"One of the most important reference books for the twenty-first century—how do we feed 9 billion people without destroying more precious ecosystems and without having to use toxic chemicals and GMOs? Every farmer, agronomist, and policy maker must read this book and, most importantly, must ensure that this valuable scientific knowledge and the proven best practices are widely adopted to make agriculture truly ecologically sustainable."

Andre Leu, president, International Federation of Organic Agriculture Movements

"Few people understand the elements of the soil and animal husbandry better than Jerry Brunetti and it is evident in this book. We ignore the knowledge within at our own peril. It is obvious that Jerry's writing comes from an 'illuminated mind.' This book should be on the shelf of every farmer and grower's library."

David Kline, editor, Farming *magazine*

"Jerry Brunetti is one of the brightest people I know in biological farming. His book is a treasure of concepts and strategies that will maximize soil fertility to grow nutritionally dense food that will improve your health. Highly recommended."

Dr. Joseph Mercola, founder, Mercola.com

"Because I hold the scientific understanding of an evolving Universe and Earth as central to transforming our planet's crises, it is a relief to listen to an interpretation of farming as primarily the work Earth has been doing for 3.8 billion years since learning to eat photons of the sun's energy and transform them into life. Everything Earth does to feed all living creatures since the creation of photosynthesis should be the essential guidance that humans need to participate in the mystery, miracle, and craft that we call agriculture. Jerry's insights into this guidance should make leaders in the present industrial food system blush with shame, as should the leaders in Western education, medicine, religion, economics, and politics for condoning it through their endorsements or through their silence."

Sister Miriam MacGillis, founder and director, Genesis Farm

"Crucial to a new generation of farmers. Jerry combines the magic of biology and the science of chemistry, and puts them both in service of a new kind of farm—which is really a whole functioning ecology."

Jack Kittredge, editor, The Natural Farmer

"Jerry Brunetti has captured both the philosophy and practice of farming in his book *The Farm as Ecosystem* as he reminds us that sustainable farming is much more than just crop and animal production. It involves the management of an ecology encompassing all of the physical, chemical, biological, and social factors that sustain a healthy society. Jerry starts with the soil and shows how everything provides an important contribution to the integrated whole of farming. He describes practical solutions based on perpetual principles to achieve an essential and rewarding contribution to mankind's successful progress. The principles developed in *The Farm as Ecosystem* will guide the avid learner to design a productive architecture as beautiful as it is efficient."

Don M. Huber, professor emeritus, Purdue University

The Farm as Ecosystem

TAPPING NATURE'S RESERVOIR —
BIOLOGY, GEOLOGY, DIVERSITY

The Farm
as Ecosystem

TAPPING NATURE'S RESERVOIR —
BIOLOGY, GEOLOGY, DIVERSITY

by Jerry Brunetti

Dec. 28, 1950 – Dec. 20, 2014

ACRES U.S.A. *Greeley, Colorado*

The Farm as Ecosystem

© 2014 by Jerry Brunetti

Acres U.S.A.
PO Box 1690
Greeley, Colorado 80632 U.S.A.
800-355-5313
info@acresusa.com • *www.acresusa.com*

Printed in the United States of America

Publisher's Cataloging-in-Publication

Jerry Brunetti, 1950–2014
The Farm as Ecosystem / Jerry Brunetti. Greeley, CO, Acres U.S.A., 2014
xvi, 336 pp., 23 cm.
Includes index, tables, and illustrations
ISBN 978-1-60173-041-1 (trade)

1. Agricultural ecology. 2. Soil fertility. 3. Agrobiodiversity.
I. Brunetti, Jerry, 1950–2014 II. Title.

S589.7 B78 2014
577.57

Contents

To my parents, Aurelio and Rena Brunetti, who instilled in me the appreciation that soil, food, taste, health, and joy are contiguous and contagious.

There are so many kindred souls in my community of ecology that I could not even begin to enumerate them all. Suffice it to say that family, loved ones, close friends, office staff here at home, *Acres U.S.A.* personnel, clients, classmates, fellow activists, mentors and the yeomen, supporters, and fellow members of sustainable and regenerative organizations have all made this text possible, due to their encouragement, love and guidance. A heartfelt salute to those nurturing the landscapes, "walking the talk," and bearing witness to this miraculous mystery of creation.

About the Author

Jerry Brunetti, 1950-2014, worked as a soil and crop consultant, primarily for livestock farms and ranches, assisting these operations as they transition away from petrochemical inputs and adopt the practices necessary for organic certification. He also worked toward improving crop quality and livestock performance and health on certified organic farms.

His "connect-the-dots" systems approach helped farmers and ranchers understand and then implement practices that demonstrate the connections between the health of people and communities and healthy land, healthy crops, and healthy livestock.

In 1979 Jerry launched Agri-Dynamics, Inc. to provide agronomy and nutritional services to livestock operations. Agri-Dynamics, Inc., now also manufactures an integrative line of complementary animal health products that are natural alternatives to pharmaceutical drugs that are particularly useful for certified organic farms, as well as nutritional supplements and pre-mixes for ruminants, swine, poultry, equine, and pets. In 1990 Jerry cofounded Earthworks, a company that provided ecologically based liquid and dry fertility products to the landscape and golf course industries. He also launched an endeavor to provide a line of bio-pesticides and liquid colloidal plant foods to both eco-minded conventional farmers and organic growers.

In 1999 Jerry was diagnosed with non-Hodgkin's lymphoma and given as little as six months to live without aggressive chemotherapy. He instead chose a holistic path of nutrition, detoxification, and immune modulation and applied his vast experience with farming and animal nutrition to his own health. Jerry passed away on Dec. 20, 2014.

The links between healthy soil, truly nutritious food, and profitable, sustainable farming are clearly evident in Jerry's personal and professional experience, and his skill for communicating this to people has won him extensive praise from holistic health professionals, sustainable farming organizations, and many farmers and consumers. He was in high demand nationally and internationally as a lecturer and speaker, and he often spoke to audiences about the relationship of "Food as Medicine" and "Farm as Farmacy."

Some of his presentations are available on DVD, including *The Keys to Herd Health, Holistic Veterinary Care* with veterinarian Hugh Karreman, and *Cancer, Nutrition & Healing*.

Jerry was a member of his local Weston A. Price Steering Committee and served as chairman on the Lower Mt. Bethel Township Environmental Advisory Council. He was an honorary board member of the Weston A. Price Foundation, a board member of the Pennsylvania Association for Sustainable Agriculture, and was active in other community-based organizations devoted to rebuilding local food systems and local democracy. In 2008, Jerry received the Sustainable Agricultural Leadership Award from the Pennsylvania Association for Sustainable Agriculture and the Eco-Agriculture Achievement Award from *Acres U.S.A.*

Introduction

O VER thirty years have passed since I first became immersed in the ever-changing and rapidly evolving world of ecological agriculture, and my understanding of agricultural practices has changed and grown with me. As a young adult I attempted to learn and implement as much as I could on a livestock operation. I witnessed enormous changes in both practice and philosophy on how to best make sustainable agriculture profitable, and I later relinquished a number of beliefs and practices in accordance with that oft-cited minimalist axiom: "Less is more."

Back in the 1970s, there were very few natural farming resources available, or at least visible, to a seeker of nature's inner workings. Environmentalism, a relatively new arena of investigation, was not at all in synch with agriculture. Agriculture was already in high gear changing its low-input strategies of diversification and self-support in order to maximize output with the fewest amounts of plant and animal species, using the most mechanized means available with the least amount of human involvement. Consequently, the Green Revolution virtually emptied rural America, thanks to very cheap "prehistoric sunlight" called fossil fuels and the newly developed hybrid plants capable of doubling or trebling their yields as long as addicted crops received their doses of petroleum-based plant foods and pesticides. In tandem with this philosophy of bigger bins, bushels, and tanker loads of milk was the family farm exodus to urban areas, deliberately instigated by government policies to reduce farm gate prices and lower the number of farmers in America.

When I was an animal science major (it used to be called "animal husbandry"), I was advised that putting animals into farms akin to concentration camps and force feeding them only several species of grains fortified with vitamins, minerals, antibiotics, parasiticides, larvacides, coccidiostats, hormones, ionophores, arsenic, recycled manure, and recycled tankage, ad nauseum, would lead to the agricultural equivalent of winning an Olympic gold medal. All of this hoopla was based on the fact that we could now extract more gallons of milk, bushels per acre, and meat per animal-days with the least amount of people doing the work—again, thanks to oil and machines. "Get big and get efficient (or get out)" were the mantras that operators heard from the U.S. agriculture secretaries, the university extension agents, the U.S. Department of Agriculture (USDA), fertilizer salesmen, and conventional veterinarians whose practices depended on "fire engine" medicine (treating acute symptoms created by stress from confinement and crowding). The lending institutions bought into it, thereby only encouraging farmers wanting an industrial economy-of-scale operation, and the inevitable debt and depreciation that followed.

This industrial model of agriculture on steroids has not only created an economic evisceration of rural communities, it has generated untold amounts of environmental damage, such as a dead zone now the size of Massachusetts in the Gulf of Mexico; a "fast food nation," as investigative journalist and author Eric Schlosser calls it, contributing to runaway diabetes and obesity; a cancer rate now at 41 percent in the United States alone;[*] and the annihilation of innumerable species due to the elimination of our precious grasslands and hedgerows.

Farmer was pitted against farmer under the myth that "inefficient" farmers were not entitled to contribute to the "problem" of farm surpluses. Under the prevailing popular theory, it would be a good thing for both agriculture and the nation to have only a few mechanized operators remaining.

And that is precisely what occurred. In 1950 there were about 3.5 million operating dairy farms in the United States. As of 2012, we're down to about 50,000. That's a 98 percent attrition! The cow numbers have remained consistent, so the rationale is that those farms remaining are the cream of

---

[*] "41 Percent of Americans will Get Cancer," UPI.com, May 6, 2010, http://www.upi.com/Health_News/2010/05/06/41-percent-of-Americans-will-get-cancer/UPI-75711273192042/.

the crop—the most talented and efficient. No doubt many in that 50,000 are indeed good farmers, but there is no doubt as well that those 3 million extinguished dairy farms had employed over 12 million people with an unfathomable amount of experience, knowledge, and talent whose loss we as a nation will forever suffer. And that's just dairy. The same consequences were seen for row crops, vegetables, fruits, nuts, poultry, swine, beef, and more.

Back in the 1970s the two main resources I depended on were the Rodale Institute and *Acres U.S.A.* The Northeast Organic Farming Association (NOFA), Maine Organic Farmers and Gardeners Association (MOFGA), Ohio Ecological Farm and Food Association (OEFFA), and TILTH were fledgling foundations. There was no Midwest Organic Sustainable Education Services (MOSES), Pennsylvania Association for Sustainable Agriculture (PASA), or Pennsylvania Certified Organic (PCO), or any of the other untold numbers of current ecological and/or grass-based organizations that now host pasture walks, farm workshops, and conferences and provide mentoring to interns and apprentices. There was no "certified" organic.

Fortunately, I was preceded by several giants of the profitable production agriculture of the first half of the twentieth century who wrote down much about how biological systems work: Sir Albert Howard (*An Agricultural Testament*), Franklin King (*Farmers of Forty Centuries*), Edward Faulkner (*Plowman's Folly*), Louis Bromfield (*Malabar Farm*), William Kenan (*The History of Randleigh Farms*), Newman Turner (*Fertility Farming*), J. Russell Smith (*Tree Crops*), Weston A. Price (*Nutrition and Physical Degeneration*), and William Albrecht (*The Albrecht Papers*). Rudolf Steiner and his eminent ambassador to America, Ehrenfried Pfeiffer, introduced an entirely new method of farming based on the energetic forces inherent in the Earth and our cosmos, called biodynamics.

There are now numerous textbooks on soil productivity/fertility available, and my preferred texts are *The Nature and Properties of Soils* by Nyle Brady and Ray Weil (I now proudly possess the fourteenth edition of this amazing textbook, which has persistently been a university reference for decades. This book contains the mother lode of information that best supports the concept of soil as a supraorganism), *How Soils Work* by Paul Syltie, *Life in the Soil* by James Nardi, *Teaming with Microbes* by Jeff Lowenfels and Wayne Lewis, *The Art of Balancing Soil Nutrients* by William McKibben, *From the Soil Up* by Donald Schriefer, *Hands-On Agronomy* by Neal Kinsey; *The Albrecht Papers* (volumes 1–6) by William Albrecht, *The Biological Farmer* by Gary Zimmer, and *Eco-Farm: An Acres U.S.A. Primer* by Charles Walters and C. J. Fenzau. All of these are fabulous resources in understanding this organism we call soil.

There were many more works, all of which are now enshrined in my library along with contemporary masters of ecological farming. Fortunately for me, I had begun reading these works at a young, idealistic age, when I was already jaded about living within the "corporate state," an amalgamation of the military, multinational corporations, a bought-and-paid-for academia, and a government run by regulatory bureaucrats recruited from the very corporations they were supposed to protect us from. The immorality and inequality of the Vietnam War was on my generation's mind, while the environment around us was clearly stressed enough for even the Nixon administration to recognize it and establish the U.S. Environmental Protection Agency (EPA).

During the early 1980s I was lucky enough to find and be mentored by some real agricultural consulting mavericks. John Whittaker, DVM, of Springfield, Missouri, was then the *Acres U.S.A.* columnist for "Whitt's End." Whitt taught me volumes about mold and mycotoxins, acidosis, and blood urea nitrogen/"funny protein," the three primary scourges of an inhumane, toxic, industrial animal agriculture. Don Schriefer of La Motte, Indiana, a regular *Acres* contributor and author of *From the Soil Up* and *Agriculture in Transition*, was one to really ask the fundamental question, "What are your yield limiting factors?" He stressed the primary importance of soil texture, residue decay, pore space, and water infiltration. Mac McCullough, a professor emeritus at the University of Georgia and frequent contributor to *Hoard's Dairymen*, was an out-of-the-box "conventional" dairy nutritionist. I say out-of-the-box because he knew that the American dairy industry was on a collision course with poor margins/low profitability because the high-forage diet was being transitioned into a swine diet that destroyed cow's feet, livers, udders, and reproductive tracts.

Today the torches of restoration, resurgence, and regeneration are being carried by many who are inspiring, motivating, and enlightening those who can listen. All one has to do is attend one of the many "calling on the clans" conferences and be inculcated with firebrand voices the likes of Vandana Shiva, Wendell Berry, Allan Savory, Wes Jackson, Chuck Walters, and Joel Salatin (to name a few).

My real mentors, however, ended up being my farmer clients. They were the ones with the vision; they were "on the ground" observing what changes were occurring with crops or stock, were able to provide me with excellent feedback, and were able to effectively build on what we both initiated. Practices that we tried and often succeeded at during that time would not even be relevant today because we've learned so much more about how to "need" so much less. We are less dependent on off-farm inputs once thought so necessary, such as fossil fuel–based fertilizers, pesticides, and drugs. This independence can only come from instituting "whole systems," which includes inviting diversity by creating ecotones (the points where different ecosystems meet and interact), such as a pasture and hedgerow, a meadow and forest, riparian edges along streams, savannahs, shelterbelts, orchards, wetlands, glades in forests, fens, ridges, forested clearings, estuaries, and so on. These ecotones are sanctuaries and nurseries for life that build resilience into not just the farm but the entire landscape. Holistic management and permaculture thus offer an embodiment of the farm as a microcosm of the macrocosm, which to me is the Earth organism.

Even though this book is demarcated into chapters of specific themes or topics, it is my hope that the reader will experience each chapter as a single thread of a textured tapestry, the image fluid rather than fixed, dependent upon the reader's aspirations, experiences, loves, and particular reverence for what is sacred and beautiful.

I hope and believe that these collective increments of ecological achievement will continue to enlighten all of us—farmers, patrons, healers, policymakers, ecologists, artisans, laborers, educators, clergy, peace officers, and military personnel—to experience what Ralph Waldo Emerson proclaimed: "To the illuminated mind, the whole world burns and sparkles with light."

Soil as a Supraorganism

The Physical Nature of Soil

I conceive that land belongs for use to a vast family of which many are dead, few are living, and countless members are still unborn.

—Nigerian tribesman

T HIS chapter will provide the reader with some collaborative thoughts as to why soil is not merely a substrate, or even a matrix, but truly a supraorganism that is self-organizing, consisting of multiple "organs" that are intelligent and cooperate with each other, and whose functions are based on form and design. Soil truly is a very complex ecosystem made up of ecosystems that know one another. The animate and inanimate are intertwined in a dance of synergy in which the whole is much greater than the sum of its parts.

For many years in the 1980s and into the 1990s, I would focus on the "three-legged stool" of soil composition, namely the chemical (minerals), the physical (sand/silt/clay and soil texture), and the biological (microorganisms and fungi). Each "leg" is completely dependent upon and an integral part of the other two. Physical structure affects pore space, which influences root growth and the activity of useful soil organisms (biology). Lime is applied to soil to increase the pH (chemistry), which affects the structure of soil (physical) as well as the nutrients plants can absorb from the soil (biology). Humus and root residue (biology) affect the appearance and structure of soil (physical) as well as its release of minerals and nutrients (chemistry).

Equally important is the biodiversity of the plants growing in such soil and of animals both wild and domestic living on the soil. Far too many

---

Supra: A prefix meaning "beyond the limits of, outside of"

biological or organic farms are woefully "understaffed" with plant and animal diversity. Are organic monocultures of corn, soybeans, and alfalfa really worthy of boasts? Organic or bio-agriculture is certainly a vast improvement over monocultures raised with pesticides, high-salt leachable fertilizers, no cover crops, or tight rotations. And clearly many, if not most, of these farms produce food and feeds that are nutritionally superior to their conventional nonorganic counterparts. But if we are to be honest, there is what is known as "organic by neglect or default." Merely growing plants without pesticides or commercial fertilizers does not automatically create healthy, tasty, nutritionally dense feeds or food (more on that later).

If natural systems are the model of how resilience and regeneration are built into soil-plant-animal ecosystems, where does one find monocultures in nature? Tropical rainforests, savannahs, prairies, tundras, deciduous and coniferous forests, and even deserts are all beneficiaries of an amazing array of biodiversity. There are virtually no monocultures in wild, natural ecosystems.

The physical, chemical, and biological systems in soils, in order to be whole, interconnected, dynamic systems, must also be impregnated with the biodiversity of nature. That biodiversity includes the innumerable species of microbes (bacteria, bacteriophages, viruses, fungi, protozoa, algae), the arthropods, miscellaneous insects, and pollinators, even birds and mammals. These biological components in turn depend on the biodiverse presence of hundreds of plant species in the local environment. That is why monocultures are hazardous to the entire supraorganism we call soil. The plants collectively synthesize tens of thousands of compounds, both primary plant metabolites (compounds necessary for the plant's survival, such as proteins, carbohydrates, fats, fibers, vitamins, minerals, etc.) and secondary plant metabolites (compounds that allow the plant to grow and develop but are not necessary for its immediate survival, such as phenols, alkaloids, terpenes, etc.). These compounds in turn affect the microbiotic community (biology), which affects soil chemistry (mineral availability), which in turn affects the physical structure of soil. In whole systems, there is no way to isolate any one of these three pillars of the supraorganism.

The physical properties of soil—essentially the size, shape, and characteristics that can be seen or felt—are key indicators of soil conditions. The soil may be sand, silt, or clay, but what kind of sand, silt, or clay? Is the soil shape plate, block, or granular? How hard or soft is the sand, silt, or clay?

How adhesive are the particles? The geological origins of the soil influence these physical characteristics because the parent rock material may have been sedimentary, magma, igneous, metamorphic, etc., and of course that means that their respective geological chemistries, and thus their specific chemical compositions and reactivities, are unique. So, the "physical" properties of a soil are clearly a combination of its geometry, or architecture, as well as its geology, the latter also being a prime factor in the soil's chemistry (i.e., mineral elements). Mathematically, sand can range in size from 2.0 to 0.05 millimeters, silt particles from 0.05 down to 0.002 millimeters (too small to see with the naked eye), and clay at less than 0.002 millimeters. Clay particles at less than 0.001 millimeter are so small that they can only be seen by an electron microscope. These tiny particles also possess colloidal properties, in which very small particles can readily disperse in liquid mediums such as blood, milk, surfactants, juices, etc.

When discussing soil management, Don Schriefer, a renowned global agronomist, emphasized that one's yields depended on the four following criteria being met, and in this order: air management, water management, decay (digestion) management, and nutrient (fertility) management. Thus a soil ecosystem consists of an atmosphere of gases (O_2, CO_2, N_2, etc.); a biosphere of plants, animals, microbes, their metabolic by-products, and their remains; the lithosphere, which consists of minerals found in clays, silt, and rock; and the hydrosphere, which includes water and exudates. All of these "spheres" are not separate but are integrated into one another. It's no coincidence that our atmosphere contains 34,000 *tons* of nitrogen over every acre! Aerobic (oxygen-loving) organisms need "free" oxygen as O_2. Anaerobic organisms also need oxygen but derive it from oxygen-laden compounds such as nitrate (NO_3) and sulfate (SO_4). Thus, anaerobic soils that are waterlogged or compacted actually lose oxygen from these compounds (as do manure lagoons) where, for example, nitrate is reduced to NO_2 (nitrogen dioxide), NO (nitrous oxide), and eventually to NH_3 (ammonia), all of which are volatile gases that leave the manure pit or the soil. Similarly, sulfate (SO_4) eventually becomes reduced to hydrogen sulfide (H_2S), another volatile gas.

Needless to say, both sulfate and nitrate are important primary plant nutrients that one cannot afford to lose. Managing water or moisture is a task quite interwoven with managing air. In order to ideally manage both, it's important to get a picture of what a "typical" soil's volume composition looks like. Most texts suggest that this ratio would consist of 45 percent minerals, 25 percent air, 25 percent water, and 5 percent organic matter. Obviously

FIGURE 1.1

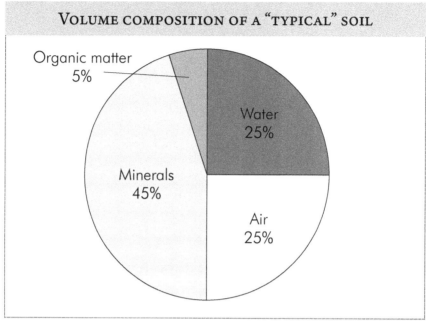

VOLUME COMPOSITION OF A "TYPICAL" SOIL

Organic matter
5%

Water
25%

Minerals
45%

Air
25%

Paul Syltie, *How Soils Work: A Study into the God-Plane Mutualism of Soils and Crops* (Fairfax, VA: Xulon Press, 2002), 31.

those numbers can vary naturally quite a bit when comparing a native prairie soil in Illinois versus rangeland in Colorado versus New England soil in New Hampshire. Nonetheless, this template emphasizes ratios that one needs to consider, whether one is growing a diverse pasture or a crop of tomatoes.

A soil ecosystem is thus more appropriately considered a family partnership, dependent on the major contributing factors of its existence: climate, topography, parent geology, and time. The 45 percent of minerals that are classified as sand, silt, and clay quite simply began as rock. Water and carbon dioxide combined to form carbonic acid [H_2O (rain) + CO_2 (carbon dioxide) → H_2CO_3 (carbonic acid)]. Carbonic acid, a mild corrosive, over time etches away at limestone (calcium carbonate) to create caves with stalactites and stalagmites [H_2CO_3 (carbonic acid) + $CaCO_3$ (limestone) → Ca^{+2} + 2(OH⁻) (hydroxyl) + 2(CO_2) (carbon dioxide)]. In these soils, the free calcium (Ca^{+2}) can now complex with phosphorus to create apatite (calcium phosphate) or with sulfur to create gypsum (calcium sulfate). Many clays are formed by rocks, like granite, reacting with carbonic acid. Granites are rich in minerals known as feldspar that are high in aluminum and silicon as well as potassium, calcium, sodium, or barium, with potassium being most prominent. Thus, the following reaction yields the basic building blocks of many other soils: $2K\,(AlSi_3O_8)$ (feldspar) + $[H_2O$ (water) + CO_2 (carbon dioxide) $\rightarrow H_2CO_3$ (carbonic acid)] $\rightarrow K_2CO_3$ (potassium carbonate) + $Al_2Si_2O_5(OH)_4$ (clay) + $4\,SiO_2$ (silicon dioxide) (sand and silt).

Rock Dust: Contemporary Glaciation

In the early 1980s, I purchased John Hamaker and Donald Weaver's breakthrough book *The Survival of Civilization*. In it, Hamaker reminded us that interglacial periods lasted 10,000–12,000 years and ice ages 100,000 years. Hamaker believed that the build-up of carbon dioxide was the catalyst of these glaciations and that the CO_2 levels were rising primarily because of a demineralization of soils, which invited glaciers to move across the landscape, grinding rocks in their path and consequently remineralizing the Earth. Their actions stimulated microbes and plants to "inhale" the CO_2 excesses, thus terminating the age of ice. Hamaker believed that as early as 1995 we would be tilting toward a new ice age. Obviously he was both correct and incorrect. The CO_2 increases are actually warming the planet—for now. And as of this writing, 1995 was eighteen years ago. However, Hamaker correctly prophesized that we would be facing intense weather events—extreme droughts and floods, high winds, record low temperatures, and blizzards like we've never encountered in areas with less-than-extreme winter climates. Hamaker's position is that weather changes are occurring because the soils have been so badly stripped of minerals that it is causing a die-back of forests, in concert with the loss of grassland and rainforest to burning and plowing. To prevent another ice age, we need to simulate the effects of the glaciers and remineralize the soil.

Based upon reports, observations, and personal experience, it appears to me that rock dust can have an impact on soil mineralization (provided enough of it is applied and it is of a fine mesh or grind) for the following reasons:

1. It is a microbial stimulant, especially in combination with organic matter. It is a source of numerous elements, and

in many instances it has paramagnetic properties that are energetic resources to the soil food web. This explosion of microbes creates what Hamaker calls skins, basically the cell membranes of the microbes. Since skins are predominantly protein, they are a rich source of carbon, nitrogen, and a few elements. As the microbes die and the skins humify, plants are able to take in both carbon and nitrogen as protoplasm. Earthworms can use both fresh and digested (humified) skins to produce microorganisms in their castings. Always use rock dusts with adequate crop residues, employ a rest period of cover crops, and keep tillage minimal to avoid disrupting fungal mycelial growth and earthworm populations and oxidizing the organic matter carbons into CO_2.

2. Rock dust, ground fine enough, can also provide plant-available minerals. This is accomplished by microbial weathering, whereby organic acids and enzymes released by microbes can liberate the minerals complexed with silicon oxides or aluminum silicates in both rock dusts and clay. A 200+ mesh product is desired because it creates a huge surface area; one ton of rock dust contains a surface area of sixteen thousand acres (and one pound of rock dust has a surface area of eight acres)!

3. Rock dust also displays paramagnetic properties. Harvey Lisle's *The Enlivened Rock Powders* and Phil Callahan's *Paramagnetism* reflect on this property of rock dust. According to Callahan, "Paramagnetism is the ability of a substance to collect or resonate to the magnetic fields of the Cosmos. It is not magnetism." Callahan's theory is that soils need to be paramagnetic in order to be productive. Oxygen is the most paramagnetic gas, which is one of the reasons why aerobic soils are more fertile than anaerobic soils. Water and plants are diamagnetic and are thus enlivened by the forces of paramagnetism, such as the moon, oxygen in the "atmosphere" around the roots, and paramagnetic rock dust. Callahan developed a meter for ascertaining paramagnetism in soils called the PCSM (the Paramagnetic Count Soil Meter, or the Phil Callahan Soil Meter). Its readings are measured in CGS, which stands for centimeter per grams seconds,

or what weight of a paramagnetic material will move one centimeter to a magnet in one second. According to the soil meter, 0–100 CGS indicates poor soil; 100–300 CGS, good soil; 300–800 CGS, very good soil; and 800 CGS and above, excellent soil. The PCSM is now available from Pike Laboratories in Jay, Maine. Callahan also demonstrated that paramagnetic rock emits light as photons. However, when the rock dust was mixed into compost, the photonic emissions increased exponentially. Good readings for paramagnetic rock dust typically range from 1,000 CGS (minimum) to as high as 9,000 CGS.

Malcolm Beck, a composter from Texas, did some trials with a blend of volcanic rock dusts plus greensand, mixed it with compost, and trialed it on tomato plants. He discovered that the treated tomato plants, which were blooming and setting fruit, survived a late frost, whereas all the controls did not. Charles Wilber's book *How to Grow World Record Tomatoes* emphasized a combination of rock dust and compost for healthy tomato growth. Wilber earned a place in the Guinness Book of World Records for getting 342 pounds of tomatoes from one plant and growing a single plant over twenty-eight feet tall!

Much attention has been given to the longevity and health of the Hunza population, who live in a remote section of Pakistan. Writers such as J. I. Rodale (*The Healthy Hunzas*, 1948), Sir Albert Howard (*The Soil and Health*, 1947), Robert McCarrison (*Nutrition and Health*, 1936), Allen Banik and Renée Taylor (*Hunza Land*, 1960), Renée Taylor (*Hunza Health Secrets*, 1964), and John Tobe (*Guideposts to Health and Vigorous Long Life*, 1965) all point to a common thread that may have contributed to these people being so vibrant and long-lived, and that was their use of "glacial milk," water from the Ultar glacier that contained rock dusts finely ground by the glacier. This rock dust was a primary source of fertility for the Hunzas, as not much animal manure was available.

Bread from Stones, the arcane work by Julius Hensel, was first published in 1894. Hensel was a contemporary of Justus von

Liebig (1803–1873), the father of N-P-K. Unlike Liebig, Hensel tried to make the case that long-lasting fertility could only depend upon non-leachable, low-salt plant foods. As of today, we know who won that argument.

The feedback from users of rock dust all over the world varies considerably as to what rock materials to use, how much to apply, and so on. Application rates of three-fourths of a ton to forty-six tons per acre have been tried.

Don Weaver, coauthor of *The Survival of Civilization*, states that a 200+ mesh dust is preferred and from a "good variety of stones." Two tons of dust per acre is an approximate minimum to produce observable first-year results. Five to twenty tons per acre is more in line with the needs of our dying Earth (twenty tons per acre is about one pound per square foot).

California organic wizards Bob Cannard and his colleague/ student Dan Weber are emphatic about using rock dust to create more resilient produce. Applying crushed oyster shells (lime), andesite, and basalt at a rate of only five hundred pounds per acre before and after planting plus direct plant applications during the growing season, Weber noticed an increase in plant stamina and a near-disappearance of insect pests. Flavors became more profound as well. In his third year as an organic grower, Weber submitted his vegetables to the Sonoma County Harvest Fair. His tomatoes and bell peppers won best of show (taste and appearance). He won six other first-place ribbons and four second-place ribbons. No doubt it was not rock dust alone that contributed to such horticultural success.

And then there is the biodynamic explanation for rock dust performing as it does. Most granite or basalt deposits contain a large percentage of silica, the most common metal in the earth's crust. According to Rudolf Steiner, the planets Mars, Jupiter, and Saturn work upon the silica in the Earth's strata. They assist those influences of the sun, as well as being delivered by the sun. All of these forces are received by the Earth, which then expresses them upward from the Earth through plants. Silica thus acts as a magnet to draw in cosmic energies and irradiate them back out through the plant. Silica is the opposite biodynamic pole of calcium. Calcium forces are drawn down into the soil and these energies, also called digestive forces, are associated with the Moon and the planets Mercury and Venus, as carried by the sun to Earth.

In between calcium (lime) and silica are the clays, typically rich in minerals and always the bearer of both silica and aluminum. Aluminum is always in the "center row" of the lime-silica dipole. For example, calcium alumina silicate is $CaOAl_2O_3SiO_2$. Thus clay is the bridge between two poles, a transport. Since both the silica and calcium forces depend upon the sun, clay is the medium that allows in the cosmic forces that emanate from the constellations at night, thanks to those forces being reflected by the moon.

In the fertile Sudan there is a triangular piece of real estate called Gezira, the apex of which is the confluence of the White Nile and the Blue Nile. The White Nile is rich in paramagnetic rock dust; the Blue Nile's wealth is organic matter from the forest's plant and animal inhabitants. The two river mixtures create a topsoil in the Nile valley that could produce high qualities of food with nary an input (see chapter 7, "The Eternal Earthworm").

It appears that diamagnetic energies, such as found in limestone, and paramagnetic energies, such as found in basalt, need to be "insulated" from one another in order to maximize the flow of energy they invite from the Earth and the cosmos. That insulation is organic matter or carbon.

It reminds me of Wilhelm Reich's orgone accumulator, which was a box or blanket constructed out of alternating layers of cotton batts and metal mesh, with cotton as the carbon and the mesh the metallic "antennae." The two substances layered together were attractants or accumulators of the orgone energy in the atmosphere that transcends all life forms. Other familiar words for this force are chi, prana, formative forces, and etheric energy.

Adding two to twenty pounds of rock dust per cubic yard of compost will create a symbiosis within the microbial population and will improve structure and aeration while also allowing faster digestion of the minerals than the soil by itself. No doubt adding biochar and compost to this soil mix will dramatically enhance the productivity of the soil.

Application rates are as follows:
United States
3 tons/acre= 14 lb/100 sq feet= 1.25 lb/sq yard
10 tons/acre= 46 lbs/100 sq feet= 4 lb/sq yard
20 tons/acre= 92 lbs/100 sq feet=8 lbs/sq yard
Metric
7.5 tons/ha=750 kg/1000 sq meter= 75 kg/100 sqm=750 gms/sq meter
25 tons/ha=2.5 tons/1000 sq meter =250 kg/100 sqm=2.5 kg/sq meter
50 tons/ha=5 tons/1000 sq meter = 500 kg/100 sq.m = 5kg/sq meter

Soil Penetrometer, photo courtesy DICKEY-john Corporation

GETTING GROUNDED

One tool I find indispensable for maintaining high soil quality physically is the soil penetrometer. This tool ascertains the amount of compaction in a soil with a gauge that rests aside the handles of a T bar instrument that measures the pounds per square inch (psi) and the depth where that compaction becomes a concern with line demarcations on the probe inserted into the soil.

Many graziers or hay producers believe that their turf-covered landscape has no compaction (unless heavy livestock "pug" it following heavy rains). Getting down with your eyes at ground level on an 8–10 percent slope during a heavy rain will teach you that if water is running laterally downhill, then it's not percolating *into* the soil. A soil penetrometer may show you have a hard pan or plow pan six to eight inches below the surface that may have resulted from previous tillage (even with draft animals!), heavy clay subsoils deficient in calcium and/or excessively high in magnesium, low organic matter soils, and ground that is worked too frequently, not allowing enough time to recuperate with growing roots that help flocculate these soils. The pans may also be geological formations of cement-like amalgamations of minerals called duripans, fragipans, or placic horizons. These can be salt-like horizons that include an accumulation of gypsum, limestone (chalk), or miscellaneous soluble salts, some of which were applied as salt fertilizers and built up over time.

Keyline subsoiler, courtesy Yeoman's Plow

Since soils hold approximately one to three inches of water per foot of depth, obviously having root systems that penetrate into the subsoil can make a massive difference in managing both flooding and drought challenges. Slicing the subsoil with tillage equipment such as the Yeoman Keyline Subsoiler can make major inroads in deepening one's topsoil, and this must be done by maintaining continuity between the topsoil and lower horizons.

The AerWay Aerator was an aeration tool that originally was conceived in New Zealand in order to shatter the pans, rather than slice them. It's a worthwhile tool, but unless one achieves a biological penetration of grasses, forbs, and legumes down into the subsoil, it's likely that the pans will return. Another aerification implement

AerWay Aerator, courtesy AerWay

that I'm impressed with is the Gen-Till, which punches holes while gently lifting the soil around the knife.

Additionally, it's important to know when slicing the pans to never do so on waterlogged soils, as this kind of intrusion will damage them. Conversely, one doesn't slice pans when they are bone dry, the reason being that clay shrinks when dry. Once they become wet again, they will swell shut. Thus, the ideal time to subsoil is when the clay is moist, like a pound cake.

Typical compaction will interfere dramatically with root growth. According to the U.S. Department of Agriculture's (USDA) National Soil Dynamics Laboratory in Auburn, Alabama, compacted soils will reduce root growth from a maximum of three inches per day to only half an inch per day, an 83 percent reduction. That's partially because roots will only enter about an inch into an oxygen-deprived environment. Take a good look at figure

FIGURE 1.2

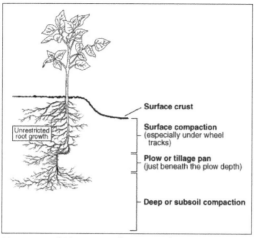

FIGURE 1.2

University of Minnesota Extension, http://www.extension.umn.edu/distribution/cropsystems/components/7400_02.html

1.2, from the University of Minnesota Extension.

Where there's no surface traffic (on the left), there is an abundance of lateral roots, compared to their absence on the right. The slice through the plow pan with a subsoiler has permitted this plants' roots to aggressively travel below the pan into the lower horizons, giving it more access to moisture and nutrients.

Concern about pans is not a modern phenomenon. The Clifton Park system of farming, developed by Robert Elliot in Britain in the late 1800s, was demonstrative of how a very biodiverse mixture of seed, sowed in April 1895, could be incorporated into a pasture.

TABLE 1.1

BREAKING UP HARD PANS AND INCREASING YIELDS ON ALLUVIAL FLAT BOTTOMLAND SOILS

Sowed April 25, 1895, cut for hay spring 1896

- 5 # cocksfoot
- 5# meadow foxtail
- 5# tall fescue
- 7# meadow fescue
- 4# timothy
- 1# wood meadow grass
- 1# rough stalked meadow grass
- 2# white clover

- 2# alsike clover
- 2# perennial red clover
- 2# kidney vetch
- 2# Lucerne
- 3# chicory
- 8# burnet
- 1# sheep's parsley
- ½# yarrow

Spring 1896 hay yield: 2 1/2 tons dry matter/acre plus heavy lamb grazing

Robert Elliot, *The Clifton Park System of Farming* (London: Faber and Faber Unlimited, 1908).

FIGURE 1.3

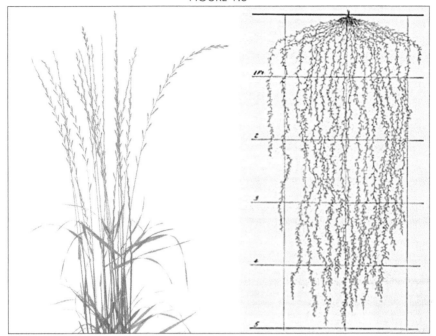

Thinkstock; John Weaver, *Root Development of Field Crops* (Lincoln: University of Nebraska, 1926).

Table 1.1 illustrates the seed mixture of the sixteen plants sowed. A year later (spring 1896), the productivity of this soil was measured. The meadow yielded two and a half tons of dry matter per acre, plus a heavy lamb grazing. Moreover, a subsoil investigation in September 1896 showed a hard pan that was fourteen inches deep and ten to twelve inches thick. The plants proven to have hardpan fracturing characteristics were chicory with thirty-inch roots, burnet with twenty-inch roots, and alfalfa (Lucerne) with eight- to ten-inch roots. No wonder Thomas Jefferson found a way to introduce chicory into the United States from Britain. Today there's much excitement in the cover crop community regarding plants like the tilliage (oilseed)/forage radish, some improved annual rye grasses, and some clovers (see chapter 11 for more information).

What's also of interest here is just how deep the roots of plants will grow given the opportunity afforded by subsoil without pans and above the water table. During 1981–1982 an extensive study was conducted at low-level waste sites at Los Alamos National Laboratory on fifty-three species found growing on these sites. Alfalfa (*Medicago sativa*) had an average rooting depth of 690 cm (over 23 feet) with a range of 38 to 3,900 cm (over 130 feet).* American author and conservationist Louis Bromfield found his alfalfa's roots 14 feet deep in the gravel subsoil on his Malabar Farm, which is in part how he built a half foot of topsoil where there was none in a handful of years in the 1940s and 1950s.

What about the research of the University of Iowa in examining a four-month-old cereal rye plant? Howard Dittmer wrote an article on the study, called "A Quantitative Study of the Roots and Root Hairs of a Winter Rye Plant," and published it in the *American Journal of Botany* in 1937 and 1938. Dittmer found the root length of this plant was 377 miles. Over 80 percent, or 275 miles, of these roots were feeder roots. The root hairs on that *single* plant numbered 14.5 billion, having a fibrous length of 6,214 miles. The surface area alone was calculated at more than a tenth of an acre. When combined, the roots and root hairs had a length of 7,000 miles with a combined surface area of 63,784 square feet, or about 1.5 acres. Now, contemplate how a single acre of winter rye may have roots and root hairs exceeding 30,000 acres, with at least a third of this mass covered by a net of fungal mycelium. If an annual can provide this much surface area, imagine what perennials can do, being that their root systems don't die off but continue to grow, deepening the topsoil overtime, increasing the carbon content of our soil, and immensely increasing the water infiltration into the subsoil. Trees exert an amazing influence on conditioning soils. Tree roots that measured a mere four inches in diameter and three feet in length can exert a force of up to 150 pounds per square inch, being able to lift a fifty-ton boulder! Mesquite trees, which thrive in the desert, have roots that venture up to one hundred feet deep.

Wes Jackson and his prairie pioneers at the Land Institute are conducting research on hybridizing annual grains with their perennial cousins. This would create a soil erosion–resistant crop that could conceivably persist for up to two decades without tillage, with nitrogen coming from legumes interspersed with the grain and no need for annual applications of herbicide; all this would hopefully translate into a buildup of topsoil instead of an average annual loss of up to eleven tons per acre per year, according to the USDA. Water quality would improve tremendously, as our surface water would not be laden with the suffocating sediment, nitrates, phosphates, and pesticides that ultimately end up in our estuaries creating eutrophication, or dead zones.

---

* See Teralene Foxx , Gail Tierney, and Joel Williams, *Rooting Depths of Plants on Low-Level Waste Disposal Sites* (Los Alamos, NM: Los Alamos National Laboratory, 1984).

Perennial grasses/legumes and forbs, by increasing soil organic matter, become huge reservoirs of moisture and nitrogen sinks. According to the USDA, a one-foot-by-three-foot block of soil, six inches thick, having an organic matter content of 4–5 percent and weighing 100 pounds, can hold 165–195 pounds of water. This soil could thus absorb a four-to-six-inch rain in one hour. Prairie studies have shown that for every ton of forage shoots produced, those prairie plants produce three tons of roots.

If that same block of soil approximates 1.5–2.5 percent organic matter, typical of most of our millions of acres of annual cropland, that hundred pounds of soil could only absorb thirty-five to forty-five pounds of water, equal to half an inch to one and a half inches of rainfall, in one hour. Dr. Ehrenfried Pfeiffer, who brought Rudolf Steiner's biodynamic agriculture to America, estimated that approximately 5 percent of the total organic matter in topsoil consists of various nitrogen compounds. Therefore a 2 percent organic matter soil would contain forty thousand pounds of organic matter per acre. Multiplying this amount by 5 percent yields a potential nitrogen reservoir per acre of about two thousand pounds. This is assuming, of course, that there are ammonifying or nitrifying bacteria present, such as azotobacters, clostridium, azasprillum, nitrosomonas, nitrobacter, and beijerinckia. Additionally, if there are legumes present, there are the rhizobia, which can convert dinitrogen (N_2) in the atmosphere into ammonium (NH_4).

AmazingCarbon.com's Dr. Christine Jones, a soil scientist in Australia, which has been struggling to endure its "once in a thousand year drought," has shown that a soil with a bulk density of 1.4 grams per cubic centimeter can absorb and store for every 1 percent increase in organic matter an additional four and a half gallons of water per top twelve inches per square yard. This is equal to an additional eighteen thousand gallons per acre. Thus, increasing soil organic matter by a very achievable 3 percent will increase that soil's water reservoir by fifty-four thousand gallons per acre. How many Texas farms and ranches could have used an additional fifty-four thousand gallons of water per acre during the 2011 drought? Dr. Jones points to Portuguese research demonstrating a scheme to pay about four hundred participating farmers to establish biodiverse perennial mixed grass/legume pastures (upward of twenty species) to improve soil carbon in an area of about a hundred thousand acres. Research demonstrated that soil organic matter (OM) starting at 0.87 percent increased to 3 percent over ten years in a Mediterranean climate. Fertilized annual pasture only reached 2.0 percent OM in the same time, while unfertilized annual pasture barely climbed over 1.0 percent OM in the same decade. Portuguese summers can be hot and dry, a real deterrent against accumulating carbon in the soil. That additional 2.13 percent organic matter translates into an extra thirty-eight thousand gallons of water per acre. That doesn't include the amount of water that is prevented from washing away during heavy rains, but rather the amount that has the chance of percolating downward into the subsoil for later access by deep root systems of pasture plants, shrubs, and trees.

The most important component of all this research is that Dr. Jones has demonstrated that it's the liquid carbon exuded from roots that produces the greatest amount of carbon in the shortest period of time. The Land Institute's analysis of our once-magnificent tall grass and short grass prairie plants demonstrates all too clearly what we have lost—and what we can readily restore with perennial root systems: namely, the survival of our species.

Another Australian miracle has been achieved on Winona Farms, a two-thousand-acre sheep and grain farm in New South Wales owned by Colin Seis (www.winona.net.au). Working with the University of Sydney in a Communities in Landscapes project (cil.landcarensw.org.au), Seis embarked on instituting a pasture cropping scheme on his farm, which entailed a rotational grazing of four thousand Merino sheep on a perennial pasture of native warm season (C-4) grasses. Once every four years, a quarter of the pastures are grazed or mowed very short and an annual cereal (wheat, oats, rye) is tilled into the sod, which is now going dormant, *without* herbicide. The following spring the annual cereals are either grazed or allowed to mature and be harvested as grain, just as the warm season native perennial grasses take off in growth. This allows Winona Farms to generate income from wool, stud animals, cereal crops, and native grass seed from *Bothriochloa macra* (red grass).

The results over ten years of this pasture cropping practice have been nothing less than sensational. Organic matter levels have climbed 200 percent. Topsoil has increased from four inches in depth to eighteen inches, while water holding capacity has increased by 200 percent. Annual costs, which were typically for fertilizer, herbicide, seed, and veterinary bills, dropped by $81,500. The following increases in minerals have also occurred: calcium up by 277 percent, phosphorus up by 157 percent, magnesium up by 138 percent, potassium up by 146 percent, sulfur up by 157 percent, zinc up by 180 percent, iron up by 122 percent, copper up by 202 percent, boron up by 156 percent, molybdenum up by 151 percent, cobalt up by 179 percent, and selenium up by 117 percent—all these increases without off-farm purchases of fertilizer! That being said, I would still recommend an application of calcitic limestone and a source of phosphorus because the soil pHs are very acidic at pH 5.4, and the P levels are only <20 ppm (parts per million) with

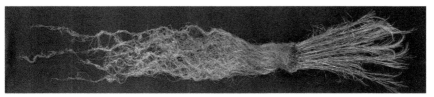

Photo of switchgrass roots. Lee R. DeHaan, Land Institute

Bray 1 Extraction. Since soil pH affects soil biology, and biology is clearly responsible for these amazing improvements, then it follows that creating a more conducive environment for soil microbes can only improve the ecological performance and/or shorten the amount of time it would take to enhance crop yields or quality.

Roots supply 80 percent of the soil carbon, and since perennials produce nine times more root mass than annuals, one can readily conclude that we need to enhance the ability of both annuals and perennials to grow deeper root systems. How to do that? The fastest way is to incorporate a physical (tillage), chemical (fertility), and biological (plant and animal) strategy.

Subsoiling the pans at twenty-four- to thirty-inch centers can provide opportunity for both annual and perennial roots to readily move downward. One can accelerate this process by applying soil amendments that help flocculate tight clays. High-calcium limestone, gypsum, and humates working together can begin the granulation process on these clays to geologically make them more friable. Biological amendments could include fish emulsion, molasses, and seaweed extract to feed microbes the proteins and energy they thrive on. Rotational grazing, especially if one correctly and effectively utilizes the mob grazing method to trample lignified carbon that can create mulch, can invite saprophytic decaying fungi and earthworms to accelerate the process. This mulch acts as an insulation blanket, conserving moisture and maintaining optimal temperatures. When grazing, as far as soil humus is concerned, it's critical to be sure one implements continuous cover, leaving a thick sward. Remember, as one travels southward, higher temperatures work against the synthesis of humus. Additionally, as one travels west of the 100th meridian, lower rainfall has the same effect in generating and maintaining soil carbon. Thus, never graze below a height of at least four inches. Generous amounts of digestible dry matter can be taken in by grazing livestock at plant heights of eight to ten inches.

FIGURE 1.4

Up to 60 percent of Photosynthetic Carbon is sent to the roots

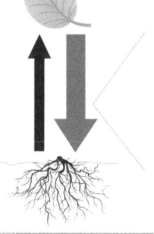

Antioxidants
Simple & Complex Acids
Complex Carbohydrates
Proteins
Essential Oils
Chelating Agents
Microbial Stimulants
Secondary Metabolites

Another important soil tool to carry along with your penetrometer is a soil thermometer. In the mid summer, bare soil can reach temperatures exceeding 95°F–100°F (30°C–40°C). At above 80°F (25°C) organic matter begins to aerobically break down rapidly. Although air temperatures can adversely affect the growth and nutritional quality of plants that are stressed from such heat, excessive soil temperatures are dramatically more damaging. Having root systems that have vigorously entrenched themselves into the subsoil accomplishes several objectives. For one, these roots create an aerobic zone with oxygen in the lower horizons. The aerobic zone is where the vast majority of biological activity takes place, where plants derive most of their nutrition and protection or immunity in what's known as the rhizosphere, or root ball. Plant roots that break down sugars and release energy for their metabolism also release carbon dioxide into the surrounding soil atmosphere. Combined with the exhalation of soil organisms, this accumulation of CO_2 reacts with soil moisture, H_2O, synthesizing carbonic acid, which breaks down parent rock materials into clay, silt, and sand, as well as chelating complexed nutrients in the soil so that they can be released for plant uptake (chelation is a biochemical phenomenon whereby an organic acid attaches to a metal ion, allowing it to become more biologically available to microbes, plants and animals). In other words, larger root systems mean larger amounts of CO_2 gas in the rhizosphere, which creates more carbonic acid, which creates better plant nutrition, meaning better growth and nutritional quality.

Since 30–60 percent of the photosynthesis compounds created in the foliage are transported into the root ball, this nectar of the roots is quite rich in humus-building compounds such as mucigel, amino acids, organic acids, sugars, and others that increase soil organic matter. The roots also provide channels that allow air, water, and nutrients to travel and earthworms to migrate.

The roots themselves act like lamp wicks. Anyone who has used an oil or kerosene lamp knows that "wicking," in which capillary action draws kerosene up the wick, is a phenomenon that one might describe as "antigravity." Thus, while the channels allow water to penetrate into the subsoil in the wet season, the "wicks" (roots) encourage that water to move upward into the topsoil during the dry season.

Design is the basis of function, so in the quest to understand how soils work, one begins by examining the architecture of nature. The natural realm has designed itself to create fractal infinity within a finite parameter. Fractal geometry is universally found throughout the natural world as a way of increasing surface area. More surface area means a greater likelihood for biological and biochemical reactions to occur. Additional surface area also means more space for habitat, where organisms can live, procreate, and die. Fractals are universal in nature. The coastline, the crown of a tree, the villi in the intestine, the meandering of streams and rivers, the circulatory system in animals, ad infinitum. The rye grass plant is an example of such potential. The same is true throughout natural systems. The DNA in each cell, for example, if its fully unraveled double helix were stretched end to end, would measure seven feet. And humans consist of about 10 trillion cells. The surface area of one's lungs, flattening the alveoli, would more than cover a tennis court. Figures 1.5 and 1.6 illustrate the relative size of soil particles to one another and the relative size of microbes to the soil particles. For example, one sand particle approximates a thousand silt particles and a million clay particles.

When viewing the relative sizes of coarse, fine, and very fine sand alongside silt, clay, and typical soil microorganisms, it becomes apparent that these aggregates create various ecotones, or habitats, for soil organisms, depending on their composition of sand, silt, and clay. The mixture of these three groups constitutes a loam. Thus by intersecting the three respective lines on the

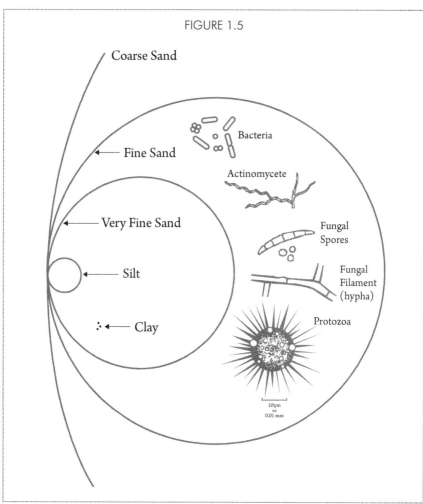

FIGURE 1.5

James Nardi, *Life in the Soil: A Guide for Naturalists and Gardeners* (Chicago: University of Chicago Press, 2007).

textural triangle, one can determine whether one's soil is a sandy loam, sandy clay loam, clay loam, silty clay loam, or silt loam.

You can determine what kind of loam you're working with by using the kneading method, in which a small ball of moist soil, the diameter of a garlic bulb, is worked into a putty-like consistency. The ball should be malleable. A high sandy soil has noticeable grit. Soil high in silt is smooth and silky. Predominantly clay soil is greasy, sticky, and shiny. Make a ribbon out of the ball using your thumb and forefinger. Work the soil into this ribbon, elongating it until it breaks apart. Interpret your observations as follows:

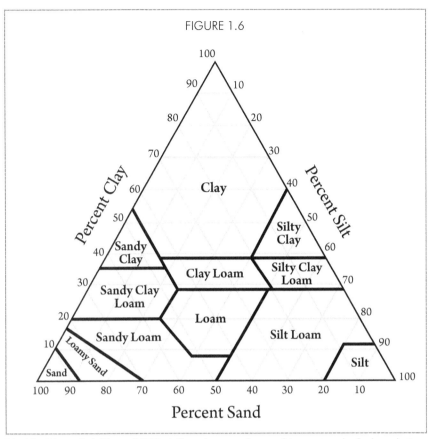

FIGURE 1.6

Modified from S. J. Thien, 1979. A flow diagram for teaching texture by feel analysis, Journal of Agronomic Education. 8:54–55. United States Department of Agriculture, Natural Resources Conservation Service, http://soils.usda.gov/education/resources/lessons/texture/.

1. Soil never formed a ball and breaks apart: sand
2. Soil forms a ball; will not form a ribbon: loamy sand
3. Soil forms a ball, but ribbon breaks off at about one inch length; AND
    a. Grittiness is a predominant characteristic: sandy loam
    b. Smooth, silky feel is a predominant characteristic with no grittiness: silt loam
    c. Smooth and slightly gritty: loam
4. Soil is sticky and firm, forming a ribbon between one and two inches in length before breaking; AND
    a. Grittiness is predominant: sandy clay loam

The Soil Smoothie Technique

Compare this method with the kneading technique. Using a quart jar (32 oz), pour one pint (16 oz) of distilled water. Add a tablespoon of a good nonfoaming surfactant or water softener. Add 1.5 cups of soil removed from the top eight to twelve inches of soil. Cap the jar, shake well until all the soil is completely in suspension, and then allow all the sediment to completely settle. The heavier sand particles settle out first, usually within five to ten minutes. A few hours later, the silt will settle on top of the sand. In twenty-four to forty-eight hours, the minute clay particles will eventually fall out, forming a layer on top of the silt.

Now using a ruler and basic math, measure the total height of all three layers. Then measure the height of each layer and determine what percentage of the total soil height this constitutes.

Now go to the textural triangle diagram and, using either method, triangulate all three determinations to come to a point within the triangle that best defines your soil type. For example, when using the jar technique, if your sand percentage was 30 percent, silt was 50 percent, and clay 20 percent, you would have a silty loam. If you had 10 percent silt, 50 percent sand, and 40 percent clay, your soil would be a sandy clay. The same conclusions can be reached using the hand kneading technique, except that the ribbons one produces will yield information directly to the kind of soil one has, without having to do the math within the textural triangle.

    b. Smooth, silky feel is predominant, with little to no grittiness: silty clay loam

    c. Smooth, silky feel with slight grittiness: clay loam

5. Soil is very sticky, firm and will form a ribbon longer than two inches; AND

    a. Grittiness is predominant: sandy clay

    b. Smooth, silky feel with no grittiness: silty clay

    c. Smoothness and little grittiness: clay

Of relevant importance is that USDA has virtually mapped almost every acre of soil in the United States as to its geological type and the potential productivity of that soil. These maps are available from the Farm Service Agency (FSA) or Natural Resources Conservation Service (NRCS) offices. Our colonial ancestors often looked at the diameter of trees to make these determinations, inspecting the spaces between the tree rings to ascertain how quickly those trees grew on that soil. Fertile soils meant faster growth, with more space between the annual rings visible in the cross-section of the tree trunk. Likewise, before purchasing or leasing land, it would be prudent to check these USDA maps to see what kind of soil you will be blessed with, or challenged with.

Understanding the physical type of your soil is important because it provides the framework as to what kind of "architecture" your soil is designed with. It also correlates to what is described in a soil test as CEC (cation exchange capacity) or TEC (total exchange capacity). Simply put, CEC/TEC is a measure of the size, or volume, of one's soil, which increases from higher amounts of clay or organic matter. Soil has a negative charge because of a) what are called isomorphic substitutions, and b) exposed crystal edges, rough from weathering, that occur on the edges of the clay lattices. Clay is constructed like a deck of cards, and montmorillonite clay consists of units made up of a sheet of alumina sandwiched between two silica sheets. There is a gap between the top and bottom silica sheets that creates a massive internal adsorptive surface area; and there is a large external adsorptive surface that would surround the lattice, or "deck of cards."

Isomorphic substitutions occur when an element with a similar atomic diameter, but which has a reduced positive charge, is substituted for either alumina or silica during the formation of the clay. For example, Al^{+3} being replaced by Ca^{+2} = net negative charge of 1; Si^{+4} being replaced by Mg^{+2} = net negative charge of 2. These net negative charges are thus able to attract positively charged minerals called cations that are in the soil solution, be they calcium, potassium, sodium, magnesium, or trace elements like zinc, manganese, copper, etc.

As these clays undergo weathering, the edges of these clay lattices fracture, exposing hydroxl (OH) groups and creating exposed crystal edges. The hydrogen in the OH^+ group can ionize in soil water and be replaced by another positively charged cation that has a stronger positive charge than hydrogen, such as potassium, magnesium, and calcium.

Since the order of the binding strength of the major cations is Ca>Mg>K>Na>H, it's typical to find the base saturation to range from:

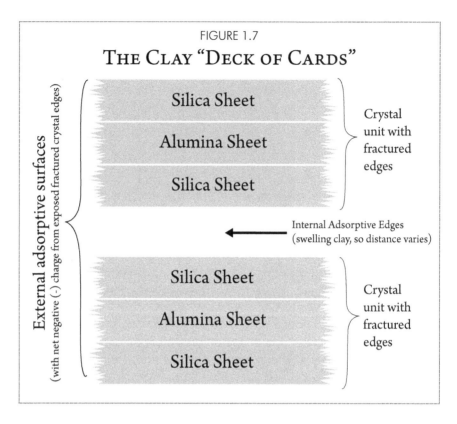

FIGURE 1.7

THE CLAY "DECK OF CARDS"

External adsorptive surfaces
(with net negative (-) charge from exposed fractured crystal edges)

Silica Sheet
Alumina Sheet
Silica Sheet

Crystal unit with fractured edges

Internal Adsorptive Edges
(swelling clay, so distance varies)

Silica Sheet
Alumina Sheet
Silica Sheet

Crystal unit with fractured edges

Ca at 50–80 percent, Mg at 10–40 percent, K at <2–10 percent, Na at 0–5 percent, and hydrogen making up the difference. What is base saturation? Imagine a table set with one hundred chairs (or 100 percent). The table is the negatively charged soil colloid whose CEC/TEC depends upon the amount of clay (or organic matter) present. The chairs are the cation elements, or positively charged minerals attracted to the negatively charged soil colloid (table). According to famed soil scientist William Albrecht, PhD, once head of the University of Missouri Soils Department and the inspiration for the formation of Brookside Labs, the ideal ratio of these cations, in order to have an adequate exchange of nutrients of the soil colloid, is calcium at 68 percent, magnesium at 12 percent, potassium at 3–5 percent, and sodium at 0.5–3.0 percent (more on minerals later). The behavior of clays in our soil matrix warrants attention because they affect much more than the CEC/TEC: swelling, plasticity, cohesion, heat given off from being wetted, adsorbing and absorbing properties, and massive surface area. How much surface area? Well according to Nyle Brady and Ray Weil's text *The Nature and Properties of Soils*, clay ranges from 10 square meters per gram of soil to 800 square meters per gram. An area about 1 hectare (less than 2.5 acres) and 1.5 meters deep, (the area and volume of a football field) consisting of 45 percent clay could have a surface area of 3.8 million square miles, or greater than the size of the continental United States. Another estimate suggests a mere pound of clay would have a total surface area of fifty football fields!

Of course, pure clay soils can become a nightmare, turning into a "brick factory" or asphalt parking lot. The missing ingredients in these scenarios are humic substances from carbon sources, such as humates, compost, or "sheet compost," the natural breakdown of lignified plant material on the soil's surface as well as the decomposition of decaying root systems. Another missing element is calcium, which acts as a flocculant that helps granulate clay clods into more friable particles. When these humic and calcitic ingredients assist in opening up soils, creating more pore space, then microbial populations and feeder roots can move in, providing yet more "living carbon" in the forms of: mucilage or "mucigel," a polysaccharide slime that acts as a lubricant and energy source; plant root exudates that contain many kinds of carbon compounds; plants and/or organisms themselves that die off, leaving organic residues of their bodies and tissues; and the enzymes these plants and organisms produce that create biochemical reactions that work upon minerals in the soil, forming new molecular complexes while disintegrating others. This ecosystem, called the rhizosphere, will be discussed in detail later.

Two separate articles written in the *New York Times* in 1985 suggest that clays, being silicon-based, act as "wild, undomesticated semi-conductors." The isomorphic substitutions referred to create "domains of disorder" providing opportunities for clays to be pleomorphic; that is, they can assemble into varied shapes. Being semiconductors, clays can store energy and information for perhaps thousands of years. Clays are also catalysts, being one of the original catalysts used to refine oil. According to these *New York Times* articles, very small amounts of clay can accelerate chemical processes by a factor of ten thousand or more!

The one author proposes that clay is potentially so "alive" that some theorize that life on this planet started in clay, rather than the sea. The theory behind this proposition is that those sheets that make up the clay's lattice, or "deck of cards," consist of an octahedral layer (the alumina sheet) and a tetrahedral layer (the silica sheet). It's speculated that because clay may replicate these complex octahedral and tetrahedral layers, it may behave similarly to DNA in a cell's nucleus, suggesting that clay can contribute to "living" molecules. In other words, a montmorillonite clay could morph into a DNA molecule.[*]

---

[*] James Gleick, "Quiet Clay Revealed as Vibrant and Primal," *New York Times*, May 5, 1987.

When wetted in water or other organic solvents, fractured, ground-up, or irradiated, certain clays can emanate ultraviolet and other light wavelengths, sometimes for years. Hitting a lump of clay with a hammer will generate a cascade of energy emissions that can sustain itself for months.[*]

This CEC/TEC absorptive/adsorptive property of clay is quite evident in the healing profession. Practitioners have used clay for multiple internal and external maladies for centuries, such as bad burns, fractures, boils, eczema, psoriasis, gum diseases, arthritis, internal ulcers, dysentery, diarrhea, constipation, and many more.

According to Raymond Dextreit, author of *Our Earth, Our Cure*, clay emits radioaesthetic emanations that heal. Conversely, Dextreit states that clay absorbs dangerous radioactive emissions that can be detected via Geiger counter experiments. I personally experienced such an experiment in Pennsylvania in 1984. A gallon of water that contained radioactive discharge detected by a Geiger counter was treated with a teaspoon of Desert Dyna-Min™ clay. The detection of the radioactivity quickly subsided. This experiment was repeated several times with the same result. Where did that radioactivity go?

Clay is a remarkable example of "fractal geometry," or what I prefer to call "fractal infinity," in the natural realm. Fractal design is the basic architecture of nature, found anywhere and everywhere. The branching of trees, the root ball of plants, the petals of flowers, the deltas of rivers, the bronchial/arterial structure of lungs, the villi and microvilli of the intestines,

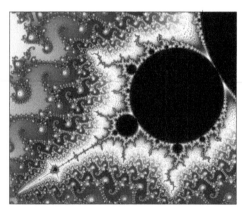

the electrostatic discharge of lightning, mountain ranges, snowflakes, the vascular system of plants and animals, the growing colonies of bacteria, ad infinitum. Benoit Mandelbrot, a researcher at IBM's Yorktown Heights facility in New York, designed a computerized fractal "creature," now called the Mandelbrot Set, a product of an exact mathematical procedure, which is not the way fractals in nature are formed. Rather, they form in noisy, random

Mandelbrot set created by Wolfgang Beyer with the program Ultra Fractal 3, via Wikimedia Commons.

---

[*] John Noble Wilford, "New Finding Backs Idea that Life Started in Clay Rather than Sea" *New York Times*, April 3, 1985.

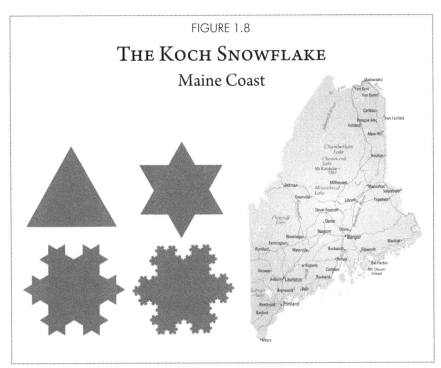

environments, a central message in Mandelbrot's book *The Fractal Geometry of Nature.*

A high school experiment called the Koch snowflake best illustrates this phenomenon. Starting out with a triangle and superimposing additional triangles at various degrees, one soon begins to see a "coastline." In the real world our terrestrial realm is outlined with such, in some localities more than others. Take the rocky coastline of Maine. If one were to drive its length from the New Hampshire border to New Brunswick border, it would approximate about three hundred miles. If one got out of the car and walked the distance, covering every linear foot along the edges of this irregular coastline bordering the ocean, the length extends to three thousand miles. That's if you are a person! What if "you" were a mouse walking along the edge of where land touches the sea? What if you were a microbe? In each example, the distance increases dramatically because the twists and turns demarcating where the water's edge touches the shoreline become increasingly smaller and smaller as perception becomes more detailed.

Another high school experiment compares the ignition potential of a large steel spike to the same amount of steel ground up into fine wool and then ignited by a propane torch. Obviously, the spike would not respond. The steel wool, however, would ignite because the surface area of the metal was enhanced by such an extent that a combustible reaction was possible.

In soils, organic compounds like humic acids and clays are classified as colloids. A colloid as Webster defines it is: "A substance made up of a *system of particles* with linear dimensions in range of about 10^{-7} to 5×10^{-5} cm, dispersed in a *continuous* gaseous, liquid, or solid medium whose *properties depend on the large specific surface area*. The particles can be larger molecules like proteins or solid, liquid, or gaseous aggregates, and *they remain dispersed indefinitely*" (emphasis added). What can that possibly mean to a farmer, rancher, naturalist, biologist, healing practitioner, or someone concerned about his or her personal ecology or health?

What all this is really emphasizing is that the "nature of nature" is rhythm. Movement and rest, chaos to order to chaos. When this colloidal substrate is infused with life, then the miracles of genesis, regenesis, and infinity itself are unleashed.

The Mineral
Nature of Soil

S o how do you ascertain the optimal quality of your soil? To take the pulse of your soil, you need to monitor the geological (minerals), biological (microorganisms), and physical (clay, silt, sand, loam, and humus) components of the soil. Fortunately, there are excellence resources for determining your soil's potential productivity and weather resilience.

To take a snapshot of the geology of your soil, utilizing a laboratory that can provide you with an assay of macro- and microelements can yield a good benchmark of your "exchangeable" macro- and microelement levels.

Following is an abbreviated summary of the importance of minerals to plants and animals and the sources that can be utilized to be applied on soils. This is by no means a soil/plant mineral primer, and those wanting to delve into the "meat" of agriculturally important minerals should peruse the texts written by McKibben, Kinsey, Albrecht, Schriefer, Zimmer, Brady and Weil, etc. (see Resources).

Labs such as Logan Labs, A&L, Midwest Labs, Texas Plant and Soil Labs, and Perry Labs are a few examples of facilities that have, in my opinion, a good track record of providing information on the geological quotient of your farm.

TABLE 2.1
ATOMIC WEIGHT

Element	Symbol	Number	Atomic Weight	Element	Symbol	Number	Atomic Weight
Actinium	Ac	89	227	Meitnerium	Mt	109	268
Aluminum	Al	13	26.9815	Mendelevium	Md	101	258
Americium	Am	95	243	Mercury	Hg	80	200.59
Antimony	Sb	51	121.76	Molybdenum	Mo	42	95.94
Argon	Ar	18	39.948	Neodymium	Nd	60	144.24
Arsenic	As	33	74.9216	Neon	Ne	10	20.1797
Astatine	At	85	210	Neptunium	Np	93	237
Barium	Ba	56	137.327	Nickel	Ni	28	58.6934
Berkelium	Bk	97	247	Niobium	Nb	41	92.9064
Beryllium	Be	4	9.0122	Nitrogen	N	7	14.0067
Bismuth	Bi	83	208.9804	Nobelium	No	102	259
Bohrium	Bh	107	264	Osmium	Os	76	190.23
Boron	B	5	10.811	Oxygen	O	8	15.9994
Bromine	Br	35	79.904	Palladium	Pd	46	106.42
Cadmium	Cd	48	112.411	Phosphorus	P	15	30.9738
Calcium	Ca	20	40.078	Platinum	Pt	78	195.078
Californium	Cf	98	251	Plutonium	Pu	94	244
Carbon	C	6	12.0107	Polonium	Po	84	209
Cerium	Ce	58	140.116	Potassium	K	19	39.0983
Cesium	Cs	55	132.9055	Praseodymium	Pr	59	140.9077
Chlorine	Cl	17	35.453	Promethium	Pm	61	145
Chromium	Cr	24	51.9961	Protactinium	Pa	91	231.0359
Cobalt	Co	27	58.9332	Radium	Ra	88	226
Copper	Cu	29	63.546	Radon	Rn	86	222
Curium	Cm	96	247	Rhenium	Re	75	186.207
Dubnium	Db	105	262	Rhodium	Rh	45	102.9055
Dysprosium	Dy	66	162.5	Rubidium	Rb	37	85.4678
Einsteinium	Es	99	252	Ruthenium	Ru	44	101.07
Erbium	Er	68	167.259	Rutherfordium	Rf	104	261
Europium	Eu	63	151.964	Samarium	Sm	62	150.36
Fermium	Fm	100	257	Scandium	Sc	21	44.9559
Fluorine	F	9	18.9984	Seaborgium	Sg	106	266
Francium	Fr	87	223	Selenium	Se	34	78.96
Gadolinium	Gd	64	157.25	Silicon	Si	14	28.0855
Gallium	Ga	31	69.723	Silver	Ag	47	107.8682
Germanium	Ge	32	72.64	Sodium	Na	11	22.9897
Gold	Au	79	196.9665	Strontium	Sr	38	87.62
Hafnium	Hf	72	178.49	Sulfur	S	16	32.065
Hassium	Hs	108	277	Tantalum	Ta	73	180.9479
Helium	He	2	4.0026	Technetium	Tc	43	98
Holmium	Ho	67	164.9303	Tellurium	Te	52	127.6
Hydrogen	H	1	1.0079	Terbium	Tb	65	158.9253
Indium	In	49	114.818	Thallium	Tl	81	204.3833
Iodine	I	53	126.9045	Thorium	Th	90	232.0381
Iridium	Ir	77	192.217	Thulium	Tm	69	168.9342
Iron	Fe	26	55.845	Tin	Sn	50	118.71
Krypton	Kr	36	83.8	Titanium	Ti	22	47.867
Lanthanum	La	57	138.9055	Tungsten	W	74	183.84
Lawrencium	Lr	103	262	Uranium	U	92	238.0289
Lead	Pb	82	207.2	Vanadium	V	23	50.9415
Lithium	Li	3	6.941	Xenon	Xe	54	131.293
Lutetium	Lu	71	174.967	Ytterbium	Yb	70	173.04
Magnesium	Mg	12	24.305	Yttrium	Y	39	88.9059
Manganese	Mn	25	54.938	Zinc	Zn	30	65.39
				Zirconium	Zr	40	91.224

I utilize Logan Labs, which uses a Mellich III extraction, and I refer to my test of choice as the "Agri-Dynamics 3" test. This test includes the following:

- total exchange capacity (soil's nutrient-holding capacity and exchange sites)
- pH
- organic matter (total, including active)
- estimated nitrogen release (ENR) or the estimated amount of organic nitrogen within the organic matter
- sulfur (anions) in ppm
- phosphate P205 in lbs/acre; (or phosphorus (P) in ppm)
- calcium in lbs/acre
- magnesium in lbs/acre
- potassium (potash or K_2O) in lbs/acre
- sodium in lbs/acre

- base saturation (% of)
- calcium
- magnesium
- potassium
- sodium
- other bases (e.g. Total of cation
- trace minerals in ppm; of Boron
- iron
- manganese
- copper
- zinc
- aluminum
- selenium
- chromium
- cobalt
- molybdenum
- silica

Note: Mellich III Extraction will yield higher amounts of trace elements than DPTA. For example the range for manganese using DPTA would be 2.0–5.0 ppm. For Mellich III it would be 10–35 ppm.

The last five are requested because selenium is not only vital to plant health, it's critically important for livestock immunity. Chromium is necessary for adequate energy metabolism in livestock. Cobalt is a requirement for all ruminants to synthesize cobalamin and to convert propionic acid into glucose, and for nitrogen fixation for legumes. Molybdenum is also a nutrient for nitrogen-fixing microbes and plays a role in nitrogen-reductase enzyme actions to make plant-available NO_3 from rhizobia bacteria and to convert nitrate (NO_3^-) into amino acids in the plant. Silica is actually a macroelement that plants utilize structurally to prevent insect and disease attack.

The following table shows the ranges I'm seeking in any soil, be it a perennial pasture, fruit trees, or an annual cropping parcel producing broad-acre crops or produce.

TABLE 2.2
SOIL REPORT IDEALS

TEC (ME) 12+	pH 6.3-6.5	Organic Matter (%) 5%+	Sulfur (ppm) 25–50ppm
Phosphate P_2O_5 (lbs/acre) 350lbs/acre	Calcium (%) 68% 1904*lbs/acre	Magnesium (%) 12% 192* lbs/acre	Potassium (%) 3–5% 208*lbs/acre
Sodium (%) 0.5–3% <100*lbs/acre	Hydrogen (%) 10%***	Boron (ppm) 1–2ppm	Iron (ppm) 50–100ppm
Manganese (ppm) 10–40	Copper (ppm) 2–5ppm	Zinc (ppm) 6–12ppm	Aluminum (ppm) <1400
Molybdenum (ppm) 0.4–0.7 ppm	Cobalt (ppm) 0.5–1.0	Selenium (ppm) 1(+)ppm	Chromium (ppm) 1–3+
Silica (ppm) +25ppm	Cadmium -----	Arsenic -----	Lead -----
Nickel -----			

*** Note: Ideal lbs/acre of Ca, Mg, K, Na, H vary soil by soil, depending upon the TEC (CEC), even though the ideal percents remain the same.
~~~~~~To convert ppm to lbs/acres multiply by 2.
Exceptions: To convert ppm of K (potassium) to lbs/acres of K20 (potash) multiply by 2.4.
 To convert ppm of P (phosphorus) to lbs/acre of P205 (Phosphate) multiply by 4.6.

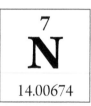

$$
\boxed{\begin{array}{c} 7 \\ \mathbf{N} \\ 14.00674 \end{array}}
$$

Nitrogen (Anion as Nitrate, NO_3; Cation as Ammonium, NH_4 Target: 3–5 Percent

Nitrogen is the most abundant nutrient required for plant growth. Not coincidentally, each acre of real estate is blanketed by an atmosphere containing 78 percent nitrogen gas, or about 30,000 tons of nitrogen as N_2! Nitrogen is the key element to synthesize protein, averaging 16 percent of protein in plants, and is therefore a key component of chlorophyll, a molecule consisting of a core element of magnesium surrounded by four atoms of nitrogen, as well as carbon, oxygen, hydrogen, sulfur, and iron. Excess nitrogen in plant tissue is a magnet for insect and disease opportunism, especially when compounded by deficiencies of sulfur, calcium, magnesium, phosphorus, and boron. Excess nitrogen creates "funny protein," overloading the bloodstream of livestock/humans with BUN (blood urea nitrogen) and stressing the immune system, liver, and kidneys. In lactating animals, this can become MUN (milk urea nitrogen), excesses of which can affect calf health, reproduction, energy balance, etc.

The mismanagement of nitrogen is the single largest agriculturally destructive practice. It burns out humus, leaches calcium, acidifies the soil, contaminates ground and surface water, and produces nitrous oxide, the most potent greenhouse gas, which then returns as nitric acid and destroys our forests by killing symbiotic fungi living amongst the trees' roots.

Nitrogen losses from improperly applied fertilizes account for 50 percent of what is applied. Plants take up three forms of nitrogen: ammonium (NH_4), nitrate (NO_3), and organic nitrogen (such as amino acids) via microbial action. NH_4, a cation, can readily attach to anions such as nitrates (NO_3), creating ammonium nitrate; sulfates (SO_4^{-2}), creating ammonium sulfate; or phosphate (PO_4-), creating ammonium phosphate, all of which are stable forms of nitrogen that don't readily leach until warmth and moisture activates soil microbes, which readily convert NH_4^+ to nitrate (NO_3^-). Since nitrate is now an anion it is leachable by water into streams and groundwater.

Ammonium (NH_4) taken into the root is converted to an amine (NH_2), which is converted to amino acids in the root, which in turn move throughout the plant to construct complete proteins. The conversion of NH_4 into amino acids requires an expenditure of energy in the roots, causing the foliage of the plant to send carbohydrates down into the rhizosphere. This process requires more photosynthesis to occur, creating more energy than is actually needed for amino acid synthesis. The surplus energy is truncated off to the microbial community surrounding the roots.

As plants take in NH_4^+ they release hydrogen, thus lowering the pH around the root hairs. This is important because an acid pH in the rhizosphere is needed to inhibit plant pathogens and increase the uptake of minerals, especially the trace elements. Trace elements are a vital prerequisite to produce the plant secondary metabolites—phenols, terpenes, alkaloids—for additional plant protection from pests. Additionally, as ammonium $(NH_4)^+$ is converted to (NO_3^-), the uptake of phosphorus increases because of the acidifying effect that the hydrogen ion released has on phosphorus uptake.

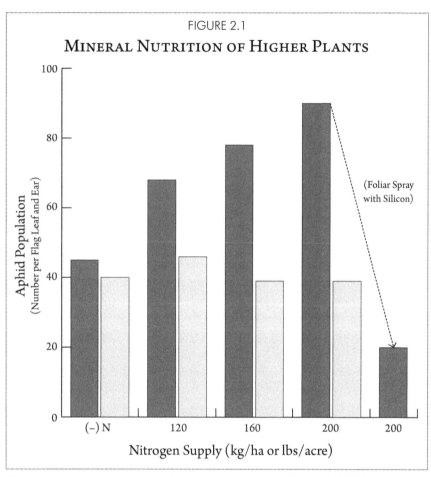

FIGURE 2.1

MINERAL NUTRITION OF HIGHER PLANTS

Effect of nitrogen supply and foliar sprays containing silicon (1% NaSiO$_2$) on the population density of two aphid's species in winter wheat. Striped bars—Metopolophium dirhodum; open bars—Sitobion avenae. (-)N denotes Nitrogen-deficient control plant." Hanisch, H.C. (1980) Kali-Briefe 15, 287–96.

Plants generally require approximately one-third of their nitrogen as nitrate, or NO$_3^-$. This is because as NO$_3$ is taken in, a hydroxyl (OH$^-$) radical is released, which is alkaline. This exchange is utilized to maintain cellular pH in the plant. However, when excess nitrogen (from any source) or only nitrate (NO$_3^-$) nitrogen is used, this OH$^-$ molecule builds up around the root hairs and adversely affects the root ecology because the pH around the root hairs becomes too alkaline, disrupting the desirable populations of microbes and inhibiting the uptake of trace elements.

Additionally, to make protein the plant must now convert NO_3^- into an amine (NH_2) in the leaf instead of the root. This process requires nitrate reductase enzyme, which requires molybdenum, which is deficient in many soils. Converting nitrate (NO_3^-) into an amine is thus an energy-consuming process for the plant, requiring as much as 10 percent of the photosynthates produced in the leaf chloroplasts. Nitrate reductase also requires sunlight and warm temperatures to form. Accordingly, it isn't being produced at night or in cool, cloudy weather, which can lead to an accumulation of nitrates and non-protein nitrogen compounds, a recipe for attracting insect and disease pests and low nutritional quality and poor shelf life.

Nitrate can accumulate into multiple undesirable substances called "funny protein." In forages, we call it non-protein nitrogen (NPN). Complete protein synthesis (called "true protein") has been arrested, and now one has a crop of "funny protein," ripe for the digestive system of more primitive organisms like fungi, bacteria, and insects. These pests do not thrive upon tissue that has true or complete protein, which is designed to be consumed by life forms with more complex digestive systems.

Nitrate excesses also mean carbohydrate deficiencies (low Brix). Thus higher levels of simpler carbohydrates like monosaccharides abound, instead of complex, more complete carbohydrates such as polysacchrides, pectins, or glucans. Excess "funny protein" means plants have a larger requirement for water—meaning less drought tolerance—and lower specific gravity (test weight), which also contributes to poor flavor and short shelf life.

How does nature reconcile the nitrogen/protein factory? Simple. She "thinks like a prairie." Crop residues on pastures, as well as dung or manure, are proteins that are digested into amines (NH_2) in the soil and then further broken down into amino acids and eventually ammonium (NH_4^+). Plant roots then reverse that process, taking in nitrogen either biologically by microorganisms as amino acids or as ammonium (NH_4).

When growing annual crops, minimum tillage can help replicate this prairie system. So can cover crops and compost tilled into the soil as slow-release sources of either ammonium (NH_4^+) or organic nitrogen as amino acids. These can be taken up as such by organisms like mycorrhizae, which would require even less energy from the plant to convert into protein than the enzyme-dependent ammonium-to-amine-to-amino-acid-to-"complete-protein" cascade.

Urea is the most popular form of nitrogen used because of its cost. It's 46 percent nitrogen and already in the amine form. However, because of the urease enzyme present in soil (from microbes), urea is converted into unstable ammonia (NH_3^+), *not* ammonium (NH_4), which is stable in the soil, especially soils with adequate organic matter. Ammonia (NH_3) is a gas and volatilizes. This conversion on the soil surface can create 50–60 percent losses of nitrogen. Incorporated into the soil the ammonia (NH_3^+) can be converted into ammonium (NH_4) or nitrate (NO_3), allowing plant roots to have access.

Essentially, there are two processes at work in the soil relative to nitrogen: nitrification and denitrification (below).

NH_2-CO-NH_2	Soil Surface	$NH_3(\uparrow)$	In	NH_4^+
Urea	Urease	Ammonia	Soil	Ammonium

Nitrification is as follows:

NH_4^+	Nitrosomonas	$NO_2(\uparrow)$	Nitrobacter	$NO_3(\downarrow)$
				$+4H^+$
Ammonium	Bacteria	Nitrogen Dioxide	Bacteria	Nitrate

In natural systems, plants readily utilize the amount of ammonium (NH_4^+) that they need, but in modern agricultural systems utilizing a lot of tillage with low-organic matter soils and applying nitrogen up front for the entire growing season, most of that ammonium (NH_4^+) is rapidly converted by Nitrosomonas and Nitrobacter bacteria to nitrate (NO_3^-) once soils have warmed.

In anaerobic soils denitrification kicks in, whereby nitrate (NO_3^-) is *reduced* by anaerobic (low oxygen) microbes which don't thrive in aerobic environments. They consume a single oxygen from the nitrate (NO_3), reducing it to nitrogen dioxide (NO_2) ($\uparrow$), then to nitrous oxide (NO) ($\uparrow$), and eventually ammonia (NH_3^+) ($\uparrow$). Sulfur is likewise reduced, creating hydrogen sulfide (H_2S) ($\uparrow$) from sulfate (SO_4^-). All of these compounds are volatile gases, which leave the soil as waste products.

It is a cornerstone requirement to manage nitrogen if one wants top-quality crops; resistance to drought, disease, and insects; and a continual building of soil carbon or humus.

- Lighter, sandier soils should be spoon-fed soluble nitrogen over the growing season.
- The cations (Ca, Mg, K, Na) need to be balanced, and the phosphate (P_2O_5) and sulfur need to be adequate as well.
- For nitrogen fixation and nitrogen metabolism, key trace minerals are essential, such as cobalt and molybdenum.
- Winter cover crops are nitrogen catchers, picking up soluble nitrogen into plant tissue for next season. Soil nitrate (NO_3) is converted into plant amines or proteins, stabilizing the nitrogen and providing plowdown of protein, which is a raw material for ammonium or (NH_4) or organic nitrogen (amino acids).
- Legumes in the crop rotation actually fix nitrogen out of the atmosphere supplying a tremendous amount of nitrogen per acre.
- Begin any stubble digestion late in the growing season. Highly lignified stubble, which is tilled under in the spring, is a slow-to-digest form of carbon that can create a nitrogen deficit in the following growing season, thus demanding more nitrogen to feed the crop.
- Add carbon sources to nitrogen amendments. Humates or humic acids can complex, or chelate, nitrogen compounds, thus stabilizing them. Molasses or sugars can provide readily available energy to microbes that take up nitrogen into their tissues, thus increasing the nitrogen-loving bacteria and creating a "nitrogen sink" in the soil, to slow down leaching.
- Providing a source of sulfur and calcium—soluble if possible—when applying soluble nitrogen can allow plants to create more complete (versus "funny") protein.
- Compost is a wonderful source of microbial protein and biological diversity as well as a mother lode of catalysts and metabolites for indigenous soil microbes. All annual crops should get some, and perennial vines and trees are no exception.
- Timing and placement of nitrogen is key. Banding may be far more cost-effective for row crops and produce. Orchards and vineyards would benefit from broadcasting due to lateral feeder roots.
- Drain wet (anaerobic) areas to prevent denitrification.
- Via aggressive, deep-rooted cover crops or subsoiling, get a deeper aerobic zone where roots and microbes, earthworms, etc. can begin enlarging and expanding the "A" horizon.

Sources of nitrogen:

- Ammonium sulfate (21-0-0-24 S), ammonium type, not organically approved
- Monoammonium phosphate (11-52-0), ammonium type, not organically approved
- Diammonium phosphate (18-46-0), ammonium type, not organically approved
- Ammonium nitrate (34-0-0), ammonium type, not organically approved
- Urea (46-0-0) ammonium type, not organically approved
- Urea/ammonium nitrate, (28-0-0; 30-0-0; 32-0-0), ammonium type, not organically approved
- Ammonium thiosulfate (12-0-0-26 S), ammonium type, not organically approved
- Chilean nitrate (16-0-0), nitrate type, organically acceptable
- Calcium nitrate (15-0-0-19 Ca), nitrate type, not organically approved
- Potassium nitrate (13-0-46), nitrate type, not organically approved
- Fish emulsion (2.5-3-1), ammonium type, organically acceptable
- Manures (range is 1–3 percent), ammonium type, organically acceptable
- Slurry manure (range is 1–3 percent), nitrate type—should be stabilized with gypsum, soft-rock phosphate, humates, and zeolite, organically acceptable

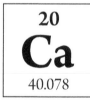

Calcium (cation): Target: 65–75 Percent

Calcium is a nutrient that is recommended to be ideally at 65–75 percent of the base saturation because is the backbone of fertility. Calcium is the vehicle that allows other nutrients to be shuttled into the plant. Calcium improves soil texture, increases the availability of phosphorus and trace elements (when calcium is not overapplied), invigorates root development (as well as stems and leaves), affects the protein quality of plants, is responsible for aiding in the synthesis of energy fractions (such as pectins in forages), and is required for cell membrane strength, resistance to fruit rotting, formation of mucilage, and the prevention of premature senescence (aging) as well as contributing to freeze resistance. Calcium deficiency stresses are mostly confined to the fruiting part or growing points. Because calcium deficiency stresses are usually caused by temporarily localized deficiencies of calcium, adding calcium to the soil at that point might be futile, as it is likely beyond the capacity of the plant to absorb and mobilize calcium where it's needed.

Foliar sprays could thus be more effective than soil applications when this occurs. Moreover, environmental factors such as drought might be more of a contributor to calcium stress than calcium levels in the soil, as calcium precipitates in the soil as it dries out. On the other hand, irrigation water high in sodium and bicarbonates could also contribute to calcium stress symptoms.

As plants grow they produce oxalic acid. Calcium helps neutralize toxic levels of oxalic acid by creating calcium oxalate, a biologically inert form of calcium. A tissue test could thus be misleading because it will include calcium oxalate as part of the total tissue calcium. Another paradox is that calcium stress disorders can occur on calcareous soils, high in phosphorous, low in boron, or irrigated with low calcium water (which leaches calcium). Calcium for animals and humans is the primary element for building strong bones and teeth and maintaining a normal blood pH and blood coagulation. It also permits the cell membranes to be permeable and is required for nerve impulse and optimal muscle functioning.

Sources of calcium are:
- High calcium limestone (35–38 percent calcium), organically acceptable
- Dolomitic limestone (21 percent calcium and 11–12 percent magnesium), to be used where calcium and magnesium are both required, organically acceptable
- Gypsum or calcium sulfate (22 percent calcium and 17–19 percent sulfur), organically acceptable (if mined), not to be substituted for limestone or dolomite on acidic soils.
- Cement kiln dust or burnt lime (more than 30 percent calcium 3–6 percent K_2O and 3–6 percent sulfur), highly available, water soluble, but not organically approved.
- Sugar beet lime (30–35 percent [+] calcium, in the form of highly available calcite), not organically approved
- Calcium silicate (30 percent calcium, 7 percent magnesium, and 12 percent silicon) is a by-product of the steel refractory industry and is not organically approved and a reasonably good source of both calcium

and silica. The mined source "Wollastonite" is organically acceptable.

- Calcium chloride (36 percent calcium and 64 percent chlorine), not organically approved
- Paper mill sludge (varies, but typically 30–35 percent calcium), quite reactive but not organically approved.
- Calcium nitrate (15.5 percent nitrogen and 19 percent calcium) is a good source of both elements for crops needing growth but is not organically approved.
- Aragonite, a seawater calcium (35–38 percent calcium), very available, organically acceptable

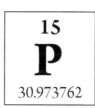

15

P

30.973762

Phosphorus (Anion) Target: 350 lbs/acre of P_2O_5; or 80 ppm of P

Phosphorus is expressed as phosphate or P_2O_5 with a triple negative charge causing it to readily lock up with cations like CA^{++}, Mg^{++}, Al^{+++}, Fe^{++}, and K^+. It is the core element of the energy currency of all life-forms, namely adenosine triphosphate, or ATP. It is essential for the synthesis of DNA (the genetic code) and RNA, which direct protein production and repair in plants and animals. Cell membranes are constructed of phospholipids, and phosphorus is essential for photosynthesis, flowering, fruiting, seed production, nitrogen fixation, root growth, and stalk strength. In animals/humans, phosphorus composes the compound apatite, which is a calcium phosphate matrix used to build bones and teeth.

Sources of phosphate:

- Soft rock phosphate (typically 18–21 percent P_2O_5, with 3 percent available), organically acceptable
- Hard rock phosphate (30–33 percent P_2O_5, with 3 percent available), organically acceptable
- Bone meal (5-12-0), organically acceptable
- Charred bone meal (0-16-0), organically acceptable
- Bird guano (15 percent P_2O_5), organically acceptable
- Hen manure/compost (3-2-1), organically acceptable
- Fish hydrolysate (3-2-1 to 5-2-1), liquid, organically acceptable
- Super phosphate (0-20-0), not organically acceptable

TABLE 2.3

NUTRIENTS & FUNCTIONS

Element	% of Element Found	Function
Oxygen	44.50000	most organic compounds
Carbon	43.60000	all organic compounds
Hydrogen	6.30000	all organic compounds
Nitrogen	1.50000	chlorophyll, enzymes, nucleic acids proteins, cell water balance
Potassium	1.30000	activates enzymes, carbohydrate translocation, protein synthesis, cell water balance
Silicon	1.20000	cell wall support, binder of membranes, protects plants from physical damage, and increases phytochrome photosynthesis system
Magnesium	0.25000	component of chlorophyll, activates enzymes, regulates cell division and general metabolism
Calcium	0.30000	cell wall structure, membrane permeability, cell elongation
Phosphorus	0.20000	main energy transfer component, most nucleic components
Sulfur	0.14000	component of proteins, involved in nodulation and respiration
Sodium	0.05000	cell water balance, carbohydrate translocation, protein synthesis
Iron	0.04000	chlorophyll synthesis, redox reactions, activates enzymes
Manganese	0.00500	redox reactions, nitrate-to-ammonia conversion, enzyme activator
Chlorine	0.00500	chlorophyll synthesis, redox reactions, activates enzymes
Aluminum	0.00400	unknown, found in all plants
Zinc	0.00300	pH of plant regulator, enzyme activator
Copper	0.00100	nitrate-to-ammonia conversion, enzyme activator, respiration
Boron	0.00070	maturation and differentiation of cells, carbohydrate translocation
Molybdenum	0.00060	nitrate-to-ammonia conversion, N fixation in legumes, ammonia-to-nitrate conversion
Cobalt	0.00020	N fixation in legumes, acid-carbohydrate conversion
Vanadium	0.00003	nitrate-to-ammonia conversion, N fixation in legumes, deactivates ammonia-to-nitrate conversion, cell division, DNA protection
Chromium	0.00002	increases iron bioavailability, carbohydrate translocation, increases cuticle thickness
Nickel	0.00001	unknown but has been shown to increases yield in plants grown under no Ni versus Ni application

- Triple super phosphate (0-46-0), not organically acceptable
- DAP, diammonium phosphate (18-46-0), not organically acceptable
- MAP, monoammonium phosphate (11-52-0), not organically acceptable
- orthophosphate (10-34-0), not organically acceptable
- MPK monopotassium phosphate (0-52-34), not organically acceptable
- Biosolids, or sewage sludge, (5-4-0), not organically acceptable
- DKP dipotassium phosphate (0-38-52), not organically acceptable

Perennial crops can utilize the more "organic" and thus less soluble forms of phosphate than can annuals, which have a shorter season to grow from seed to harvest. If soils are low in P_2O_5, and/or low in other elements, such as calcium, zinc, or humus, then a more sustainable approach would be to apply some soluble form of phosphate as well as some slow-release phosphate such as rock phosphate. I like the bone meal and guano sources because they are balanced with both fast and sustained-release phosphorus and contain a suite of other elements, like calcium and trace elements.

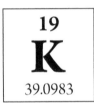

Potassium (Cation) Target: 4–5 Percent Base Saturation

Potassium is a major element that curiously does not incorporate into organic compounds but actually remains in the ionic form (K+) in solution within the cell. It is an activator of at least eighty enzyme systems essential for starch synthesis, photosynthesis, protein synthesis, and translocation of sugars. It also enhances water uptake—a "poor man's irrigation"—thus drought tolerance, winter hardiness, resistance to fungal and insect pests, and it has importance for flavor and color as well as stalk strength. In animals/humans, it is a vital element for the nervous system, a healthy vascular system, and is one of the key elements for the cellular sodium-potassium pump that allows cells to take in nutrients, water, and oxygen and eliminate waste.

Potassium is readily attached to clay colloids, and the amount of insoluble potassium can be quite massive, as much as 10,000 pounds per acre in the top six inches of soil, with even more (30,000 pounds per acre) in subsoils. These locked-up volumes of potassium are not readily available to plants and do not even show up on a soil test as they are not located on the exchangeable sites of the clay colloids. Adequate calcium applied to flocculate, or granulate, the clay in acid soils will help, as will increasing the organic matter, which invites bacteria and fungi to produce enzymes and acids to help release potassium.

Thus when considering the amount of potassium in soils, there are four "reservoirs" in the soil bank. The exchangeable potassium is attached to the soil colloids and found on a CEC or TEC lab analysis. It is readily available to plants but comprises only about 1 percent of the total potassium. Solution potassium is also available to plants, is found in the water film surrounding soil aggregates, and comprises about 0.5 percent of the total soil potassium. It is also very susceptible to leaching. Potassium that is held tightly between the clay lattices comprises 1–10 percent of the total potassium but is only released slowly to plants. The majority of soil potassium, 90–98 percent, is locked up in mineral complexes. Negligible amounts of this potassium source are released to crops.

Perennials have an advantage over annuals in mobilizing potassium (and other elements) not only because they can efficiently access the exchangeable and solution sources of potassium. Perennials also have the resources of larger amounts of plant exudates (e.g., enzymes, organic acids, etc.) to extract those hard-to-access sources of potassium that annuals cannot, as they only have a root system that lives two to three months instead of many years. Perennials' roots are persistently working on the complexed potassiums in the clay lattice, and perhaps even resistant mineral complexes,

Higher pH soils (greater than 6.7 percent) don't readily accept potassium inputs, and if combined calcium and magnesium base saturations exceed 90 percent it is very hard to build potassium levels. Ratios are important, namely a 1:1 with magnesium in parts per million and a 1:3 ratio with magnesium in terms of base saturation percent.

Additionally, high sodium levels can compromise potassium availability. High-sodium soils are found more commonly in arid states under irrigation, especially if the irrigation water is recycled wastewater from municipalities, food processing plants, or high-sodium wells.

If the sum of potassium and sodium exceed 10 percent of base saturation there can be an issue with manganese uptake. Excess nitrogen will drive down potassium, and excess nitrogen or potassium will both drive down boron. If manganese is excessive while zinc is deficient, this can be a sign of potassium unavailability to the plant, regardless of potassium soil levels.

Sources of potassium:
- Potassium sulfate (0-0-50-17 S), soluble and organically acceptable
- Potassium chloride (0-0-60-40 Cl), soluble and organically acceptable
- Potassium hydroxide (0-0-83 K_2O), not organically accteptable; also under wood ashes
- Dipotassium phosphate (0-38-52)
- Monopotassium phosphate (0-52-34), soluble and not organically acceptable
- Potassium nitrate (13-0-44), soluble, not organically acceptable
- Sul-Po-Mag (22 K,11 Mg,22 S), soluble and organically acceptable
- Glauconite, Jersey greensand (7 percent K_2O, plus iron, multiple trace elements), organically acceptable
- Wood ashes (6.0–10.0 percent K_2O); the name *potash* actually is derived from the words *potassium* and *wood ashes*. Both soluble and sustained release, organically acceptable
- Manures (all manures contain 1–2 percent potash), soluble and sustained release and organically acceptable. Manures that are slurry anaerobic liquids are very soluble and also contain anaerobic by-products (indoles, skatoles, mercaptans, ammonia, and sulfides) that can be quite toxic to soil life. The best manures are composted and only have a slightly lower analysis than raw manure, but with greater beneficial impact on soils and crops.

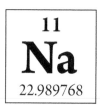

Sodium (Cation) Target:
0.5–3.0 Percent Base Saturation or 40–50 lbs/acre
Sodium is an element that isn't considered "essential," but in fact it is part of the cationic mineral balance which affects the soil's pH and electrical conductivity, plant sap pH, and governs the osmotic pressure in cellular tissues and fluids in plants as well as animals/humans. This I consider essential.

Excess sodium is usually the issue, as it works in the opposite way as calcium. Calcium granulates clay, and sodium prevents clays from granulating, so excesses can damage soil structure.

In areas that have excessive potassium in the soil, usually where a lot of animal manure accumulates, the potassium levels in the forages can be so elevated as to be toxic to ruminants. Getting the calcium levels up to optimum and then applying a coating of a hundred pounds of plain rock salt, three hundred pounds of gypsum (calcium sulfate), and one pound of boron per acre can make a difference in improving protein quality, energy levels, and the palatability of the pastures. In C4 plants (warm-season annuals like corn, sorghum, etc.) and warm-season perennials (switchgrass, gammagrass, big bluestem, etc.) sodium is needed to bring about a higher utilization of carbon dioxide (CO_2), allowing C4 plants to synthesize more carbohydrates than cool-season (C3) annuals (like wheat, barley, oats, rye, etc.) and cool-season (C3) perennials (like ryegrass, bluegrass, orchard grass, etc.).

Most sodium buildup comes from irrigation. Saline waters need to be dealt with because, over time, sodium will readily displace the other critical cations—calcium, magnesium, and potassium—and the salts can contribute to nutrient deficiency in the plants and a saline buildup around the roots, inviting dehydration of both plant roots and soil microbes.

One method to counter saline water is to add potassium silicates, humic acids, and soluble gypsum, which contains calcium and sulfur. The calcium displaces the sodium, which combines with sulfur to create sodium sulfate, a water-soluble salt that can leach out of the rhizosphere.

Creating hardpans by tilling soils that are too wet, compaction from heavy equipment, pugging by livestock, and humus-destroying overtillage will cause drainage problems that allow sodium and other salts to accumulate.

Sources of sodium:
- Rock salt (39 percent sodium, 61 percent chloride)
- Sodium sulfate (32 percent sodium, 23 percent sulfur)

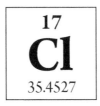

17
Cl
35.4527

Chloride (Anion) Target: 0.02–0.04 percent

Chloride is a secondary element not given much notice, as typically plants don't require huge amounts of it. That being said, there are more than 130 chlorinated organic compounds found in plants, and the average concentration in plants is 0.20–2.0 percent. Back in the 1990s a few other nutritionists and

I stumbled upon the fact that corn silage containing more than 0.40 percent chloride had a lot more resistance to molds and mycotoxins. The chlorine requirement for most plants appears to be in the range of 0.02–0.04 percent. Chloride affects the opening and closing of the leaf's stomata. It is also a factor in producing antibiotic and fungicidal compounds.

On the other hand, chloride/chlorine excesses are more of a concern than deficiencies, particularly in arid and semi-arid areas. Most of the time it is because of the continual use of potassium chloride or muriate of potash instead of potassium sulfate. I do not believe that potassium chloride is an intrinsic evil, but it has become a detriment because of overuse. When overused, potassium chloride increases the salt index of the soil, dehydrating roots and soil microbes. It could also create an excess amount of chlorine, a sanitizer and thus soil sterilant. Those that would advocate using salt—whether sea salt or sea solids—but warn against potassium chloride have not reviewed their chemistry. Sodium chloride, or table salt, contains 61 percent chlorine; potassium chloride contains 48 percent chlorine.

Sources of chloride:
- Rock salt (61 percent chlorine, 39 percent sodium)
- Potassium chloride (48 percent chlorine, 52 percent potassium

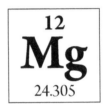

Magnesium (Anion) Target: 10–15 Percent Base Saturation

Magnesium is one of the core elements of chlorophyll, a compound that is also rich in nitrogen. Chlorophyll is the green pigment found in the chloroplast, the plant organelle responsible for converting water and carbon dioxide in the presence of sunlight into sugar. It is a carrier for phosphorus, which is necessary for seed germination and required for the synthesis of amino acids, vitamins, pigments, oils, carbohydrates, and lipids. In fact this element is critically necessary for over three hundred enzyme systems in animals. Magnesium acts like glue with soil particles, thus the sandier soils could use more magnesium, perhaps 20 percent base saturation, or a calcium:magnesium ratio of 4:1 versus a 7:1 Ca:Mg base saturation percent ratio in heavier soils. Curiously, magnesium has a 1.4 additional advantage over calcium in raising pH. Excess calcium will suppress magnesium uptake and, ironically, excess soil magnesium (by depressing calcium) will suppress uptake of magnesium into plants.

Dolomitic and serpentine soils are rich in magnesium. Serpentine soils contain little calcium as well (unlike dolomitic soils), giving a Ca:Mg ratio of less than 1.0, whereas dolomitic soils are typically greater than 2.0 Ca:Mg.

In livestock/humans, magnesium is critical for all muscle function (including the heart) and is actually necessary along with calcium, phosphorus, boron, zinc, and strontium to construct strong bones and teeth. It is required to prevent tetany (staggers) in cattle, especially on nitrogen-rich (high-protein) spring grass, and also for maintaining the acid-alkaline balance in the gut and circulatory system.

Sources of magnesium:

- Dolomitic limestone (21 percent calcium, 11–12 percent magnesium), organically acceptable
- Magnesium carbonate, or magnesite (24–28 percent magnesium), organically acceptable
- Serpentine, or magnesium silicate (30 percent magnesium, 20 percent silica), organically acceptable
- Magnesium sulfate, or Epsom salts (9.9 percent magnesium, 13–17 percent sulfur), soluble, organically acceptable
- Magnesium hydroxide (41 percent magnesium), organically acceptable (but only as the mineral brucite), soluble
- Magnesium chloride (25 percent magnesium), soluble, organically acceptable

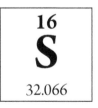

Sulfur (Anion) Target: 50–75 ppm

Sulfur is the fourth major nutrient (following nitrogen, phosphorus, and potassium) relative to plant requirements. Sulfur (as sulfate, or SO_4) is utilized by plants as much as they depend on phosphate, or P_2O_5. Sulfur is necessary to partner with nitrogen to make complete protein (not "funny protein"). There are only twenty-two amino acids, and three of them are sulfur-rich: methionine, cysteine, and cystine. But there are over fifty thousand proteins made up of nitrogen-based amino acids, and sulfur is an important constituent of many of them.

Sulfur is necessary for nitrogen fixation, the formation of chlorophyll, and is an essential component of vitamins (such as thiamine, or B-1) and enzymes. It facilitates the translocation of sugars, and in semiarid grasslands sulfur is the next most limiting nutrient following nitrogen.

One of the more important attributes of sulfur is its role in the synthesis of glutathione. Glutathione is a tripeptide consisting of three amino acids, namely glycine, glutamic acid, and cysteine. Cysteine, a sulfur-bearing amino acid, is derived from methionine, another sulfur bearing amino acid. Glutathione is the universal antioxidant in plants and animals/humans. Not only is it a cell membrane protector, it is also a heavy metal chelator or detoxifier that can shuttle toxic metals like lead, cadmium, arsenic, mercury, and even excessive amounts of nutritional metals like copper out of tissues in both plants and animals/humans. Many soils are naturally or artificially contaminated with these kinds of heavy metals, and plants depend on ample amounts of glutathione to remove them.

In order to produce glutathione, one needs adequate amounts of all those raw materials that contribute to quality protein: nitrogen (preferably as ammonium from organic compounds), sulfur, calcium, phosphorus, magnesium, boron, molybdenum, and cobalt.

Sulfur is oxidized in soils for plant use by autotrophic bacteria called Thiobacillus, including five species that can operate in a soil pH range of 2–9. Sulfur tends to leach, being an anion, and it can accumulate in poorly drained soils or in greenhouses without rainfall. To hold onto sulfur soils need to be rich in humus. Because our soils have become depleted of organic matter, which in itself is a raw material for sulfur, SO_4 levels have decreased. Manure and compost are the grower's best source of nonpurchased sulfur.

Sulfur is an effective remediator of excesses in the soil and can facilitate the reduction of magnesium, calcium, sodium, and potassium. The goal in good-quality forage is to have at least 10 percent of the nitrogen tissue test as sulfur. It would be no exaggeration to say that in over three decades of looking at soil tests, 90 percent show a sulfur deficiency. Goals for soil sulfur are fifty to seventy-five parts per million, or one hundred to two hundred pounds, of sulfur (which is 150–225 pounds of sulfate).

In animals/humans, sulfur is a keystone element to build insulin, heparin, fibrinogen, connective tissue (collagen, cartilage), keratin, elastin, biotin, and thiamine. It's a component of detoxifying compounds, such as isothiocyanates, indoles like sulforaphane, or di-indole methane, all found in cruciferous plants like cabbage, turnips, kale, etc., as well as sulfated amino acids found in the allium (garlic/onion) family. Many medicinal botanicals are rich in miscellaneous sulfur compounds like dandelion and burdock.

Sources of sulfur:

- Elemental sulfur (greater than 90 percent sulfur), used in very alkaline soils to react with excess calcium or magnesium, organically acceptable
- Gypsum or calcium sulfate (22 percent calcium, 17 percent sulfur), organically acceptable
- Potassium sulfate (50 percent K_2O, 17 percent percent sulfur), organically acceptable
- Sul-Po-Mag (22 percent sulfur, 11 percent magnesium, 22 percent potash), organically acceptable
- Ammonium sulfate (21 percent nitrogen; 24 percent sulfur, a good balance of nitrogen with sulfur, not organically approved
- Magnesium sulfate (9.9 percent magnesium; 15–17 percent sulfur), organically acceptable
- Ammonium thiosulfate (12 percent nitrogen, 26 percent sulfur), not organically approved

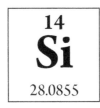

Silica Target: >25 ppm

Silica is the mineral with the largest concentrations in the soil, yet because of that it is considered a nonessential nutrient. When looking at tissue tests, however, the silica content rivals calcium, phosphorus, magnesium, sulfur, and in some cases even nitrogen.

Plants utilize silica in concert with calcium and boron to create "armor plating" by biologically converting inert silica in the soil to water-soluble monosilicic or orthosilicic acid, which is transported to the phylosphere or leaf to create a cuticle (the armor) that discourages fungal and bacterial disease and insect attack.

Silica can also be useful in increasing plant tolerance to salinity by immobilizing sodium. More stalk strength is the result of silica as well, resulting in less lodging. Grasses are a rich source of silica, anywhere from 1–6 percent. Rice, a cereal grass, can contain up to 15 percent silica in the stalk. Experiments with growers spraying silica on vegetables, fruit trees, and turfgrass have been quite encouraging in arresting diseases. It is best used in combination with soluble calcium and trace elements known to be deficient on the tissue test, as well as with humic and fulvic acids. Silica in livestock/ humans is a macroelement that is synergistic with calcium, magnesium, boron, and copper in the formation of connective tissue, bone calcification, and skin elasticity.

Silica not only creates a physical deterrent to chewing insects, it can repel sucking insects as well because of its possible ability to reduce the amount of soluble nitrogen in plant tissue. The accompanying bar graph illustrates how a silica application dramatically reduces aphid infestation on wheat. It also demonstrates that some aphid species are attracted to excess nitrogen or amino acids in the plant tissue while others are not.

The amazing depression of aphid attack on the winter wheat following a silica foliar spray is not apparently associated with just the physical changes on the leaf surface, but also for the soluble silicic acid in the plant cytoplasm, or tissue solution.

Sources of silica:
- Rock dust, granite, basalt, etc., organically acceptable
- Diatomaceous earth (89 percent silica), organically acceptable
- Potassium silicate, "water glass" (27 percent silica, 13 percent potassium), organically acceptable with some certifiers
- Clay minerals, soft rock phosphate, carbonotite, Dyna-Min
- Humic and fulvic acids

There is understandably much confusion by growers trying to ascertain the difference between plant food *elements* such as N, P, K, and Ca and plant food *compounds* as they might be utilized by laboratories that have different reporting methods. Table 2.4 may also be useful when a grower needs to figure out how much of a given plant food compound is needed to create the desired amount of any given plant food element in a fertilizer formula. The conversion table was assembled by the International Plant Nutrition Institute (www.ipni.net).

MINERALS TO RESIST DROUGHT?

The key to drought resistance is a massive root system. To the extent that key elements contribute to a large rhizosphere, they can contribute significantly to drought resistance. Since phosphorus is an energy element, (adenosine triphosphate) and because it is mobile—that is, it can move

TABLE 2.4

PLANT NUTRIENT CONVERSION TABLE

To convert Column 1 to Column 2, multiply by:	Column 1	Column 2	To convert Column 2 to Column 1, multiply by:
4.43	N	NO_3	0.23
1.22	N	NH_3	0.82
4.72	N	$(NH_4)_2SO_4$	0.21
2.86	N	NH_4NO_3	0.35
1.20	K	K_2O	0.83
0.63	KCl	K_2O	1.58
0.71	CaO	Ca	1.40
0.56	$CaCo_3$	CaO	1.78
0.60	MgO	Mg	1.66
2.99	MgO	$MgSO_4$	0.33
3.43	MgO	$MgSo_4 \cdot H_2O$	0.29
2.09	MgO	$MgCO_3$	0.48
0.16	$MgSo_4 \cdot 7H_2O$	MgO	6.25
2.29	P	P_2O_5	0.44
0.46	$Ca_3(PO_4)_2$	P_3O_5	2.18
2.00	S	SO_2	0.50
2.50	S	SO_3	0.40
3.00	S	SO_4	0.33
0.13	$MgSO_4 \cdot 7H_2O$	S	7.68
0.25	$(NH_4)_2SO_4$	S	4.00
0.23	$MgSO_4 \cdot H_2O$	S	4.31

From D. M. Ball, C. S. Hoveland, and G. D. Lacefield, *Forage Crop Pocket Guide* (Norcross, GA: International Plant Nutrition Institute, 1999).

upward and downward (i.e., mobile in the plant's xylem/phloem)—it needs to be available where the roots and the roots' symbionts like mycorrhizae are located. Likewise, roots require adequate available calcium at the growing tips to create a healthy strong root cap that allows roots to migrate through the soil. This can only be done when enough calcium is available to build strong cell membranes. Ironically, if calcium is confined to the top few inches of the soil due to compaction, it can elevate soil pH to such an extent that the availability of calcium to the plant drops. For this reason, some believe such compacted soils need disturbance in order to assist calcium in moving downward. The same challenges are also associated with phosphorus, as it too tends to accumulate on compacted soils in the top several inches.

Potassium, called "poor man's irrigation," affects drought resistance because it controls osmotic pressure in the plant, especially the opening and closing of the stomata in the undersides of the leaf of the plant. Failure to open and close in a timely manner translates into water losses. Potassium diffuses throughout the soil, thus compaction hinders roots in picking up enough potassium to get the job done. Zinc is an element that directly affects phosphate availability. Boron directly affecs calcium availability. Copper, because it contributes to the formation of the xylem in plants, indirectly affects the availability of calcium and boron as well as phosphorus and potassium. A combination of phosphorus, calcium, potassium, zinc, copper and boron uniformly distributed throughout the rhizosphere is thus good insurance to provide drought resistance to crops, especially annuals. Because no-till operations, especially without cover crops, can often invite an accumulation of these elements in the top few inches (even to excess amounts), it may be advisable to have soil tests conducted in the top two to three inches (5–8 cm) as well as the next underlying five to eight inches (13–20 cm).

It may be that what could be necessary to improve root accessibility to excess surface nutrients is not more plant food applied but a soil tillage disturbance, such as from a Gen-Till or AerWay. In the case of an aggressive tillage requirement, rotovator or mold board plow could be used to mix nutrients throughout the root zone. That being said, the best way to have a mix of nutrients throughout the rootzone, which in my opinion should be thirty-six to forty-eight inches for annual crops, is to first avoid or eliminate compaction. That entails limiting traffic to dry soils, limiting axle loads to less than ten tons, preferably less than five tons, using flotation tires, practicing "vertical" tillage (e.g., zone/strip tillage), and creating and using traffic lanes to make permanent avenues that confine compaction to a limited site. Most importantly, as far as I'm concerned, is the need to plant deep-rooted cover crops that fracture existing hard pans/plow pans as well as preventing them from becoming reestablished. Consider tillage radishes, annual ryegrasses, some deep-rooted legumes, and a rotation into perennials such as alfalfa, orchard grass, fescue, and ryegrass, if the latter cover crop is going to be tilled (rotovated, chisel plowed, etc.) and subsequently cultivated and/or sprayed with herbicide.

These practices allow for a better mixing, or homogenization of the soil so that there is a more uniform migration of applied surface nutrients to migrate downward, building more root mass, which means more plant nutrition and drought resistance.

Trace Elements

The Mighty Micronutrients

The old agriculture of the 19th and 20th century is dying, and consumers can hasten that death, and they should. They are, after all, the walking wounded, offended by the chemical amateur. The consumer cannot hide in an organic garden or sleep in a subway of ignorance. Consumers will get clean agriculture when they demand it, casting their demands in knowledgeable terms and nailing those terms to the market door.

— Charles Walters

TRACE elements have been recognized for at least three-quarters of the past century as relevant to crop quality and animal health and productivity. Most conventional growers look at the vital necessity of supplying ample amounts of N-P-K to achieve a yield that may be profitable enough in a "good" year, weather-wise. But because "good" years are now becoming anomalies, stress to crops will be increasing and the costs of addressing related challenges continue to increase. It behooves many of us to ask why we choose to be either so ignorant or so disinterested in the critical importance of trace elements, which are vital compounds to both plant and animal/human vitality.

All that being said, when considering trace elements, there are a few ground rules to consider: be sure that the macroelements (e.g., Ca, P, Mg, S, K, N) are in adequate supply and preferably in balance as recommended on a comprehensive soil test, and if levels of trace elements are very low, do not apply the full amount to achieve the optimal levels. For example, some soils may be very low in copper, zinc, or boron, to the extent that it could require fifty pounds per acre of zinc sulfate, twenty to thirty pounds per acre of copper sulfate, or thirty to forty pounds per acre of borax. At these amounts,

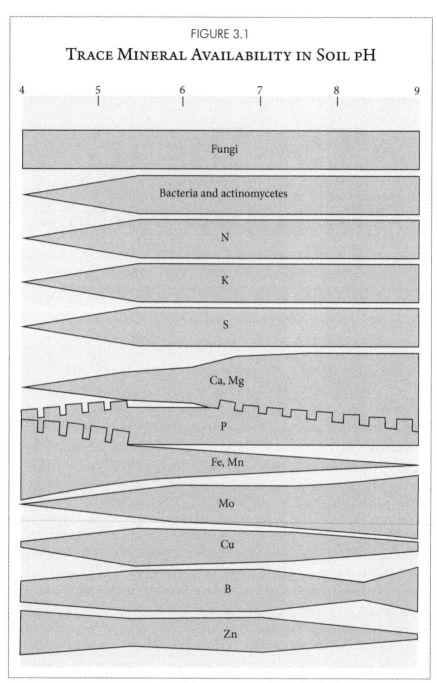

FIGURE 3.1

TRACE MINERAL AVAILABILITY IN SOIL pH

Nyle Brady and Ray Weil, *The Nature and Properties of Soil* (Upper Saddle River, NJ: Prentice Hall, 1996), 385.

these compounds are very detrimental to soil microbial systems and even herbicidal, risking the death of the crop.

In these instances, spreading out the application over months, even years, is advisable, and if the plants' tissue tests indicate an elemental deficiency, then foliar feeding can be successfully implemented, and at a sizeable savings in cost.

Figure 3.1 on the previous page illustrates that, with the exception of molybdenum, trace mineral availability is optimal in acidic pHs. Macroelements are most available at slightly acidic to alkaline pHs. Thus, a "mid-6" (6.3–6.5) pH seems to be the ideal range for both macro- and microelements.

TABLE 3.1

RELATIONSHIPS BETWEEN LOW LEVELS OF CERTAIN TRACE ELEMENTS AND ENHANCED SUSCEPTIBILITY TO INFECTION IN CULTIVATED PLANTS

Element	Host	Infecting Organism
Boron	Barley	Mildew, *Erysiphe graminis* D.C.
	Wheat	Rust, *Puccinia triticina*
		Rust, *Puccinia glumarum*
	*Sunflower	Mildew, *Erysiphe cichoracearuni**
	Beet	Mildew, *Phoma betae*
	Cauliflower	Mildew, *Botrytis* sp.
	Flax	Mildew, Bacterial infection
Copper	Wheat	Rust, *Puccinia triticina*
Manganese	Oats	Bacterial infection
Molybdenum	Lucerne	Lowers resistance to infection in general
	Lettuce	
Zinc	Rubber	*Oidium heveae*
		Phythophtora sp.

*Sunflower infection by mildew is used as an indicator of boron deficiency in the United States.
E. J. Butler and S. G. Jones, *Plant Pathology* (London: Macmillan, 1949).

Table 3.1 was assembled in 1949, over sixty years ago, demonstrating that the agricultural scientific community was aware that trace element deficiencies meant an increased likelihood of plant disease. In other words, it

TABLE 3.2

THE INFLUENCE OF TRACE-ELEMENT FERTILIZATION OF
THE SOIL ON THE NITROGEN, TRYPTOPHAN, AND
METHIONINE CONTENT OF LUCERNE AND THE AVERAGE
WEIGHT GAINS OF RABBITS FED ON IT

Soil Treatment	% N	Tryptophan (mg/g)	Methionine (mg/g)	Average Gain in Weight of Rabbits
None	3.12	1.86	4.57	740
Mg alone	3.20	—	—	744
T.E. alone	3.19	—	4.20	699
Mg + T.E.	3.05	2.52	5.44	849

V. L. Sheldon, W. G. Blue, and W. A. Albrecht, "A Biosynthesis of Amino Acids According to Soil Fertility," *Plant & Soil* 3, no. 4 (January 1951): 361–65.

was not a "pesticide deficiency" but a nutritional shortfall that meant plants had compromised immunity and were thus vulnerable to diseases.

Table 3.2, based on William Albrecht's work, illustrates that making complete, true (not "funny") protein* requires the trace element spectrum and that the evidence is not only revealed in the tissue tests, but in the performance of the animals consuming such produce.

So what constitutes plant immunity, especially as it relates to mineral nutrition? Besides synthesizing complete proteins, complete carbohydrates, adequate lipids for healthy cell membranes, and producing enough chlorophyll to maintain the energy fly wheel as the plant is building its frame, root ball, fruits, and seeds, there is another category of plant physiology called the plant secondary metabolites (PSMs). Essentially, there are three main categories of PSMs: phenols, terpenes or terpendoids, and alkaloids.

The phenols include the compounds of flavonoids, (flavones, flavonols, flavan-3-ols, isoflavones, flavanones, and anthocyanins). Isoflavones, also called phytoestrogens are actually compounds produced in legumes which ward off mildews. Not surprisingly, legumes are dependent on minerals like calcium, potassium, phosphate, and boron, all of which are necessary as raw materials to build phytoestrogens.

Phenols also include the non-flavonoid family (phenolic acids, tannins, hydroxycinnamates, stilbenes, and lignins). A popular phenolic acid is

---

* Funny protein is a term given to me by John Whittaker, DVM that I use to describe non-protein nitrogen, such as nitrate, free unbound amino acids, nitrite, ammonium, etc.

salicylic acid (aspirin), essential for a plant's immune response, called systemic acquired resistance (SAR), produced as a response to an adversarial attack, similar to an immune reaction in animals and humans.

Tannins are recognized by holistic livestock nutritionists to be effective deterrents against internal parasites and bloat and a detoxifier of "funny protein." They perform as deterrents against insects and excessive grazing by animals, and also act as sunscreens against ultraviolet radiation.

Stilbenes are often produced by plants as phytoalexins, or compounds released often as a SAR response to an insect attack. Ptero-stilbenes found in the blueberry family are one such example. Another is resveratrol, found in red grape skins and especially in Japanese knotweed (*Polygonum cuspidatum*).

Lignins, another phenolic, are second only to cellulose as the most abundant plant carbon compound on Earth. Its importance is attributed to its strength in the cell wall and its role in water transport. It is clearly a plant shield against environmental extremes of pests such as fungi, bacteria, insects, and root nematodes, and its synthesis is dependent on adequate copper and manganese uptake. It is also a plant's protection against elevated temperatures and drought.

Terpenes are the largest group of PSMs, numbering over twenty-two thousand including over six hundred carotenes, or carotenoids. Research of over half a century ago showed magnesium, copper, manganese, zinc, and iron are all required to synthesize carotenes (tetraterpenoids). Beta-carotene, alpha-carotene, lutein, lycopene, zeaxanthin, cryptoxanthin, etc. are the most popular. Terpenoids are volatile, (e.g., the essential oils or monoterpenes) and perform as repellants and communication molecules to warn their neighbors of the presence of an adversary, such as insects. They also are molecules that attract the predatory insects that feed upon the parasitic species. For example, these moleculese attract hornets to attack and feed upon caterpillars. They are antifungal, antibacterial, anti-nematode, and also perform as "sunscreens" against ultraviolet radiation. The plant hormones gibberellins and abscicic acid are diterpenes and also perform as a SAR immune reaction as phytoalexins in response to adversarial challenges. Bee propolis is also a diterpene, which makes it a powerful anti-microbial.

Alkaloids tend to be higher in root systems and are quite repellant/toxic to pests. Nicotine is an insecticidal alkaloid; caffeine is toxic to slugs. The conclusion to all of this is that nutrition is the foundation for immunity.

French research published in 1935[*] showed that strawberries were more vigorous and more resistant to oidum and Red Spider mites with 24

---

[*] Jean Dufrenoy, "Problemes physiologiques en physiologic vegetale," *Annales Agronomiques* (1935): 34.

elements, than they were with "only" 12 elements. (How many growers even use 12 elements?)

Russian research P. Polyakov in 1981 stated, "The treatment of plants with micronutrients intensifies the physiological processes and thus causes the pathogenic agent to be inhibited or destroyed, as happens with varieties which are naturally immune." What he's saying is that immunity cannot only be acquired via plant genetics; it also demands good nutrition.

He oversaw an experiment with sunflowers grown annually over a four-year period, measuring their resistance to gray mold (Sclerotinia). All that was done was a seed soak for ten hours in a 0.10 percent solution of the following individual elements: manganese, cobalt, boron, and copper. These results on disease incidence were as follows:

TABLE 3.3

PERCENTAGE OF ATTACKS ON SUNFLOWER
BY SCLEROTINIA (GREY MOLD)
ACCORDING TO MICRONUTRIENTS USED TO SOAK THE SEEDS
(Averaged Over Four Years)

- Seeds soaked ten hours in salt solution of 0.1 percent
- Two litres of solution sufficient to soak seeds needed for (1) hectare

Controls	Manganese	Cobalt	Boron	Copper
16.3%	4.4%	4.9%	6.4%	7.7%

"The treatment of plants with micronutrients intensifies the physiological processes and thus causes the pathogenic agent to be inhibited or destroyed, as happens with varieties which are naturally immune." P. Polyakov (1971) Change in sunflower under the influence of microscopic elements (sclerotinia); Sel'skokl Biol. T.6,3 pp 471–72

This translates into a 53–73 percent reduction in disease over the controls—merely by soaking the seeds! A 0.10 percent solution is equivalent to *one pound* of any of the above elements in one hundred and twenty-five gallons of water.

My hunch is that results would be better if those four elements were blended, but at the same finished as a 0.10 percent concentration. Perhaps zinc, silica, iron, iodine, selenium, and even some macroelements like calcium and potassium would be worth trying.

Francis Chaboussou's classic *Healthy Crops* makes a strong case against overapplying nitrogen. Measuring boron levels in cherry tree leaves detected:

- No nitrogen: 24 ppm boron
- 100 lbs/acre nitrogen: 14 ppm boron
- 200 lbs/acre nitrogen: 16 ppm boron
- 300 lbs/acre nitrogen: 15 ppm boron

Boron can also be reduced dramatically when applying excess potassium. So perhaps the take-home lesson here is to supply an appropriate amount of boron when applying nitrogen or potassium.

The following two tables, also from *Healthy Crops*, demonstrate that healthy versus virus-infected tomatoes had appreciably higher amounts of calcium, copper, manganese, zinc, boron, and cobalt, and lower levels of nitrogen, nickel, and molybdenum.

TABLE 3.4

FOLIAGE ANALYSIS OF TOMATOES
WATER-SOLUBLE ELEMENTS IN MG/KG/PPM

	NH_4	PO_4	K	Ca	Mg	Fe	Cu	Mn	Zn	B	Co	Cd	Ti	Ni	Mo
Healthy Tomatoes	1000	3125	4850	3375	1475	115	62.5	40.0	137.5	160	7.5	5.0	2.5	92.5	12.5
Virused Tomatoes	1250	3125	4900	1925	1400	107.5	15.5	11.5	115	110	T	T	T	137.5	32.5

Francis Chaboussou, *Healthy Crops: A New Agricultural Revolution* (Austin, TX: Acres U.S.A., 2005), 179. T=Traces

TABLE 3.5

FOLIAGE MINERAL RATIOS IN HEALTHY
VERSUS DISEASED TOMATOES

	K/Ca	Ca/Mg	P/Ca	K/Mg	Fe/Mn	P/Mn	N/Cu	N/P
Healthy Tomatoes	1.40	2.28	.092	3.28	2.87	78.12	16.00	0.32
Virus Tomatoes	2.40	1.39	1.62	3.50	9.24	271.70	80.64	0.40

Francis Chaboussou, *Healthy Crops: A New Agricultural Revolution* (Austin, TX: Acres U.S.A., 2005), 179.

Additionally (perhaps more importantly), further insight to plant health and minerals revealed the critical importance of ratios between minerals, especially K:Ca, Ca:Mg, P:Ca, Fe:Mn, P:Mn, and N:Cu. Thus, the take-home advice on tissue tests is the same as the soil tests. Pay attention to both the *levels* and the *ratios* of all elements, and adjust accordingly.

Other researchers came to similar conclusions as Dufrenry and Polyakov. The following table demonstrates clearly the importance of the production of "complete" true protein in plants relative to insect resistance.

TABLE 3.6

RELATIONSHIP BETWEEN MINERAL NUTRIENT DEFICIENCIES, NUMBER OF SQUASH BUGS (*ANASA TRISTIS*) PER PLANT AND SOLUBLE NITROGEN CONTENT OF SQUASH

Nutrient Supply	Squash Bugs (per plant)	Soluble Nitrogen (ug/g-1 fresh weight)
Complete fertility	1.70	32.10
(—) N	0.66	4.50
(—) P	2.11	93.70
(—) K	2.45	98.90
(—) S	3.42	143.70

P. S. Benepal and C. V. Hall, "The Influence of Mineral Nutrition of Varieties of *Cucurbita pepo* L. on the Feeding Response of the Squash Bug *Anasa tristis* De Geer," *Proc. Am. Soc. Hortic. Sci* 90 (1967): 304–12.

Note the direct relationship between the elimination of nitrogen and the much lower levels of squash bugs and the very low amounts of soluble nitrogen in the leaf. The other noteworthy item is that squash bug pressure really accelerated when sulfur was eliminated from the fertility mix. The runner-up to eliminating nitrogen as a fertilizer relative to squash bug pressure was having a "complete" fertility package available. My supposition is that if a suite of trace elements were included in the trials, the outcomes would have been even more variable because of the interactions between trace elements and macrominerals, and because of the direct influence trace elements have upon the synthesis of those plant secondary metabolites, which are themselves repellent to insects.

It is important to note that most sucking insects prefer amino acids over simple sugars, and they prefer simple sugars over complex sugars, such as polysaccharides. Free amino acids in the plants' cytoplasm are the result of a metabolic or physiological interference inhibiting the conversion of those amino acids into a finished product, namely a complete or true protein. High content of free amino acids in plants is a result of either excess nitrogen and/ or deficiencies of cofactors like potassium, sulfur, boron, molybdenum, zinc, cobalt, etc. Chemical pesticides can also create this outcome.

The main types of resistance that plants have to insect pests are physical (surface texture, hairs, color), mechanical (fibers, or the amount of silica), and chemical/biochemical (plant secondary metabolites, which act as toxins or repellents). Colors of leaves are important for recognition and orientation. Mineral nutrition has a role in all three of these factors.

TABLE 3.7

Netherlands Cancer Mortality & Soil Types

Soil Type	Total Number of Deaths From Cancer per Annum per 100,000 Inhabitants Above 50 Years of Age Per Period					
	1900–10	1910–20	1920–30	1930–40	Avg. 1900–30	Avg. 1900–40
Reclaimed Peat Soils	658	706	661	689	675	678
Peat Soils	605	667	667	688	647	657
Sea Clay Soils	595	654	667	693	630	652
Sandy Soils	562	622	653	651	612	622
Cover Sand Soils	544	611	653	603	603	603
River-Clay Soils	551	603	635	631	596	605
Loess & Other Soils Rich in CaCO$_3$	350	479	578	833	469	435

S. W. Tromp and J. C. Diehl, "A Statistical Study on the Possible Influence of Soil and Other Geological Conditions on Cancer," *Experientia* 10, no. 12 (December 1954): 510–18.

André Voisin, writing about minerals and health in his book *Soil, Grass and Cancer*, provides some compelling research (see table 3.7) compiled in 1954 by S. W. Tromp and J. C. Diehl, elucidating for the reader research conducted in the Netherlands from 1900 to 1940.

Of course, this was at a time when people consumed foods locally, and therefore the nutrition in those foods reflected the soil fertility or deficiencies inherent in that region. The point was that those dwelling on the loess soils, rich in calcium and other elements resulted in those inhabitants having a 30 percent lower incidence of cancer. William Albrecht conducted similar research using the World War I draft records as tell-tale evidence as to where the healthiest soils were located. He perused the data to find where the highest acceptance rates and the highest rejection rates to the draft were in the United States. The highest rejection rates were in areas like the Ozarks and Appalachia that had thin, rocky soils that were not blessed with the full mineral buffet. The highest acceptance rates to the draft were in the plains states like Iowa, Nebraska, and Illinois, which were enriched by glaciation millennia ago creating the calcium-phosphate "apatite" soils and further enriched through intensive mob grazing by perhaps the largest animal biomass since the dinosaurs: the bison. These animals were estimated to number somewhere between 50–75 million head, until the U.S. military and the white settlers collaborated to exterminate them. Today, only several hundred thousand bison remain, or less than 1 percent of the original herd. Kentucky's Bluegrass Country is renowned for its thoroughbred racehorse industry. It was because of these apatite soils that strong skeletal development could occur to build the strong legs needed for racing. Likewise, the best mules were bred in that apatite-rich ribbon of soil in central Tennessee that produced animals capable of the endurance and strength needed to do farm work.

Trace elements are vital components of enzymes, which are catalysts that govern many thousands of physiological and metabolic functions in plants and animals/humans. In addition to metallic ions, the synthesis of enzymes also requires co-enzyme factors, organic molecules such as vitamins, quinones, and PSMs. Chlorophyll could be called a magnesium-based enzyme (it also needs nitrogen, sulfur, and trace elements). Chlorophyll is actually protected by carotenes from UV radiation, and enzymes have the miraculous ability to speed biological reactions up to one million times. In fact, even seaweed extracts and seawater, both storehouses of ocean elements, apparently increase carotene production. More carotenes (and other PSMs) mean more chlorophyll, which means more photosynthesis, which means better crop production and performance. As mentioned previously, a number of metallic factors enhance carotenes. Enzymes can therefore be called metalloproteins, and it is estimated that half of all proteins contain a metal of some kind.

Looking at the Mulder Mineral Wheel, it becomes evident that mineral excesses create mineral availability deficiencies of other elements, even if they are present in adequate amounts. Excesses themselves, especially of trace elements, can be toxic (heavy metals) and suppress critical enzyme systems,

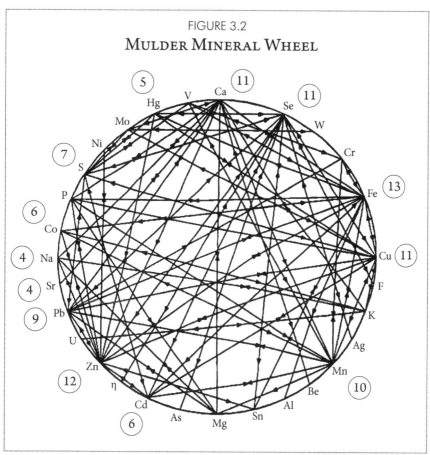

FIGURE 3.2

MULDER MINERAL WHEEL

David L. Watts, *Trace Elements and Other Essential Nutrients* (Henderson, NV: Meltdown Intl, 1995), 17.

leading to plant senescence or disease/insect attack. Tissue and forage tests are really useful in this regard, and visual observation of leaf, stem, root, tuber, and fruit are quite honest in telling the story of what is going on with your crop. Numerals beside certain elements denote the number of other minerals affected by that element.

An excellent book on the latter practice is *What's Wrong with My Plant? (And How Do I Fix It?): A Visual Guide to Easy Diagnosis and Organic Remedies* by David Deardorff and Kathyrn Wadsworth. This work provides the reader with very descriptive photographs, illustrations, and text that specifically provides the reasons why plants are in trouble, be it insects, disease, mineral or water deficiencies, or mineral or water excesses. I highly recommend this text as a reference manual.

TABLE 3.8

Optimum Parameters for Forage Nutrient Density

Nitrogen: 3.2–3.5% (20–22%)   NDF: 38–43%

Protein Solubility   NDFd 48: 40–60%

ADF insol CP: <.90%   Lignin: 5–10%

ADF: 28–30%   IVIDMD 48: 75–85%

WET CHEM RESULTS

	Legumes	Grasses
Ca	1.5–2.0%	1.2–2.0%
P	0.35–0.50%	0.25–0.40%
Mg	0.35–0.50%	0.30–0.50%
K	2.0% (1:1 with Ca)	2.0–3.0%
S	0.32–0.35%	0.32–0.35%
	(N:S ratio at least 1 part sulfur, 10 parts nitrogen)	
Cl	0.30–0.40%	0.30–0.40%
Na	0.15–0.20%	0.15–0.30%
Si	0.50–1.5%	1.0–3.0%

TRACE MINERALS

	Legumes	Grasses
B	40 ppm+	25 ppm+
Cu	15 ppm+	15 ppm
Mn	35 ppm+	55 ppm
Zn	30 ppm+	45 ppm
Fe	<200 ppm	<100 ppm
Al	<100 ppm	<100 ppm
Mb		3 ppm
Co		0.13 ppm
Se		0.20 ppm+
I		0.5 ppm
Cr		1–3 ppm

Agri-Dynamics

Table 3.8 provides target levels of minerals for legume and grass forages. If one is growing apples, tomatoes, or onions, etc., it would be prudent to purchase a textbook or manual that has the tissue test ranges that demarcate the optimum ranges for fruit, vines, produce, or cereal crops, as these individual crops will vary as to levels that encourage quantity and quality.

A basic rule of thumb for foliar feeding these nutrients is to begin applying deficient elements when the tissue tests are 50 percent of the optimum. Meanwhile, focus on getting the soil mineral levels up to the ideals demarcated in the basic soil test parameters, and especially focus on your soil biology (see chapter 4 for a comprehensive look at taking the biological pulse of your soil). The microbial resources in the soil not only increase the uptake of applied nutrients, but these bacteria, fungi, protozoa, actinomycetes, algae, earthworms, arthropods, beneficial nematodes, and so on are also responsible for releasing the complex storehouse of nutrients naturally and geologically present in your soil, as well as those elements that were previously applied as plant foods and became complexed, or "tied up," in the soil and can only be made available to plants by the soil's biological systems.

Pike Agri-Lab Supplies in Jay, Maine, directed me to an excellent online resource from the University of Florida, "Plant Tissue Analysis and Interpretation for Vegetable Crops in Florida."* This web article includes guidelines for collecting samples; proper handling of the sample; basic plant nutrition; the process of identifying each vegetable crop's nutrient

TABLE 3.9

MOBILITY OF ELEMENTS IN PLANTS
(ABILITY OF AN ELEMENT TO BE RELOCATED WITHIN
THE PLANT UNDER A DEFICIENT SUPPLY)

High	Intermediate	Low
Nitrogen (NO_3^- and NH_4^+)	Iron	Calcium
Phosphorus	Manganese	Boron
Potassium	Zinc	
Magnesium	Copper	
Sulfur	Molybdenum	
Chlorine		
Nickel		

* www.edis.ifas.ufl.edu/ep081.

deficiencies; and the deficiency, sufficiency, and toxicity ranges from plant nutrient concentrations.

Table 3.9 is a guide as to what nutrients are most and least mobile within plant tissue, and can act as a template for what nutrients to consider as foliar amendments due to compromised uptake out of the soil solution.

THE MAJOR MICRONUTRIENTS

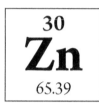

Zinc (anion) Target Levels: 6–12 ppm or 12–24 lbs/acre

Zinc is a vital element that I refer to as the "energy micronutrient" because it is a partner with phosphorus. Typically an ideal ratio of the two is ten parts of *elemental* phosphorus to one part of zinc, assuming the phosphorus levels are normal, or not excessive. Its role along with phosphorus is in the production of ADP (adenosine diphosphate) and ATP (adenosine triphosphate), the energy currency of life, both plant and animal.

A critical enzyme, carbonic anhydrase, located in both the chloroplast and cytoplasm, helps convert CO_2 into carbon compounds like sugars, cellulose, pectins, etc. Zinc partners with copper to produce Cu/Zn-superoxide dismutase (or SOD), a potent antioxidant enzyme that protects the plant (and animal/human) cell membrane from oxidation. Mycorrhizae fungi are essential to maximize zinc (and copper) uptake from soils. Paradoxically, overfertilizing soils with phosphorus can suppress the root colonization of mycorrhizae and thus the uptake of zinc. Zinc is critical for the uptake of soil moisture and thus is a "drought trace element" along with potassium, a macroelement. It affects the production of auxins, plant hormones, which in turn regulates leaf size. Soil microbes, for example azotobacter, a free-living (non-rhizobial) nitrogen-fixer, depend on zinc. In animals and humans, over two hundred enzyme systems rely on zinc. It is essential for cell growth, reproduction, and sexual maturity. It's synergistic with vitamin A for strong immunity, including the development of the thymus gland, which produces thymic hormones associated with antibody production and natural killer cell levels and function.

Sources of zinc:
- Zinc sulfate (23–36 percent), organically acceptable
- Zinc oxide (78 percent), organically acceptable
- Zinc chelates (5–15 percent), organically acceptable

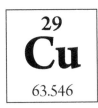

Copper (cation) Target Levels: 5–10 ppm or 10–20 lbs/acre

Copper is the protein trace element; that is, it has a role of increasing the uptake of the preferred form of nitrogen, namely ammonium (NH_4). It is essential for the production of chlorophyll, root metabolism, sugar synthesis, stalk strength, and elasticity because it affects the production of structural carbohydrates like cellulose, hemicellulose, and lignin, and it is vital protection against fungal diseases. Copper was shown to have a contributing effect on the production of both ascorbic acid (vitamin C) and beta-carotene (provitamin A) as far back as the 1950s.

TABLE 3.10

THE INFLUENCE OF COPPER ON THE ASCORBIC ACID AND CAROTENE CONTENT OF GREEN BARLEY

	Ascorbic Acid (mg/100 g)	Carotene (mg/100 g)
No treatment	29.2	4.00
10 lb $CuSO_4$ per acre	45.1	5.40
100 lb $CuSO_4$ per care	46.5	6.60

Increasing copper applications results in appreciable increases of both ascorbic acid (vitamin C) and carotene (pro-vitamin A) in barley.

Karl Schutte and John Myes, *Metabolic Aspects of Health: Nutritional Elements in Health and Disease* (Kentfield, CA: Discovery Press, 1975), 66.

Copper is a precursor to the enzyme polyphenol oxidase, which is an important factor for the synthesis of lignin and alkaloids to resist pests, as well as flowering and maturation. Copper is also a contributor to other plant phenols (plant secondary metabolites, or PSMs). Copper deficiencies can be created by high-calcium soils, peat soils, high-iron (ferralitic) soils, excessive zinc levels, sandy soils, and excessive nitrogen and phosphate applications. Copper excesses often arise as a result of copper fungicides being regularly applied. Copper at these levels is toxic to all soil microbial systems. The goal of an ecological farmer is to get copper *into* the leaf rather than *onto* the leaf. Many dairy farms use copper sulfate foot baths then dump the copper water on the same soil repeatedly, or throw it into the manure lagoon. In either instance copper has become a biocide. Being a metal, it doesn't regularly degrade and is thus capable of long-term damage to soil biology.

Molybdenum can be a thief of copper, even though soil levels may be adequate in copper. Often, excessive "moly" levels are found in strip-mined areas, and they can really create reproductive challenges, immune compromises, foot rot, coat discoloration, etc. in livestock-fed pasture or forages grown on such land.

In animals and humans, copper is a vital constituent of hemoglobin (along with iron and cobalt), which is the oxygen-carrying protein of the blood. It performs as an antioxidant and is critical for the formation of the myelin sheath around the nerves and associated with elastin, a connective tissue protein in blood vessels and joints. Two important enzymes—catalase, which quenches oxygen free radicals, and tyrosinase, which activates vitamin C—are copper dependent. Copper is needed for internal parasite resistance and healthy hair, hooves, nails, and skin. Copper partners with zinc to produce Cu/Zn SOD, or superoxide dismutase, an enzyme that protects the cell membranes in plants and animals/humans from oxidative damage.

Sources of copper:

- Copper sulfate (23–25 percent), organically acceptable

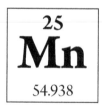

Manganese (cation) Target Levels: 40–80 ppm

Manganese is critical for seed germination and early maturity of plants. It has a role in metabolism of nitrogen. It's needed for the assimilation of CO_2 to produce plant carbohydrates. Like Cu/Zn SOD, manganese is a key component to produce the enzyme Mn-SOD, another superoxide dismutase. This antioxidant is found mostly (90+ percent) in the chloroplast, or chlorophyll-producing organelle in the plant. Also, the symbiotic rhizobia and their root nodules are rich in Mn-SOD. Like copper, manganese is needed to synthesize lignin, the plant protectant against heat, drought, diseases, and insects. Manganese is a precursor for fatty acids and sugars in the chloroplasts, a very important element for the production of carotenes.

Research conducted in 1951, as shown in table 3.11, demonstrated that manganese applications elevated the levels of vitamin E in soybean leaves, another potent antioxidant.

TABLE 3.11
THE INFLUENCE OF MANGANESE SULFATE
ON VITAMIN E IN SOYBEAN LEAVES

June 25, 1949 (lbs. MnSO₄/acre)	Vitamin E Content PPM					
	July 5	July 13	July 21	August 1	August 9	Average
75 (13.5 Mn)	11.7	13.4	13.1	9.8	10.1	11.6
150 (27.0 Mn)	14.0	11.4	15.5	9.1	10.5	12.1
0	13.1	7.1	8.2	6.4	6.0	8.2
5* (0.90 MN)	12.6	9.5	12.9	11.1	12.3	11.7

*Foliar Application, 4x
O. J. Burger and S. M. Hauge, "Relation of Manganese to the Carotene and Vitamin Contents of the Growing Crop Plants" *Soil Science* 72, no. 4 (October 1951): 303–14.

In livestock, deficiencies have resulted in silent heats, reproductive failures, abortions, and a predominance of male births. In animals and humans manganese is required for utilization of biotin, vitamin C, and thiamin (or B-1). It is essential for cartilage formation, neurotransmitter synthesis, and a component found in the mitochondria, the powerhouse of each and every cell.

Studies done at the University of Wisconsin in 1951 showed that fodder having less than twenty parts per million of manganese produced in cattle ovaries with a weight of about 0.65 milligrams. Fodder having manganese levels greater than fifty parts per million produced ovary weights of 2.0 milligrams, or more than a 300 percent increase.[*]

Manganese is a precursor for the enzyme arginase, which helps convert toxic blood ammonia to less toxic urea.

---

[*] O.G. Bentley and P. H. Phillips, "The Effect of Low Manganese Rations upon Dairy Cattle," *Journal of Diary Science* 34 (1951): 396–403.

Sources of manganese:
- Manganese sulfate (28 percent), organically acceptable
- Chelated manganese (5-15 percent), organically acceptable

Iron (Cation) Target Levels: >50 ppm

Iron is the second most abundant metal in the Earth's crust, following silica. There usually is no shortage of iron, but there often is an unavailability of iron due to alkaline soils, cold wet soils, and sulfur deficiencies. Excesses of phosphorus, manganese, and zinc (at low pHs) can also interfere with iron availability. It fixes magnesium to the chloroplast, thus the reason it is a "green-up" element, helping prevent chlorosis. Typically, foliar feeding of iron is usually the way to address an iron shortfall.

Humic acid can be a contributing factor to make iron more available. In livestock/humans, iron is needed by numerous enzyme systems and is the core element of hemoglobin, the oxygen-carrying protein in the blood. It's required for DNA synthesis, liver function, and immune competence.

Boron (Anion) Target Levels: 2-3 ppm or 46 lbs/acre

Being an anion, boron doesn't attach to a negatively charged soil colloid, thus it is found in the soil solution or is complexed with the humus fraction of organic matter. Boron is a potent partner with calcium and in fact is the catalyst that facilitates the release of calcium out of the soil into the plant. But excess calcium applied to soils will hinder boron solubility, and thus uptake. Potassium uptake is also improved with boron, and the same paradox applies: excess potash suppresses boron solubility and its availability to plants. Sugar translocation, the synthesis of nucleic acids and plant hormones, and the activation of cell division depend upon boron.

Since boron is found to be active in the xylem, foliar feeding can help in nourishing foliage and fruit, but to impact the roots soil boron needs to be addressed as a soil application.

Because boron is a water-active, or labile, trace element, hindrances on water movement throughout the plant will reduce the translocation of boron. Excess water and cold soil temperatures can contribute to this stagnation, and foliar feeding of boron as either sodium borate or boric acid would be a good idea. Not surprisingly, drought can be a detrimental factor in the uptake of boron. Since boron affects pollen variability and pollination itself and promotes flowering and the setting of seed, it needs to be carefully monitored in soil and tissue tests if those concerns are a priority. Boron deficiency will manifest as hollow stems in alfalfa, brassicas like cabbages, and soft pith in apples.

Legumes and dicots in general have a larger requirement for both calcium and boron than do grasses; grasses and cereals will therefore have a higher requirement for silica than do legumes or dicots. In other words, there appears to be an association between dicots and legumes, which produce more pectins than grasses and therefore need more calcium and boron. Grasses and cereals, which produce more structural carbohydrates like cellulose, hemicellulose, and lignin, depend more on silica and have a lower requirement for calcium and boron than do legumes and dicots. But make no mistake, boron is a critically important trace element for all crops.

Boron is also important for assimilation of nitrogen in plants as well as assisting plants in translocating accumulated carbohydrates from daytime photosynthesis in the leaf down into the root overnight. Don Schriefer stated years ago that high Brix levels detected early in the morning were an unhealthy sign that adequate amounts of the photosynthates were not sent into the root overnight, whereas healthy plants typically translocated 30–50 percent of those leaf photosynthates into the root system.

Back in the 1930s the University of Vermont published research that concluded alfalfa plants supplied with adequate amounts of boron had more resistance to leafhoppers than did deficient alfalfa. No doubt the reason is that boron is a precursor to those protective plant secondary metabolites, especially the elavanoid cyanidin, that deter these chewing insects. And not surprisingly, leafhoppers seem to thrive in dry weather, when moisture and therefore boron uptake are compromised. I would therefore include boron as boric acid in a foliar mix to be applied on crops susceptible to leafhopper, especially during hot, dry weather.

TABLE 3.12

RELATIONSHIP BETWEEN BORON SUPPLY AND INTENSITY OF RED SPIDER MITES (*TETRANYCHUS PIEROEI*) ATTACK ON OIL PALM

B supply (mg 1⁻¹)	Mites (no./m⁻²)	Feeding Holes (no./cm⁻²)	Correlation between Feeding Holes are Leaf Cyanidin Content	
			Feeding Holes (no./cm-2)	Cyanidin (ug/g-1)
0	1.8	67	60–65	2–5
0.5	1.7	60	30–50	10–18
5.0	1.2	30		
50.0	1.0	20	10–30	20–32
500.0	0.9	17		
1,000.0	0.9	12		

J. A. Rajaratnam and L. I. Hock, "Effect of Boron Nutrition on Intensity of Red Spider Mite Attack on Oil Palm Seedlings," *Experimental Agriculture* 11 (1975): 59–63.

Table 3.12 illustrates how cyanidin deters attacks by red spider mites on oil palm. As the boron levels increased, the cyanidin levels did as well. As the cyanidin levels rose, damage (feeding holes) declined proportionately. The cyanidins are in what's known as the cyano group, which includes cyanide, a naturally derived poison found in numerous plants, including cruciferous vegetables and legumes.

A number of years ago, I was on tour in Western Australia and met a "holistic" agronomist who told me the experience he'd had in the Wheat Belt. Conventional "experts" caution wheat farmers against using boron due to its toxicity. Consequently, insect pests soared and the use of insecticides in this region was extraordinary. Residents had to hide in their homes while the aerial warfare of spraying the region with poison was under way. This agronomist found that these soils were very deficient in calcium (along with other elements) and when all those elements were brought up to ideal levels, the boron was no longer toxic to the crop. The wheat now had resistance to its insect enemies, apparently due to the cyanidin production triggered by the boron (and other phytoalexin PSMs associated with boron), thus eliminating the health-destroying and ecologically devastating practice of poisoning the local environment with insecticides.

In livestock and humans, boron is once again a catalyst-partner with calcium and phosphorus to build strong bones and teeth. Boron is a precursor to the parathyroid hormone that regulates blood calcium levels. Cows with a propensity for milk fever (low blood calcium) need to have boron deficiencies addressed. Additionally, boron appears to be a contributing factor to prevent and reverse hairy heel warts, a disease of the hoof in livestock. Boron is a catalyst that activates vitamin D in the kidney into calcitriol, the active form of this "vitamin-hormone" necessary for a strong immune system. Boron is a raw material for the sex hormones estrogen, progesterone, and testosterone as well, which may partly explain its role in preventing osteoporosis, by helping to maintain healthy hormone levels in older individuals.

Sources of boron:

- Borax (11 percent or 14 percent, sodium borate), organically acceptable
- Sol-U-Bor (20.5 percent, soluble sodium borate), organically acceptable
- Boric acid (17 percent soluble), organically acceptable (preferred source of soluble boron—more available)

TABLE 3.13

Effect of Molybdenum on the Growth and Nitrogen Content of Alder Plants (Alnus glutinosa) in Molybdenum-Deficient Soil

Parameter	Molybdenum Application (μg per pot)	Leaves	Stem	Roots	Nodules
Dry weight (gram per pot)	0	1.79	0.59	0.38	0.007
	150	5.38	2.20	1.24	0.132
Nitrogen Content (%)	0	2.29	0.92	1.79	2.77
	150	3.58	1.17	1.83	3.26

J. H. Becking, "A Requirement of Molybdenum for the Symbiotic Nitrogen Fixation in Alder," *Plant and Soil* 15 (1961): 217–27.

Molybdenum (Anion) Target levels: 0.4–1.0 ppm or 0.8–2 lbs/acre

Molydbenum is a trace mineral that, unlike most, increases in availability at a higher pH. The primary significance of this microelement is that it is an essential raw material for the enzyme nitrogenase, which is required for nitrogen-fixing bacteria, especially those residing in the root nodules of legumes. Table 3.13 demonstrates the increase in both dry weight and nitrogen content of the leaves after an application of molybdenum into the soil.

Table 3.14 demonstrates the significant impact that molybdenum had on miscellaneous crops in New Zealand. As you can see, these increases are tremendous. Alfalfa (Lucerne) and rape (canola) increased from 43–603 percent. Pastures on clay soils went up in yield from a low of 38 percent to a high of 390 percent. That's a lot of extra feed for a very small investment.

Additionally, molybdenum is a core element of the nitrate reductase enzyme, the enzyme necessary to convert nitrate (NO_3) into amines (NH_2), then into amino acids and eventually protein. Plants taking up nitrogen as ammonium (NH_4) are not as dependent upon nitrate reductase enzyme (and therefore molybdenum) because the amines (NH_2) are readily synthesized in the root, providing amino acids that are taken in by the leaf.

Again, nitrate reductase enzyme needs sunlight, so complete, true proteins are not efficiently made at night or during cloudy weather. Excess phosphates and especially excess sulfates can be antagonistic to moly, but excess moly will inhibit the uptake of copper, even though adequate amounts of copper are in the soil.

In livestock/humans, molybdenum can help detoxify nitrate, prevent nitrosamine formation, and enhance immunity to parasites.

To reduce undesirable levels of nitrates in plants, make a soup mix containing about ten pounds of magnesium sulfate, four to six ounces of sodium molybdenate, two gallons of molasses, one pint of fulvic acid, and one pound of soluble humic acid powder in forty gallons of water per acre.

Sources of molybdenum:

- Sodium molybdenate (47 percent molybdenum), organically acceptable
- Ammonium molybdenate (58 percent molybdenum), not organically approved

TABLE 3.14

POTENTIAL CROP IMPROVEMENTS IN WAITAKI COUNTY, NEW ZEALAND, BY THE USE OF MOLYBDENUM FERTILIZERS

Crop and Soil	Control (No Molybdenum)	Yields (With Molybdenum)	Percent Increase
Lucerne on sandstone soil	3,060	13,920	355
Lucerne on clay soil	13,664	19,488	43
Rape on sandstone soil	7,616	53,536	603
Rape on clay soil	8,288	14,784	78
Pasture on clay soil:			
a	3,300	6,233	89
b	2,038	9,357	359
c	3,561	17,450	390
d	995	1,505	51
e	4,968	7,028	44
f	2,080	2,868	38
g	13,700	20,500	50
h	12,200	18,800	54

Crop yields are given in pounds per acre of green matter. Dosage of molybdenum not given. All the soil sand crops treated gave a marked response to molybdenum. Both clay and sandstone soils gave crop increases of over 300 percent.

Karl Schutte and John Myes, *Metabolic Aspects of Health: Nutritional Elements in Health and Disease* (Kentfield, CA: Discovery Press, 1975), 48.

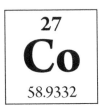

27
Co
58.9332

Cobalt (Cation) Target levels: 0.5–1.0 ppm or 1.0–2.0 lbs/acre

Cobalt, like molybdenum, is an absolute essential for nitrogen-fixation microorganisms. Three fundamental enzymes depend on cobalt: methionine synthase, needed for healthy plant protein production; ribonucleotide

TABLE 3.15
EFFECT OF COBALT ON PEANUTS

Cobalt Treatment	Number of Nodules per Plant	Total Nitrogen at Maturity (% Dry Weight)	Pod Yield (kg/ ha-1)
Control (-CO)	91	2.38	1232
Seed Treatment	150	2.62	1687
Foliar Sprays (2x)	123	3.14	1752
Seed Treatment and Foliar Sprays (2x)	166	3.38	1844

Petra Marschner, ed., *Marschner's Mineral Nutrition of Higher Plants* (Academic Press, 2011), 429.

reductase, essential for DNA synthesis; and methylmalonyl coenzyme A mutase is required to produce "heme" in the root bacteria, which is the iron component of leghemogloblin, a red iron containing protein pigment essential for the bacteria to fix nitrogen. Curiously, hemoglobin in animals and humans is a red oxygen-carrying pigment of red blood cells.

Table 3.15 demonstrates how cobalt is associated with yield and nutrient density on a legume.

Just two foliar sprays plus dusting the seed with cobalt sulfate increased yields by 50 percent over the controls. In animals and humans cobalt is the core element of vitamin B12, or cobalamin. This compound is essential for a ruminant's liver to convert one of the key fatty acids produced from fermentation, called propionic acid, into glucose. Cobalt is important to fertility, cellular longevity, the absorption of fats and carbohydrates, and may be a factor in preventing ketosis and Johne's disease in ruminants.

Sources of cobalt:
- Cobalt sulfate (20 percent cobalt)

OTHER TRACE MINERAL CONSIDERATIONS
Selenium (Anion) Target Levels: 0.5–1 ppm or 1–2 lbs/acre
Selenium is a protective element for both plants and animals/humans. Selenium is not considered an element useful for plant growth or health, but it can be a valuable partner with sulfur in producing selenoamino acids such as selenomethionine and selenocysteine. Cysteine and methionine are sulfur-bearing amino acids, and those forms of selenium stimulate the immune

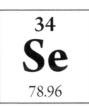

34

Se

78.96

systems of animals and humans. Certain plants are selenium accumulators, such as broccoli, cabbage, or other brassicas.

Selenium as a plant food should be applied as sele*nate* versus sele*nite*. Not very much is needed of either. As a foliar, ten grams (about a third of an ounce) of actual selenium per acre is applied. There are some reports that selenium in tissue in levels as low as ten parts per million can reduce some aphid infestations by up to 50 percent.

In animals and humans, selenium is a powerful partner with glutathione, creating an enzyme called glutathione peroxidase, which is necessary for immune cells called neutrophils to be active. Selenium is also a partner with iodine in the thyroid,in that it converts the T-4 thyroid hormone into the active T-3 form. Selenium is also an antagonist and binder of heavy metals like mercury, cadmium, and lead.

Sources of selenium:

- Sodium selenate (41 percent selenium)
- Sodium selenite: (45 percent selenium)

53

I

126.90447

Iodine (Anion) Target Levels: 2–5 ppm

Iodine is never discussed even remotely as being a nutrient for crops. However, a book entitled *Iodine and Plant Life: Annotated Bibliography, 1813–1949*, published in 1950 by the Chilean Iodine Educational Bureau, would strongly suggest otherwise. Referring to the nitrogen cycle in *The Chemical Activities of Bacteria* by Dr. Ernest F. Gale, the authors point out that nitrogen-fixing azotobacter bacteria are greatly influenced by small amounts of iodine in the soil environment: one part of iodine to 200,000–500,000 parts of soil, or two to five parts per million of iodine. Iodine was

TABLE 3.16
IODINE AND PLANT LIFE

Genus	Iodine Dry Matter (%)
Fucus	0.06
Ecklonia	0.40
Phyllophora	0.50
Laminaria	0.60

Iodine and Plant Life: Annotated Bibliography, 1813–1949 (London: Chilean Iodine Educational Bureau).

TABLE 3.17
INCREASES IN IODINE CONTENT AFTER APPLYING POTASSIUM IODINE

	Pounds per Acre Applied	Iodine Content Increases
Pasture	0.53	5 x (500%)
Fodder Beet Root	1.80	2 x (200%)
Fodder Beet Leaves	1.80	9 x (900%)
Lettuce and Turnips	2.10	25% to 8 x (800%)
Vegetables	2.20	25% to 80 x (8,000%)
Vakerion	2.90	43%
Beans and Turnips	5.20	3 x (300%) to 120 x (120,000%)
Lettuce and Turnips	10.60	4 x (400%) to 13 x (1,300%)

also used successfully as a plant protectant against diseases and nematodes. However, only "free" I_2 iodine worked as a plant protectant; iodides or iodates—mineral salts of iodine—were not effective.

Research done on heavily damaged citrus groves in California in the 1950s suggested that "free" I_2 iodine was very effective in eliminating nematodes, even bringing back trees with severe die-back. I have experimented with a cold-process free I_2 iodine (an iodophor) with very encouraging reports on seed-borne nematodes in ginger, turfgrass diseases, and nematodes with a solution called Eco-Dyne/Bio-Dyne.

Iodine for animals/humans is a vital micronutrient for not only producing thyroid hormones but also for synthesizing iodo-lipids and iodo-proteins, very important for immune function. Iodine is also required to help remove toxins, heavy metals, other halogens like bromine and fluorine, and actually performs as a natural antiseptic against pathogens in the bloodstream.

Sources of iodine:

- Potassium iodide (76 percent)
- Idophor iodine (3.5 percent iodine)
- Chilean nitrate: (0.022 percent iodine)
- Kelp (see table 3.16)

Tables 3.16 and 3.17 provide iodine averages of seaweeds and terrestrial plants and do not take into consideration the seasonal variations. The basic rule is that the iodine accumulation increases with sunlight exposure or photosynthesis. Thus, kelp harvested in late summer should have higher iodine levels than that harvested in spring.

Applying potassium iodide to cropland at the levels indicated in able 3.17 increased the iodine content accordingly to different crops.

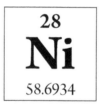

28
Ni
58.6934

Nickel (Cation) Target Levels: 1–2 ppm or 2–4 lbs/acre

Nickel is molecularly related to iron and cobalt, and it is a recognized essential trace element for microbes, especially because of the enzymes they produce for nitrogen metabolism. The most recognized nickel enzyme is urease, which converts urea into nitrate, a process necessary for protein synthesis because otherwise toxic levels of urea can accumulate in the plant.

Additionally, nickel appears to provide a significant contribution to seed germination. Studies conducted on nickel regarding plant diseases are very encouraging, especially on rust fungi and nematodes. A solution of two hundred to a maximum of four hundred parts per million of nickel (as nickel sulfate) appears to have a fungicidal effect, although there is a likelihood that nickel's disease-suppressing impact is a result of an induced resistance of a "phytoalexin" response, whereby plants can produce plant secondary metabolites on demand because of nickel's contribution in helping plants deter fungal pathogens. In animals, nickel enhances the rumen microbial population. Nickel appears to have a synergistic relationship with zinc, calcium, and magnesium, and healthy soils can typically have up to five parts per million of nickel. Deficiencies are often found in conventional orchards where excessive amounts of copper, iron, manganese, zinc, calcium, and magnesium have been applied. Nickel fortunately is a naturally occurring trace mineral in most phosphate fertilizers. Nickel deficiency can be addressed by a foliar application of ten to one hundred milligrams of elemental nickel per liter, or 0.10–10 grams per hundred-liter (twenty-six gallons) spray tank.

Sources of nickel:

- Nickel sulfate (38 percent nickel); rate of use is a seed application at about the rate of cobalt or molybdenum (i.e., one to two parts per million or four pounds per acre).

Micronutrients are often ignored because many crop advisers, extension agents, and growers believe there are adequate amounts in most soils. The N-P-K mind-set asserts crop production is mostly *not* dependent upon trace elements, a huge mistake when one considers how significant trace elements are in concert with soil biological systems; their requirements by plants to synthesize protective compounds like plant secondary metabolites, and their important partnerships with major elements, which collectively influence plant production, pest resistance, and nutrition/shelf life. Perennial systems have the advantage of long-lived deep root systems that can prospect and harvest all elements more efficiently than annual crops can, as annuals life spans are a mere two to three months. But even fruit, nut, berry, and forage crops will readily respond to micronutrient inputs, as the scientific literature has demonstrated. Thus micronutrients actually contribute to a profitable crop as much as the major elements do, especially in times of climatic stress such as excessive moisture, drought, unexpected freezes, and abnormally elevated temperatures.

Used wisely, micronutrients are quite cost effective; so much so that every eco-farmer cannot reach a plateau of crop resilience and sustainability without them.

The Biological Nature of Soil

Humankind has not woven the web of life. We are but one thread within it. Whatever we do to the web, we do to ourselves. All things are bound together. All things connect.

—Chief Seattle

W HEN researching the growth pattern of bacterial colonies, scientists in Japan and Israel discovered that branching patterns of *Bacillus subtilis* become increasingly sparse as the nutrient density became scarce or as the gel medium that it grew upon became harder. Scientists discovered these changes to branching patterns were caused by cellular communication, called chemotaxis, which means that bacteria emit biochemicals that act as communication molecules to encourage microbes to move away from not-so-friendly environments. In other words, the fractal complexity and density depended on food availability and friendliness of the environment (soft gel medium versus hard gel medium). The microbial biomass is the unseen ecology of our planet's biology, even though microbial systems make up 50 percent of the Earth's total biomass and 80 percent of all the Earth's biodiversity is microbial.

Humans comprise 10 trillion cells that compose their organs, tissues, etc. The microflora that live in us and on us are approximately ten times that amount, or 100 trillion cells. Since human cells are twenty times larger than microbe cells, human cells compose the bulk of the space we take up. Over 80 percent of these bacteria dwell in the intestinal tract, where there are literally three to five pounds of these symbiont probiotics, consisting of five

FIGURE 4.1

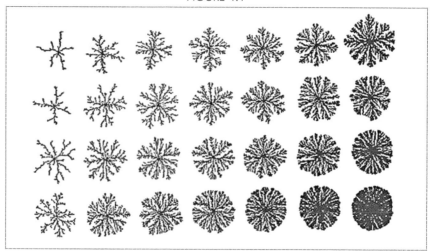

Eshel Ben-Jacob, professor of physics, Tel Aviv University. Philip Ball, *The Self-Made Tapestry: Pattern Formation in Nature* (New York: Oxford University Press, 1999), 137.

hundred to a thousand species. Less than 25 percent of these microbes have been identified.

Soils contain an estimated 2–3 million species of bacteria and an estimated 1.5 million species of fungi, and only 2–5 percent have been described or named! We have a robot searching for life on Mars while we ignore or marginalize the most significant life-forms that allow this planet to be alive. As in animals, the vast majority of these microbes dwell in the "digestive system" of the plant, the root ball or the rhizosphere. Also as with animals, the majority of the immune system of plants is in the "gut" because high populations of beneficial, symbiotic microbes are both the plants' and animals' primary first line of defense to synthesize compounds that not only protect the digestive system or root ball/rhizosphere but also supply compounds that can be taken up by plants to protect its tissues above ground. Generally we refer to these plant protectants as plant secondary metabolites, compounds that are beneficial to the plant but are not directly necessary for its survival. Soils that have a well-balanced soil food web, have excellent physical and mineral properties, and depend upon biodiversity and high populations of these diverse microbial species are typically referred to as "immune soils." Practices that can enhance the disease-suppressive properties of soils are:

1. liming acid soils
2. compost

TABLE 4.1

ESTIMATED NUMBERS OF COMMON MICROORGANISMS
FOUND IN *HEALTHY* AGRICULTURAL SOILS

Organism	Estimated Number Number/gram	Average Weight per Upper Foot of Soil Low High lb/acre
Bacteria	3,000,000–500,000,000	500–1,000
Actinomycetes	1,000,000–20,000,000	800–1,500
Fungi	5,000–15,000,000	1500–2,000
Protozoa	1,000–500,000	200–400
Algae	1,000–500,000	200–300
Yeasts	1,000–100,000	
Nematodes	50–500	25–50

Paul Syltie, *How Soils Work: A Study into the God-plane Mutualism of Soils and Crops* (Fairfax, VA: Xulon Press, 2002), 34.

3. proper irrigation and water quality (pH, TDS, bicarbonate, alkalinity, salinity, EC, etc.)
4. aeration and drainage
5. reduced or zero tillage
6. cover crops (preferably multiple biodiverse species)
7. balanced fertilizer applications
8. tight crop rotations
9. crop residues returned to surface or shallow "sheet composting"
10. seed inoculation with mycorrhizal and trichodermal fungal spores, etc.

According to Brady and Weil's *The Nature and Properties of Soils*, the reproductive potential of bacteria is incomprehensible. A single bacteria allowed to divide every hour would yield 17 million cells in twenty-four hours. In *six days* this reproductive juggernaut would yield a volume of organisms greater than the volume of the Earth! Of course, bacteria being a primary food for everyone else, this situation will never be anything but a fantastic hypothesis, but it does impress upon one the amazing volume of "livestock" that make up life in the soil, and how much energy and fertility these "livestock" contribute to the productivity and well-being of natural systems, be they forest or farm.

❖

Aerobic organisms utilize free (atmospheric) oxygen for their metabolism. Zero to six inches below the soil is where most of the microbial activity is occurring. This fact is often referred to as the fence post principle, which states that most microbial activity happens at the point where an untreated fence post will decompose, beginning at the soil surface and extending a few inches below the surface.

Atmospheric gases are typically 21 percent oxygen and 250–350 ppm or 0.025–0.035 percent carbon dioxide (CO_2). The soil atmosphere is generally about 15 percent oxygen and 2,000–4,000 ppm or 0.2–0.4 percent carbon dioxide. The exhalation of soil life creates this difference and, of course, that CO_2 is a primary raw material that plants recycle through their stomata to incorporate into the chloroplast. There it can combine with water (H_2O) to create sugars (CHO), which are in turn the building blocks of numerous other carbon complexes, such as starches, cellulose, hemicelluloses, lignin,

waxes, oils, resins, pectins, fructans, glucans, and numerous plant secondary metabolites like terpenes, alkaloids, and phenols.

The photo shows me drawing the trapped soil atmosphere out of a four-inch diameter cylinder tapped into the soil surface and capped. This is allowed to sit overnight before I draw out the air and gases

Photo by Will Winter

that have accumulated in that containment. Halfway between the cap and the syringe is a CO_2 monitoring indicator capsule that captures the CO_2 in the trapped atmosphere and registers the amount via a color code. Needless to say, the CO_2 amounts generated in soils that are either pastured or cover cropped versus soils that have been subject to continuous tillage without any cover are significantly different. Ninety percent of the carbon dioxide produced by life on this planet primarily originates from bacteria and fungi. According to James Nardi, a research scientist at the University of Illinois at Urbana-Champaign, a single acre of rich soil can easily surpass the metabolic activity of fifty thousand human beings.

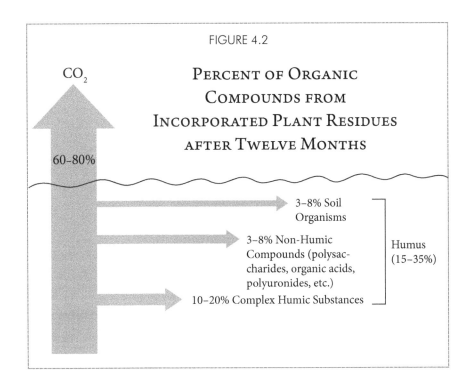

FIGURE 4.2

PERCENT OF ORGANIC
COMPOUNDS FROM
INCORPORATED PLANT RESIDUES
AFTER TWELVE MONTHS

CO_2

60–80%

3–8% Soil Organisms

3–8% Non-Humic Compounds (polysaccharides, organic acids, polyuronides, etc.)

Humus (15–35%)

10–20% Complex Humic Substances

Brady and Weil indicate in their book *The Nature and Properties of Soils* that the "living (liquid) carbon" is retained more in the soil than is the carbon (crop residue) that we have been mostly focused on, since on the average two-thirds of the crop residue is going to be discharged as CO_2 gas. That's why, when growing annuals, it is important not only to have their residues digested in the soil but also to get that bare ground covered quickly with living plants.

The challenges we are facing because of climate change have much to do with the vast amounts of carbon lost from our soils and the soil ecosystem's diminishing ability to rapidly and effectively sequester carbon dioxide, thanks to soil erosion levels now exceeding 24 billion tons per year worldwide (or 4 tons for every human) and the practice of burning forests and grasslands half the size of Africa every year. According to Allan Savory, founder of Holistic Management, merely increasing the soil organic matter on just the planet's 4.9 billion hectares of rangeland (not cropland) by 2.0 percent would sequester 2,880 billion tons of CO_2, compared to the 44 billion tons of CO_2 emitted by human industrial activities per year.

Anaerobic microbes, although they utilize oxygen, don't use free atmospheric O_2 oxygen but rather consume oxygen from other molecules, such as nitrate (NO_3^-) and sulfate (SO_4^{2-}). This is a process known as reduction (instead of oxidation) and will eventually convert nitrate to ammonia (NH_3^+) and sulfate to hydrogen sulfide (H_2S), both volatile gases that will cause valuable nutrients to leave the land. Facultative organisms are those that can adapt to utilizing oxygen either as atmospheric O_2 or as a complexed oxygen compound such as NO_3^- or SO_4^{2-}.

Manure lagoons are challenged by the issue of depleted oxygen. One partial solution is to feed an edible clay, such as Desert Dyna-Min™, to livestock so that these compounds begin to be adsorbed in the GI tract as well as in the manure. Another solution is to dust about a quarter of an ounce (7–8 grams) of the following in the manure gutter or on the bedding pack daily per adult cow:

- Soft rock phosphate (if there is a P_2O_5 deficiency in the soil; otherwise use an edible clay like Desert Dyna-Min™). The phosphate clay attracts the ammonia (NH_3^+) and causes it to react with the phosphate (P_2O_5), creating monoammonium phosphate (MAP), a very stable form of nitrogen.
- Gypsum or calcium sulfate, now often used as bedding in stalls. The calcium sulfate reacts with ammonia, creating another stable form of nitrogen called ammonium sulfate. Note: Excess gypsum in manure lagoons can generate toxic, deadly amounts of sulfide (H_2S) gas.
- Adding humates will provide an additional chelating component, as the very large humic molecules can react with nitrogen, ammonia, calcium, phosphate, sulfate, et cetera, while providing a stable carbon complex in the soil.

The CirCulator, courtesy of Gary Wegner

The CirCulator™, technology owned by CIRCUL8 CEO Gary Wegner, is also intriguing. Consisting of four paddles powered by an electric motor and attached to a buoy that floats in the center of the lagoon, the device constantly keeps the manure slurry slowly moving from bottom to top, top to bottom. This constant movement prevents layering, which creates intense, toxic hypoxic zones that only encourage anaerobes, which produce undesirable, toxic volatiles like ammonia, sulfide, mercaptans, skatoles, indoles, etc. If you've ever inspected ground doused with "black water" from conventional lagoons, you'd see the evidence of these toxins by the huge number of dead earthworms lying on the soil surface. What is this toxic soup doing to the other aerobic creatures dwelling in your topsoil?

The CirCulator apparently allows the proliferation of phototropic (sunlight) facultative microbes that create what's known as "red water," which does not kill earthworms and is so user-friendly one can rinse one's hands in this effluent and it doesn't leave a residual stench on the skin. As more and more livestock producers, from small to very large, are installing anaerobic waste lagoons, it's imperative that we realize how detrimental this form of manure can be. It's highly leachable; highly anaerobic, thus toxic; and produces highly volatile compounds that escape into the air, fouling our atmosphere and losing nutrients off the farm.

The reason circulated ponds do not stink is that they do not lose the 80 percent of nitrogen and 80 percent of sulfur that conventional lagoons normally lose. It appears that phototrophic microbes (such as purple sulfur bacteria, or PSB) that thrive in these ponds have the ability to sequester nutrients and transport them to the soil. For example, during photosynthesis, PSB can take a molecule of hydrogen sulfide produced by another microbe, break the bond between the sulfur and hydrogen, store the sulfur in their living protein, release hydrogen, and get energy from the process. The phototrophs also find ways to store nitrogen in their living protein so that ammonia and hydrogen sulfide don't leave the system. These valuable nutrients are extremely beneficial in the soil, and we should do whatever we can to not let them go into the air. Hydrogen sulfide is a lethal gas, in addition to being a very foul smell. Eliminating odors while protecting the environment seems like the right thing to do.

Moisture is second only to air as a vital resource for life, microbial life included. We do reside on a watery planet. The vast oceans constitute 97.25 percent of this planet's moisture. Ice (glaciers) constitutes another 2 percent, and groundwater (most of which is over two thousand feet deep) another 0.7 percent. This means the remainder of our fresh water supplies is less than 0.05 percent! Of that 0.05 percent, 60 percent is found in our lakes, 7 percent in our rivers, 6 percent in our atmosphere, and 33 percent is found in the soil. Therefore, our responsibility is to hold onto that 33 percent of 0.05 percent available water by a) increasing infiltration and arresting runoff, and b) increasing the organic content of our soils.

Soil holds onto water via a capillary film around each soil particle. When each soil particle holds a full thickness of that film it is said to be at "full field capacity." The soil feels moist to the touch but does not form a mud ball. The

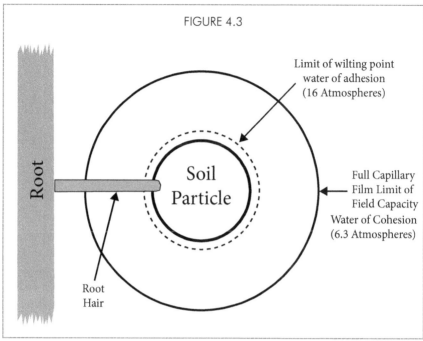

FIGURE 4.3

Root

Soil Particle

Root Hair

Limit of wilting point
water of adhesion
(16 Atmospheres)

Full Capillary
Film Limit of
Field Capacity
Water of Cohesion
(6.3 Atmospheres)

Don Schriefer, *From the Soil Up* (Austin, TX: Acres U.S.A., 2000).

pore space, filled with air, is approximately at 25 percent, and water at another 25 percent. Water on soil particles and the soil pores is capillary water. This is water that can move upward toward the soil surface or downward and laterally toward root surfaces as water is removed by surface evaporation or root uptake. Because clay and organic matter possess more pores and surface area, their total water holding capacity is larger. Good soil structure is critical for these capillary columns of water to rapidly move to where they are most urgently needed. Between the wilting point and field capacity, a sandy soil can hold only 8 percent plant-available water, compared to a silty loam, which can hold 28 percent.

Capillary films actually try to maintain an equal film thickness from the water table to the soil surface, which is called capillary attraction or surface tension. Again, this principle is based on the lamp wick phenomenon, so it's now easier to understand why we want deep roots, no plow/hardpans, and a lot of soil carbon.

Drought affects plants when the capillary film surrounding the soil particle shrinks, increasing the requirement of atmospheric pressure to the root hairs to pull in the moisture. When the transpiration losses through the leaves exceed the ability of the root to remove the soil film, the plant reaches the wilting point. Plants recover from wilt at nighttime because transpiration losses are less than during the daytime heat. When plants cannot recover during the nighttime, the wilting point is irrevocable and plant life ceases. Soil oxygen (aeration) helps determine the suction strength of the roots, and adequate soil nutrition affects the roots' abilities to grow downward and outward.

If one looks at water loss and gain through the following tabulations, it becomes quite evident that human influences have a huge impact on how much water we conserve or waste with agricultural management practices. If precipitation and irrigation amount to 100 percent of the total incoming water, one needs to do addition and subtraction to estimate the total net water resource to a crop. The amount intercepted by plants and evaporated is 5–30 percent. Runoff can be 0–30 percent. Percolation into the soil, a plus, can be as high as 40–80 percent. Drainage losses can average 10–30 percent. Capillary rise into the plant, also a plus, will be 0–10 percent. Evaporation losses directly from the soil can range from 5–50 percent. Evapotranspiration losses through the leaves can be 15–60 percent. All these numbers added and subtracted, and then reconciled to what the soil originally received as precipitation or irrigation (the 100 percent), means that the net amount of incoming moisture available to plants will be somewhere between 30–65 percent of what was originally provided by rain or irrigation, a very wide range.

Humans may be able to control irrigation, but not precipitation. Arresting runoff and enhancing percolation are major variables at the mercy of humankind's stewardship. Evaporation from the soil (from a lack of vegetative cover and/or low organic matter) is yet another factor dependent on human involvement. Not having hardpans increases percolation, reduces runoff, and enhances capillary rise during dry weather. Having cover crops also reduces runoff, increases downward water percolation, and reduces temperature (and thus evaporation). Organic matter or carbon holds more water, buffers the soil from heat and evaporation, and decreases runoff while also enhancing downward infiltration.

The primary factors that affect soil temperature are:
1. the slope or angle that the sun's rays strike the surface;
2. the season, dependent upon the latitude;
3. rainfall or irrigation: total amount, frequency, and water temperature (e.g., well versus reservoir versus rain);
4. wind speed and its direction (which is why we need hedgerows and shelterbelts);

5. humidity (the East, Midwest and Southeast are much more humid than the Rocky Mountain states, the Southwest, and California);
6. cloudiness (the Northeast is more cloudy than western states);
7. ground cover (perennial polycultures and cover crops);
8. the amount of tillage and soil disturbance (oxidation of carbon/ organic matter);
9. soil structure and permeability (amount of organic matter, soil calcium, lack of hardpans/plowpans);
10. soil density (e.g., a geologically rich mineral soil versus an organic peat soil).

If soils are adequately saturated with moisture, the cooling effect of water evaporation from the soil means that one pound of water can lower the temperature of a cubic foot of mineral-dense soil by 28°F!

Temperature is directly associated with soil moisture and dictates what is active when. Soil temperatures actually peak approximately one to two hours later than the daytime temperatures. Figure 4.4 shows how solar radiation is received per unit of land area, depending on what direction the slope faces and its degree of incline. Sunlight striking a southern slope at a ninety-degree angle generates a lot more concentrated solar radiation than sunlight striking a northern slope at a forty-five-degree angle.

FIGURE 4.4

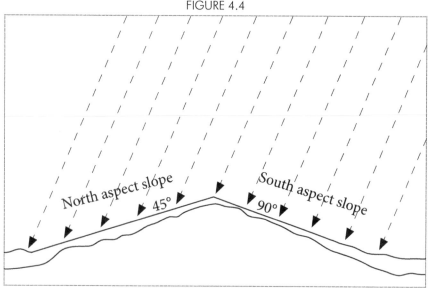

Nyle Brady and Ray Weil, *The Nature and Properties of Soil* (Upper Saddle River, NJ: Prentice Hall, 1996), 298.

GROW FOODS AND GO FOODS

Microorganisms also need nutrients, primarily nitrogen and carbon, or what William Albrecht referred to as "grow foods" (proteins) and "go foods" (carbohydrates). Where the rubber meets the road is the rhizosphere. The rhizosphere actually makes up only 1–5 percent of the total soil volume and extends only 1–5 millimeters away from the root surface (1 millimeter = 1/25 of an inch). The carbon and nitrogen cycle is dictated by the "living carbon," or exudates that are deposited into the rhizosphere by the plant.

This photosynthetic food is very complex. There are basically two categories of exudates, which are low molecular weight solutes that are found in high concentrations in the plant's cytoplasm. The first category includes exudates that are simply lost via passive diffusion of which plants exert little control. These are called basal exudates. The second types of exudates are those that are released for a specific purpose, thus the plant exerts a close degree of control.

FIGURE 4.5

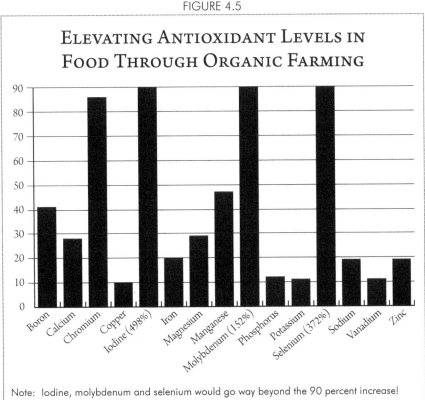

ELEVATING ANTIOXIDANT LEVELS IN
FOOD THROUGH ORGANIC FARMING

Note: Iodine, molybdenum and selenium would go way beyond the 90 percent increase!

Data from Charles Benbrook, *Elevating Antioxidant Levels in Food through Organic Farming and Food Processing*, Organic Center for Education and Promotion, January 2005.

TABLE 4.2

Carbon Compounds Released by Roots into Rhizosphere

Amino Acids	Organic Acids	Vitamins	Purines/ Nucleosides	Enzymes	Inorganic ions/gaseous molecules
α-Alanine	Citric	Biotin	Adenine	Acid/	HCO_3^-
α-Alanine	Oxalic	Thiamin	Guanine	alkaline	OH^-
Asparagine	Malic	Niacin	Cytidine	phosphates	H
Aspartate	Fumatic	Pantothenate	Uridine	Iavertase	CO_2
Cystine	Acetic			Amylase	
Glutamate	Butyric				
glycine	Valeric				
Leucine	Piscidic				
Lysine	Formic				
Methiomine	Aconitic				
Serine	Lactic				
Threonine	Pyrivic				
Proline	Glutaric				
Valine	Malonic				
Tryptophan	Aldonic				
Omithine	Erythronic				
Histidine	Tetronic				
Arginine					
Homoserine					
Phenylalanine					
Aminobutyric acid					
Aminoadipic acid					

E. A. Paul and F. E. Clark, *Soil Microbiology and Biochemistry* (San Diego: Academic Press, 1996).

Figure 4.5 demonstrates how organic farming practices can dramatically increase the uptake of minerals, due to a biological impetus. Minerals such as iodine, selenium, vanadium, chromium, and molybdenum are not typically applied as plant foods, yet their uptake appears as if they were fed those elements.

Table 4.2 illustrates those carbon compounds or photosynthates released by roots into the rhizosphere, and what I call the "nectar of the rhizosphere."

It includes amino acids, organic acids, sugars, vitamins, purines/nucleotides, enzymes, and inorganic ions/gaseous molecules.

Many plant secondary metabolites need to be added to this list, including phenols (e.g., flavonoids), terpenes, and alkaloids. Those exudates, or root secretions, of the second category that have specific purposes may be utilized in chemotaxis, which is an intentional movement of roots toward or away from a chemical stimulus: hormonal secretions for plant growth, maturity, and reproduction; biochemical defense compounds against fungal, bacterial, insect, and nematode enemies; compounds solubilizing certain tied-up nutrients such as iron, phosphate, manganese, et cetera (this is especially important in order to solubilize iron and phosphate, which are often complexed with soil aluminum); providing microbial secretions to enhance microbial growth and activity; and providing enzymes that can decontaminate miscellaneous toxins. For example, poplar tree exudates can decontaminate the herbicide atrazine, and wild rye exudates can denature 2-chlorobenzoic acid. These exudates are also biochemical attractants and repellents, regulating the soil microbial community. Phenols, for example, are thought to be involved in the genetic triggering of the legume-rhizobium interaction critical for legumes to fix nitrogen via their rhizobial bacterial partners.

TABLE 4.3
MUCIGEL MENU

Amino and Organic Acids

• Asparagine	• Glutamine	• Phosphatides
• Methionine	• Phenylalanine	• Indole
• Adenine	• Histidine	• Salicylic Acid
• Serine	• Arginine	• Purines
• Aspartate	• Alanine	• Pyrimidines
• Valine	• Glycine	• Nucleic Acids
• Glutamate	• proline	• Tartaric Acid
• Leucine	• Vitamins	• Oxalic Acid
• Lysine	• Sugars	• Malic Acid
• Tryptophan	• Tannins	• Citric Acid
• Tyrosine	• Alkaloids	• Scopoletin

Pinocytoses: Uptake of complex molecules through root cell membranes (e.g., amino acids, amino sugars, nucleic acids, etc.)

An exudate compound called lumichrome stimulates root carbohydrate respiration, assisting in the release of CO_2 into the rhizosphere, which can cause CO_2 levels to increase up to 17 percent in the root ball, which in turn can create a luxury supply of carbonic acid, H_2CO_3 (CO_2 + water), causing a dissolution of calcium carbonate (lime) to produce elemental calcium uptake. Another special kind of root exudate is mucilage or mucigel. Its composition is listed in table 4.3. Its purpose is to protect the root apical zones, or root tips, from premature sloughing. It lubricates the roots to assist them in moving through the soil like an earthworm. The mucigel improves soil and root contact, especially in dry soils. It increases the uptake of minerals ions and helps to create soil aggregates to improve soil aeration.

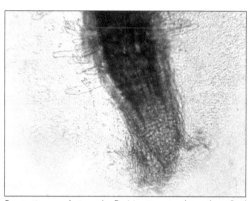

Root tip exudates. J. P. Martin et al., eds., *Soil Microbiology and Biochemistry Slide Set* Madison, WI: Soil Science Society of America, 1976), number 53.

In addition to the root exudates, soil carbon is also derived from root lysis, or the sloughing off of root cells, as well as root death. Actually, soil carbon is quite a stew of many kinds of carbons: fats, oils, waxes, resins, gums, sugars, starches, cellulose, lignins, tannins, pigments, and derivatives (including chlorophyll, cyanidins, etc.), polysaccharides as gels, and slimes secreted by bacteria and fungi (such as glomalin from mycorrhizal fungi). These carbons can constitute up to 40 percent of the organic matter of soils, including alcohols, hydrocarbons, organic acids, aromatic compounds, and mineral-carbon compounds. There are literally hundreds of compounds and thousands of combinations. Some are water soluble, but three to five times as many more are non–water soluble, and eight to ten times as many are volatile. That is why great soil is so aromatic; you can smell the phenols, terpenes, alkaloids, and sulfated fatty and amino acids. This is the *terroir*, the breath of the land.

The actual hierarchy of the soil food web comprises a predator-prey relationship. A special kind of connection exists among the community of this web, and as one can see with figure 4.6, it all begins with plants, the mother ship that is the liaison between sunlight and the alchemy of photosynthesis and the "livestock" in the soil.

FIGURE 4.6

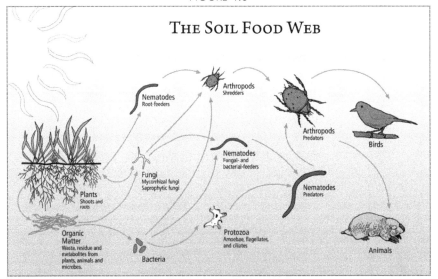

THE SOIL FOOD WEB

Courtesy USDA [Public domain], via Wikimedia Commons.

This chapter is not intended to be a primer on soil biology/microbiology but rather will address some of the principles associated with the production of fertile soils as they have been formed by the myriad of "livestock" inhabiting our soils (the herbivores, predators, decomposers, and symbionts). This group is appropriately called the soil food web, and I have a personal fascination and experiences worth noting in this area. Brady and Weil's *The Nature and Property of Soils* provides a very good general classification by size of some of the important groups of soil fauna and flora, as illustrated in figure 4.6.

The microbial community in turn begins the cycle of life; of prey and predator; of producers, consumers, and decomposers. Since bacteria (Eubacteria, or true bacteria) make up the largest percentage of biomass, both in actual numbers and in weight, they are the primary producers. They also happen to be about 60 percent protein, so they are a rich source of nitrogen. They also serve as nitrogen sinks, capturing nitrogen that would otherwise leach away or volatize.

At 1 billion per gram of soil, an acre would contain 1.5 tons of bacteria, and the estimates of their species calculated by researchers at Los Alamos National Laboratory in New Mexico place their distinct species numbers at about 1 million per gram, even though only less than seven thousand species have been described! It's unfathomable to imagine the number of species of

TABLE 4.4

SOIL FLORA AND FAUNA

Body Width (mm)	Major Taxonomic Groups	Examples
1. Macrofauna (72) All heterotrophs, largely herbivores, detritivores, and omnivores	Vertebrates Arthropods Annelids Mollusks	Mice, moles, voles, gophers, etc. Ants, beetles, centipedes, grubs, millipedes, spiders, termites, etc. Earthworms Snails/slugs
2. Macroflora Mostly autotrophs	vascular plants bryrophyte	Feeder roots of annuals/perennials Mosses
3. Mesofauna (0.1–2.0) All heterotrophs, mostly detritivores All heterotrophs, mostly predators	arthropods arthropods annelids	mites, springtails mites, protura enchtracid (pot) worms
4. Microfauna (<0.1) Detritivores, predators, bacteriavores, and fungivores	nematodes rotifera protozoa tardigrades	miscellaneous nematodes rotifers amoeba, ciliates, flagellates Macrobiotus sp. (water bears)
5. Microflora (<0.1) Mostly autotrophs Mostly heterotrophic Heterotrophs and autotrophs	Vascular plants Algae Fungi Lichens and microbiotic crusts Bacteria cyanobacteria actinomyctes archae	Root hairs of annuals/perennials Green, yellow-green, diatoms yeast, molds, rusts, mildews, and mushrooms Aerobes, anaerobes blue-green algae Many kinds of actinomycetes Methanotrophs, halophiles, thermoplasma

From Brady and Weil, *Nature and Properties of Soils.*

bacteria that inhabit our planet with its innumerable environments, from rainforests to deserts, oceans to swamps, volcanic vents to glaciers, and the digestive systems of invertebrates, humans, and other animals.

The archaea group of microorganisms, those that scientists like James Nardi refer to as extremophiles, are able to thrive in harsh environments, such as high salt, very high or very low temperatures, waterlogged circumstances, etc. They were not considered to be commonly found in garden/agricultural soils until recently, yet it's now understood that the archaea population can number as much as 250 million per gram of soil at times, up to half the total bacterial population in that soil.

Much has been written about the nitrification (oxidation) process by bacteria in soils. Ammonium (NH_4^+) is converted by nitrosomonas bacteria to nitrogen dioxide (NO_2^-), which is then converted by nitrobacter bacteria into plant-usable nitrate (NO_3^-). This conversion is known as nitrogen fixation. Recent findings at Penn State University have found that the rhizobia bacteria originally used to inoculate soybeans when they were brought into the United States have become naturalized in our soils, growing wild. Inoculant companies have developed their own strains of rhizobia for improving yield. The downside of marginalizing the wild rhizobia is that they apparently provide a much greater degree of resistance against the Asian soybean aphid, which began infesting U.S. soy fields about ten years ago, requiring pesticide applications to arrest the loss of as much as 40 percent of the crop. The naturalized rhizobia bacteria impart some kind of pest resistance, most likely because the soybeans are able to synthesize effective plant secondary metabolites antagonistic to aphids that they are otherwise unable to produce with the new inoculant commercial strains.

AN INVITATION TO BECOME A LEGUME

Another exciting breakthrough in nitrogen-fixing bacteria originates out of the University of Nottingham's Center for Crop Nitrogen Fixation. Professor Edward Cocking and colleagues found a specific strain of nitrogen-fixing bacteria in sugar cane that could intracellularly colonize all major crop plants. Remarkably, this development potentially allows all the cells within a plant to fix atmospheric nitrogen! This technology, labelled "N-Fix," is not a genetic modified/bioengineering technology, either. Rather, it is a seed inoculant, enabling plant cells to become nitrogen fixers, a hopeful boon to annual crop production, which uses wasteful and contaminating amounts of nitrogen. Commercialization of this non-GMO breakthrough is expected by 2015–2016.

In the same vein of investigating the "cellular wisdom" that exists among microbes and plants, researchers at the University of Missouri's Bond Life Sciences Center, under the direction of professor Gary Stacey, discovered that, for reasons yet unclear, non-legumes have not yet made a "pact" with nitrogen-fixing rhizobia bacteria that allow legumes to convert nitrogen gas into plant food that can be used to build proteins. Legumes recognize these bacteria as their allies, rather than as pathogens, by sensing a signal from the bacteria. The legumes then create nodules where the bacteria gather in order to be fed by the plant in exchange for fixing nitrogen out of the soils' atmosphere for the plants growth. The rhizobia found ways to produce biochemicals that inhibit the plant's defense responses, so they can be recognized and accepted as bacterial "friends." Non-legumes, like corn and tomatoes, were also found to receive the rhizobia signal, which in turn inhibited their plant defense mechanisms against the friendly rhizobia but for whatever reason did not initiate the next step of forming nodules to allow the rhizobia to become symbiotic partners with those plants.

The scientific challenge is thus to find ways to get non-legumes to activate mechanisms that will produce nodules that the rhizobia bacteria can inoculate. If the research at the University of Nottingham or University of Missouri bears fruit, it could have enormous implications on reducing the $8 billion spent yearly by farmers on nitrogen and the destructive amounts of nitrogen fertilizer leaching into our waterways and aquifers. In the meantime, we are blessed with the miracle of nitrogen fixation by the rhizobia with legumes and nitrogen fixation by the actinomycetes bacteria and the blue-green algae with non-legumes and legumes.

Only recently has it been discovered that there are perhaps twice as many archaea species as eubacteria species that are capable of oxidizing nitrogen. Only about 280 species of archaea have been described, yet in upland soils they are estimated to make up 10 percent of the microbial biomass. Like bacteria, archaea are known as prokaryotes, meaning their cells lack a nucleus surrounded by a membrane. Curiously, the genetic construction of archaea is more similar to that of plants and humans than to other bacteria.

Bacteria populations skyrocket in the rhizosphere compared to elsewhere in the soil, to the tune of ten to several hundred times as much. Two types of bacteria inhabit soils. Heterotrophic bacteria utilize organic substances in the soil for their sustenance and transform these organic compounds into plant nutrients. Autotrophic bacteria have the ability to synthesize their own organic compounds from carbon dioxide as well as transform inorganic substances and mineral elements into plant-available nutrients. Bacteria can also be categorized by their shape—bacillus (rod-shaped), spiral, and coccus (spherical)—and whether they are aerobes, which live in free-oxygen environments, or anaerobes, which live in environments absent of free oxygen. There are also facultative aerobes and facultative anaerobes, meaning that they can inhabit both environments, but the facultative anaerobes prefer oxygen-absent environments, and the facultative aerobes prefer oxygen-rich environments.

Bacteria are primary decomposers, but fungi are more significant in that regard. Bacteria use enzymes to fracture bonds that hold organic complexes together. Some bacteria, for example, are able to decompose the most common carbon raw material on our planet, cellulose, by producing enzymes like cellulase. This is an important relationship in creating soil humus. Since bacteria are able to ingest what they decompose, they create non-leachable plant nutrients that are locked up in their bodies until they either die or are eaten by predators like protozoa and nematodes.

Actinomycetes are bacteria that resemble fungi because they produce spores and grow filaments. They are the creators of that great earthy garden soil smell, and actinomycetes have been a lucrative resource to the pharmaceutical industry as a source of antibiotics such as neomycin, tretracycline, actinomycin, and candicidin. One of the more popular antibiotics produced by this organism is streptomycin, the first antibiotic proven to cure tuberculosis, discovered in 1943 by soil scientist Albert Schatz, PhD (1920–2005).

Schatz's forward thinking about soil formation was associated with the principles of chelation. In fact, he authored a text in 1954 titled *Chelation (Sequestration) as a Biological Weathering Factor in Pedogenesis* and another on the same subject in 1963, titled *The Important of Metal-Binding Phenomena in the Chemistry and Microbiology of the Soil.*

Actinomycetes are also nitrogen-fixers, able to extract nitrogen gas (N_2) and convert it to ammonium (NH_4) by associating with non-legume plants, invading their root hairs, and forming knobby larger nodules than rhizobia do with legumes. The rhizobia, blue-green algae, and actinomycetes collectively fix about 140 million metric tons of nitrogen each year, twice the amount of nitrogen fertilizer manufactured by the plant food industry.

Algae are often thought of as waterborne creatures found in swamps, ponds, streams, and rivers, but they have actually been found to be some of the hardiest terrestrial occupants of any other microbial form. Algae may be plants (e.g., kelp) or protists (e.g., bacteria, like cyanobacteria), and all utilize sunlight to photosynthesize sugars and give off carbon dioxide to form that mild corrosive called carbonic acid that can "eat" rocks. The blue-green algae (cyanobacteria) are also capable of fixing nitrogen.

In the top several inches of soil, where there is sunlight, algae can be found in high numbers—as many as 100 million per gram—and can consequently generate quite a bit of organic matter to soils. According to Nardi, in some Arizona soils, algae annually contribute six tons of organic matter to the top three inches of each acre.

Algae are also found in extreme climatic conditions, such as deserts, and when they are dormant they can survive temperatures of boiling (212°F/100°C) as well as intense cold (-320°F/-195°C). Algae have evolved to form partnerships with other organisms such as fungi, mosses, and bacteria. In desert environments, these partnerships create what's known as a microbiotic or cryptobiotic crust, where mutualistic collaborations of algae or cyanobacteria and their fungal/liverwort/moss partners protect these fragile and/or semi-arid lands with a glue-like covering that conserves moisture, fixes nitrogen, adds organic matter, prevents wind and water erosion, and conserves and recycles nutrients. These crusts can be irreparably destroyed, however, with off-road vehicles and trampling by hooves and feet.

Many years ago, I read the autobiographical account of the mystic G. I. Gurdjieff, called *Meetings with Remarkable Men*, a report of Gurdjieff's travels to isolated regions of Central Asia and the Middle East. His expedition found that they could keep their pack animals fed while traveling through a vast span of desert without vegetation by experimenting beforehand with two camels, two yaks, two horses, two mules, two donkeys, ten sheep, ten goats, ten dogs, and ten cats. The food created and tested with these species was the following recipe: seven and a half parts sand, two parts ground mutton and a half part salt. Not only was this gruel palatable to these animals, they actually were able to gain weight! Of course, Gurdjieff and his crew knew that the nutrition in the sand was some form of "organic substance." It is my belief that this organic substance was the cryptobiotic or microbiotic crust rich in protein, carbohydrates, fats, vitamins, and minerals.

Lichens are another example of symbiosis between fungi and algae, consisting of blue-green algae (cyanobacteria), golden and brown algae, and the ascomycota fungi. These organisms can survive drought, the hardest of rocks, and subfreezing temperatures. They are primary decomposers of lignin and stone, where the algae produce the photosynthetic carbons and nitrogen fixation to nourish the fungi while the fungi harvest the minerals found in the rock or tree bark. Lichens are extremely abundant, occupying 8 percent of the earth's land surface, and can live hundreds to thousands of years upon their rock host.

Lichen on rock, Thinkstock

Lichen produce hundreds of organic acids to achieve this long life, as well as producing natural antibiotics to protect their territory. Some of these unique acids are named after the specific lichens that produced them, such as lobaric acid of the Labaria species, gyrophoric acid from the Gyrophora lichen, and the ervenic acid from the Ervenia group. A popular "herbal" remedy is made from the Usnea lichen, which produces usnic acid. These organic acids are actual chelators, which brings me back to Dr. Albert Schatz's research on chelation as a primary factor in influencing the formation of soil (pedogenesis). Chelation, derived from the Greek word *chela*, meaning "claw," allows the formation of a ring-shaped chemical structure, based on six carbon atoms, that enables organisms such as lichens to clamp onto free-floating metal ions. This phenomenon is attributed to the biochemistry of chelation, in which one or more electrons can be shared between two elements. Another interesting fact about lichens is that up to 36 percent of their dry weight consists of these chelating organic acid compounds, giving them the superhero ability to dissolve iron and other metals in rock! Lichens are eaten as a delicacy in Japan and China, and some consider them to be the Biblical manna of the Israelites.

Chelation is a ubiquitous process throughout nature. A fascinating story possibly explains how the Incas in Peru could achieve an engineering feat in the fifteenth and sixteenth centuries unparalleled in excellence to this day thanks to naturally occurring chelation. Cut stones that make up the walls of Saksaywaman, an old fortress in the former Inca capital of Cuzco, weigh between ten tons and up to three hundred tons each. According to Yale University's explorer Hiram Bingham, author of *Lost City of the Incas*, these giant polygonal blocks were fitted together so precisely that it is impossible to insert the point of a knife between them. No mortar was used, and obviously the Inca didn't have diamond-tipped steel cutting blades to create these cuts. In fact, they had no metal cutting tools whatsoever.

Humic Substances-Geological Carbon

The following is excerpted from Lawrence Mayhew's article "The Principles and Practices of Using Humic Substances in Agriculture."

Carbon as the organic fraction of soils consists of a large variety of carbon compounds ranging from microorganisms, plant and animal cells, their residues at various stages of decomposition, and humus. The need for complex organic soil carbon is critical for chemically controlling nitrogen, phosphorus, sulfur, and micronutrient nutrition to the microbial communities and plants, as well as providing better water holding capacity, pH buffering, and increasing the metabolic activities of microbes.

Humic substances are the stable carbons that are the result of biological activity over long periods of time, and if there is a very lengthy time variable, the fully decayed materials will recombine (secondary synthesis) into extremely complex super-mixtures of black carbon that have no recognizable physical structure (amorphous), no specific chemical structure, and cannot be separated into distinct chemical components.

Geological carbon formation is quite a different process than above-ground composting, which is a rapid and usually hot process; whereas humic substances in soils, peat bogs and geological deposits (e.g., leonardite/lignite) are developed over long lengths of time (up to a thousands of years) at much lower temperatures, resulting in humic materials that have some biochemical differences.

Terrestrial-based humic substances include leonardite, oxidized lignite, oxidized sub-bituminous coal, humalite, carbonaceous shales, peat, and shilajit, an exudate found in rock formations in the Himalayas and a renowned Ayurvedic medicinal.

Traditionally, the active fractions of these geological deposits were marketed based upon their level of humic acids and fulvic acids, which in turn were determined by their solubility in dilute acids (fulvic acids) or alkali (humic acids). The classical methods for determining humic and fulvic acids are flawed because other minerals such as calcium carbonate are not removed from the humic fraction; because carbohydrates and proteins and other low molecular weight substances are not removed from the fulvic fractions, these guarantees of humic/fulvic acids are skewed.

Consequently, the Humic Products Trade Association (www. humictrade.org) has developed and validated a standardized method for analyzing humic and fulvic acids in cooperation with the USDA and the International Humic Substances Society (www. humicsubstances.org). The methodology was recently approved by the Association of American Plant Food Control officials (AAPFCC) Laboratory Services Committee.

The traditional "snake oil" reputation of humic substances is rapidly receding, thanks to numerous trials conducted by scientists who have published their findings in respected peer-reviewed professional journals. Consequently, 11 million acres were treated with humic substances in 2012 in the United States alone, at a value of $90 million. Fifteen major fertilizer distributors now market humic acids in the United States.

The data gathered from various soil types have demonstrated that commercial humic substances will increase overall crop yield and quality as well as soil health. Most notably, increases in length and weight of shoots and roots, the number of lateral roots, root initiation, and increased flowering and fruit set and nutrient availability and nutrient uptake are also positively impacted (especially nitrogen and phosphorus).

The numerous mechanisms involved that are likely to be responsible for such effects have been investigated by scientists for over 180 years, including but not limited to: chelating of cations (especially Ca^{++}, NH_4^+, K^+), the complexing of anions (NO_3^-, PO_4^{-3}, SO_4^{-2}), and the interactions with clays that increase soil aggregate stability by cation "bridging," by the bonding of hydrous oxides, and by active surface sites facilitating the release of plant nutrients. Other indirect effects may include stabilizing nutrients, stabilizing soil enzymes, reducing nutrient leaching, and increasing water holding capacity. Commercial humic products provide the greatest crop response on sandy soils of low organic matter content and also in high calcium (calcareous) soils, but significant crop responses were also found in soils with moderate organic matter and fertility. An exhaustive amount of references can be found on the aforementioned benefits.

Incan wall in Cuzco. Thinkstock

The explanation for this precise cutting may come from the story of nineteenth-century English explorer of South America Percy Fawcett, who left an account, prior to his disappearance in 1925, of being told by natives about a certain bird that used a plant to soften rock into "clay" prior to pecking at a circular depression for a nest, and this process only took a few days. Apparently, another Englishman had told Fawcett how he had walked through certain plants about one foot high with dark red leaves. By the time he crossed the terrain his four-inch-long spurs had been destroyed, eaten down to one-eighth of an inch in length. He was advised by the locals that this plant's juice dissolved his spurs. The alleged plant, identified later by a Peruvian priest-archeologist, was called *harakkeh'-ama* in Quechua, the native Incan language. The bird was identified as the pito bird, believed to be the *Colaptes pitius* or Chilean flicker. The Inca used the pito method to soften the stones prior to cutting them into the exact shapes needed to build their fortress. The plant juice evidently contains compounds, such as those found in lichen, that dissolve rock via a chelating process that probably involved various organic acids and enzymes.

Chilean flicker. Ben Tubby, CC-BY-2.0, via Wikimedia Commons

Other examples of chelation reside in what are collectively known as humic substances. Humic substances are found throughout our ecosystems because they are continuously created by microorganisms and plants. Because they have been synthesized since the genesis of life on Earth, humic substances are the largest source of sequestered carbon known. They are both widely researched and yet are not even close to being fully understood. Like clays, they possess behavior that is not static and perform multiple functions as needed, when needed. That is, humic substances have an ability to change their characteristics in order to perform multiple functions as needed by the soil and plant community. Geological deposits of humic substances are derived from what's known as "humates," which are found in oxidized coal deposits such as leonardite and lignite. These compounds contain the active fractions humic acid and fulvic acid.

The oil industry discovered many years ago that by inserting humates into wells challenged when the drilling bits encountered corrosive salt domes, these humic substances could chelate the salt to save the drilling bits. Chelating the salt means that the salt becomes complexed or incorporated into the humic substance, which now buffers or insulates the drilling bit from the corrosive action of the salt. Consequently, it didn't take long for agriculture to find buffering benefits from humates applied to salt-damaged soils negatively impacted by irrigation water deposits of excess sodium, calcium, and bicarbonates. Humates mixed with limestone could assist in the downward migration of calcium into deficient subsoils in Florida citrus groves.

Humates not only chelate positively charged cations like calcium, magnesium, sodium, and potassium, they can also chelate and thus hold on to leachable negatively charged anions such as boron, nitrate, sulfur, iodine, selenium, molybdenum, and chromium. Blending humates with non-leachable, insoluble phosphate $(P_2O_5^=)$ renders the phosphorus more available to plants.

I and other colleagues have used various humic substances in our business for over three decades, including as a soil and fertilizer amendment and an additive to foliar sprays to improve plants' intake of these tank mixes. Humic acids are recognized to increase plant cell membrane permeability by up to 35 percent, which may explain why a major agro-chemical company found out that adding humic acid extracts to their tank mixes allowed applicators to dramatically lower the amount of herbicide needed to achieve the same contact "burn-down." The same phenomenon occurs when adding these substances to a tank mix containing nitrogen, especially one containing urea. The humic acid chelates the nitrogen so that it doesn't readily volatilize in the tank or on the leaf surface while enhancing the absorption of the nitrogen.

Mixing humates in animal feed is a worthwhile practice for the same reasons. It has an attraction to those negative compounds found in the GI tract, like ammonia, methane, skatoles, mercaptans, etc., while being able to bind with those nutrients needed to be absorbed, chelating them, and improving uptake. Recently my company, Agri-Dynamics, has developed two similar formulas, one for horticulture and another for livestock. Both contain a mixture of nonalkali-derived seaweed extract, humic acid extract, and miscellaneous proprietary vitamins and minerals. What we experienced was not expected. In livestock, enteritis in birds, pigs, and calves stopped instantly; internal parasites were often discharged from many animals across multiple species. Immune systems perked up quickly, and homeostasis returned in short order. In plants given a similar formula, insect attacks stopped, and plant vigor and rate of growth increased.

Because of their fractal structure, humic substances create an enormous surface-to-mass ratio, which of course increases the habitat for soil microbes and also the soil's ability to bind to water molecules. Scientific papers going back to the 1960s have found that humic acids have cytokinin-like behavior (as is found in kelp extract), inhibit indoleacetic acid oxidase, increase stem elongation, increase phosphate activity (more uptake of phosphate), increase root formation, increase resistance to wilting in low humidity, enhance chlorophyll synthesis, enhance seed germination, and much more. Many of these references can be found in the chapter "Humic Hope" of the textbook *Organic Soil Conditioning* by William Jackson, PhD.

Fulvic acids are the low molecular-weight fraction of humic substances and appear to act in a hormone-like way to increase the plants physiological activities, especially the governing of oxygen intake, a very important component of a plant's resistance to climate stresses such as high temperature and drought. Fulvic acids appear to be especially strong chelators and thus can be effective in enhancing the translocation of elements in the soil and leaf as well as decontaminating contaminants like pesticides. Another interesting and important consideration of these low molecular-weight substances is their ability to solubilize silicon, which of course enhances cell defenses and photosynthesis.

A unique, naturally occurring fulvic material Agri-Dynamics has been using is actually extracted as a "leachate" from a prehistoric forest deposit. It has been laboratory analyzed and found to contain nearly seventy mineral elements. The chelating properties of this substance are so profound that one can mix calcium nitrate with 75 percent phosphoric acid and not get a precipitation reaction. Only one pint per acre in a tank mix is sufficient to affect other ingredients in the mix, to keep them in solution, to enhance their uptake to the plant, and to provide numerous trace elements from the extract. This extract is clearly a plant-derived substance as it is highly concentrated in phenolic compounds called tannins, or tannic acid. It thus makes for a valuable ingredient in liquid livestock remedies to discourage the growth of

FIGURE 4.7

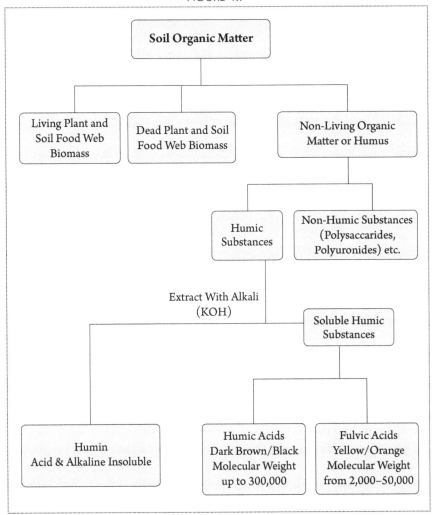

Brady and Weil, *The Nature and Properties of Soil*, 511.

pathogens and parasites. Because this elixir has such a compatible affinity to so many compounds that normally would be mutually antagonistic, and because it has so many applications to livestock, horticulture, and agriculture, Agri-Dynamics named this leachate/extract Fusion™. The benefits of this extract are apparently due to fulvic acids' ability to chelate two to six times more metals than higher molecular weight fractions, such as humic acid, and can carry three to ten times their weight in iron oxide.

TABLE 4.5

TABLE OF HUMIC AND FULVIC ACIDS

Element	Percent of Humic Acid	Percent of Fulvic Acid
Carbon	56.1	45.8
Hydrogen	4.6	5.4
Nitrogen	3.2	2.1
Oxygen	35.3	44.8
Sulfur	0.8	1.9

R. L. Wine, *Statistics for Scientists and Engineers* (Englewood Cliffs, NJ: Prentice Hall, 1964), 354–61.

Clearly humic and fulvic acids are very potent, rapidly reactive, and very complex organic molecules that have a vast array of characteristics useful for soils, microbial activity, plant physiology, and animal health and performance. Obviously, this very limited sampler of information on what is nothing less than a very complex amalgamation of chemistry, physics, and biology is only an attempt to introduce to the reader the importance and benefits of these compounds found in the natural world that act as powerful and miraculous catalysts that make life possible.

Ecological farming practices are the primary resources of these remarkable substances, their synthesis being the result of vigorous, healthy plant and microbial relationships and their synergy. Figure 4.7 organizes organic matter into its basic categories.

But if one needs to prime the pump of geological time on landscapes that have deteriorated over recent decades because of mismanagement and abuse, these substances, thank goodness, have been "banked" in a treasure trove of deposits that now allow them to be available for use and so can provide those critically essential missing links that exponentially increase the health, vitality, and productivity of any farm or ranch.

SHALAJIT: HUMUS FOR HUMANS

Shalajit is a substance used in an Ayurvedic medicine, a holistic practice that originated in India thousands of years ago. Shalajit is typically a pale-brown to blackish-brown exudate of variable consistency that seeps out of rock layers in various mountain ranges, especially the Himalayan and Hindukush ranges of India. It is a complex mixture of organic humic substances and plant and microbial metabolites. It is believed to have been derived from vegetation

Biochar: Perennial Humus?

In the 1990s, remarkable discoveries were made of the "terra preta do Indio," or the "Indian dark earth," in the Amazon Basin. These findings have raised huge questions about how the impoverished tropical soils could become so fertile, and remain so for at least a millennia. Rather than adapt to the nature of the tropics, these pre-Columbian natives actually "created" a natural system that could effectively feed themselves and many generations to come.

These tropical soils are typically called oxisols, ultisols, and spodosols and are very high in oxides of iron and aluminum and low in silicates. They are poor in cations calcium, magnesium, and potassium and leach readily. They are also acidic. Trials conducted in unproductive landscapes with biochar demonstrated that soils enriched with charcoal and fertilizer were almost 900 percent more productive by the second year than plots treated with fertilizer alone.

Apparently, ongoing studies here in the United States have suggested that biochar can greatly increase the cation exchange capacity in the soils, something desperately needed not only in tropical soils, but sandy soils and clay/loam soils low in both active carbon or dissolved organic matter and total organic matter. A meta-analysis of biochar field trials suggests that the main benefits of biochar are a liming effect to neutralize acidity, increase in water holding capacity, and improved nutrient availability. Some Japanese researchers have found that the surface area of char made from cedar increased from 120 square meters per gram at 400°C to 460 square meters per gram at 900°C. One metric ton of char requires 330 cubic feet of wood, providing a density of 720 kg per cubic meter, or 0.72 gms per cubic centimeter. The carbon content of biochar is 76 percent. Soil organic matter is typically 60 percent carbon. Coal ranges from 65–90 percent carbon.

Using biochar alone generated varied results, from no difference to 12–14 percent increases in unfertilized plots at four to sixteen tons per acre. However, other research in places like Australia saw an increase in wheat of 340 pounds (or 5.7 bushels) per acre (an 18 percent increase in yield), with 2.5 tons per acre of biochar, plus half the rate of recommended fertilizer.

How much char to apply? Of course, economics plays into this answer, especially if you're purchasing it. Domestic trials suggest a *maximum* of 10 percent in the top six inches of soil; but that's hardly realistic except over long periods of time with regular, light applications. (The top six inches of soil equals about 800,000 pounds per acre; 10 percent of that is 80,000 pounds, or 40 tons!)

A reasonable application could be five hundred pounds per acre per year; or one hundred to two hundred pounds per acre in the seed furrow or transplants. However, key to this working are the following points: 1) Biochar is hydrophobic; that is, it repels moisture. Mixing it with moist amendments like soil, compost, or wet rock dusts will hydrate it. 2) Inoculate and fertigate the biochar with nutrients that can immediately supply both microbes and nourishment deep within the many pores of this potential microbial habitat. You could use compost tea or worm tea, and I would "charge" those teas with fertility ingredients (per one hundred gallons of tea) such as one quart of seaweed, one gallon of fish hydrolysate, one gallon of molasses, and one quart of humic acid. Saturate the biochar with this "soup" until moist; on a small scale, add the biochar to a container of this soup mixture for two or three days.

Ideally, then incorporate this treated biochar into your soil so that the microbes can begin their job of expanding their habitat, creating both active carbon (dry organic matter) and residual organic matter in tandem with the root residues, which are lignified and thus provide a sustained release of organic matter over time.

Over ten years ago, Agri-Dynamics formulated a similar analog to biochar that performed wonderfully in the near pure sand golf greens by blending zeolite with high-quality compost, granite dust, humates, glauconite, kelp meal, and some natural fertilizers rich in potassium, sulfur, phosphorus, and magnesium. It was recommended to be blended at 10 percent with the sand. Afterward, it was swept in core aerification plug holes, twice yearly. Did that formula ever stimulate root growth and plant health! This was on bentgrass only one-sixteenth of an inch in height. Zeolite's architecture, like charcoal, is a honeycomb-structured polysilicate mineral that originated from volcanic eruptions. In fact, the kitchen countertop gravity pour-through water filters contain a blend of granules of activated charcoal and zeolite to purify water because their huge surface areas can capture so many pollutants.

Perhaps a blend of biochar, zeolite, compost, compost tea, humates, and mineral amendments can be a "restoration mix," a greenhouse bed amendment, a potting soil additive, a transplant additive, a seed coating.

My take on the numerous research studies—summarized on www.biochar-international.org, the fabulous website of the International Biochar Initiative—is that this two-thousand-year-old soil building and remediation practice can be cost-effective and consistently productive provided it is included as part of a holistic systems strategy, whereby other amendments needed by fragile or damaged soils can be incorporated, be they macroelements, trace elements, ground covers, mulch, compost, vermicasts/vermitea, rock dusts, liquid nutritional soups, etc.

Recall, that Native Amazonians didn't merely use biochar to create terra preta—they contributed pottery shards (clay) and fertility from animal and human waste.

Several books worth perusing are *The Biochar Revolution*, edited by Paul Taylor; *The Biochar Solution* by Albert Bates; and *The Biochar Debate* by James Bruges.

fossils that have been compressed under layers of rock for hundreds of years, undergoing a great deal of metamorphosis due to the high temperature and pressure. During summer months, hot weather causes it to become more liquid-like, like a sap or latex juice flowing out of the rock crevices yielding a gummy exudate.

Being a naturally occurring substance, the composition of shalajit varies from location to location and is influenced by factors such as the species of the plants involved, the geology of the rock, local temperatures, altitude, and humidity. It is traditionally recognized to be a potent rejuvenator and immunomodulator, an anti-aging resource, and it is prescribed for anemia, digestive disorders, gallstones, jaundice, chronic bronchitis, inflamed spleen, edema, diabetes, and osteoarthritis to name but a few ailments. A fabulous text on the subject is *Humic Substances in Drug Development* by Rajesh Khanna, S. P. Agarwal, and R. K. Khar.

The fungal inhabitants of our soils are perhaps the most significant with regard to being primary decomposers and producers of some carbonaceous compounds that are second to none in building organic matter. Up to 50 percent of those substances consumed by fungi are incorporated into the fungal mass, compared to 20 percent being incorporated by the soil bacteria. Only about a hundred thousand species of fungus have been identified, even though an estimated 1.5 million species are yet to be cataloged. The total fungal biomass on an acre of soil can range from 1,000 to 15,000 kilograms per hectare (or about 1,000 to 15,000 pounds per acre). Fungi are very versatile in their function. For example, the trichomycetes family lives in association with specific arthropods, actually living in the guts of soil citizens such as millipedes. Primary decomposers are called sugar fungi because they attack the simple carbon sugars that are found in abundance in the leaf litter of a crop that has shed its summer vegetation, or that was mowed or pulled as weeds.

Sugar fungi are the organisms that contribute to the heat of a compost pile containing vegetation debris by releasing energy from the consumption of this carbon resource. Fungi, like higher life-forms, are made up of cells that have distinct, enclosed nuclei, and they construct their cell walls from a compound called chitin, the same raw material that makes up the exoskeleton of insects and crustaceans. An enzyme called chitanase is now made from

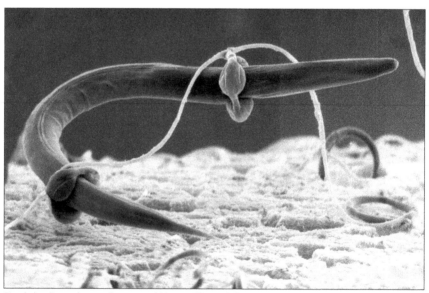

Drechslerella anchonia. Courtesy of Nancy Allin and George Barron

shrimp/crab/lobster waste to be used as a natural pesticide against fungal diseases and some insects.

The tougher parts of a plant's make up are cellulose, hemicelluloses, and lignin. And because fungi are not made up of these plant carbon chains, they can readily decompose them. The family of sac fungi, Ascomycota, primarily attacks the cellulose and hemicellulose, leaving the toughest carbon chain of all, lignin, to the Basidiomycetes, which produce mushrooms, bracket fungi, and smuts. Some fungi, like the *Drechslerella anchonia*, actually behave like carnivorous plants, waiting for their prey with snares and then baiting them with a biochemical attractant. The snares are triggered by touch, causing fungal enzymes to parasitize and digest the prey.

Fungi numbers are not typically counted by numbers of individuals, such as bacteria, but rather by the length of their hyphae, or fungal filaments, which can be massive. James Nardi notes that a *single* fungus found in Michigan actually covered a thirty-eight-acre parcel; yet another fungus discovered in the Pacific Northwest covered fifteen hundred acres. That means these fungi would be the largest living creatures on the planet and could be up to ten thousand years old. Typically, a thimbleful of healthy soil may contain several miles of Arbuscular mycorrhizae fungi hyphae!

The fungi that may be the most economically and ecologically significant, however, are the mycorrhizae, fungi that create a mutually beneficial relationship with their host plant. What has been only recently discovered is that more than 90 percent of all plants on Earth form mycorrhizal relationships.

Unlike the saprophytic fungi which derive their nutrition from dead and discarded plant vegetation, mycorrhizae obtain their energy from "living carbon," or plant exudates given up by the host plant, a sizable investment considering 5–30 percent of that plant's total photosynthate production may be given to its mycorrhizal partner. But in exchange for such a gift, the absorptive surface area of the plant's root mass (weight) may increase up to ten times, thus greatly enhancing the plant's ability to take up more moisture and minerals such as zinc, iron, copper, potassium, boron, nitrogen, and especially phosphorus.

Essentially, there are two groups of mycorrhizae: the ectomycorrhiza and the endomycorrhiza, also known as Arbuscular mycorrhizae because the latter group penetrates the root cell walls and forms highly branched structures known as arbuscles. The ecto group includes hundreds of species that associate with hardwoods and conifers. They cover the surface of the feeder roots and can actually increase the surface area of a tree's roots by seven hundred to a thousand times.

Table 4.6 demonstrates how mycorrhizae actually enhance the uptake of nutrients in tomatoes in both saline and non-saline irrigated water. The "salty" water showed the greatest percentage of uptake of minerals, except for sodium. It is generally recognized that mycorrhizal fungi can increase the absorption of soil nutrients by a factor of 100–1,000.

What is intriguing about these Arbuscular mycorrhizal (AM) relationships is that they can interact in a four-way entanglement that can really boost productivity.

In 2013 researchers at the University of Aberdeen in the United Kingdom discovered an amazing communication phenomenon amongst plants that are symbiotically partnered with mycorrhizae fungi. Their research entailed growing an untreated control block of beans that were not inoculated with AM fungi and another block that were inoculated. They eliminated any possibility of plants being able to cross communicate with volatile substances via the air by covering them with bags. Researchers then infested some of the beans with aphids. What was fascinating was that inoculated beans that were "wired" via fungal filaments to those challenged with aphids were able to mount a defense, synthesizing repellents against the aphids and sending out volatile emissions as signals to predatory wasps, calling in an "air strike" against the wasps' favorite prey, the aphids. Beans not connected to plants via fungal hyphae that were challenged by aphids did not get an early warning of the impending pest and thus became easy prey to the aphids. This suggests

TABLE 4.6

Effect of Seedling Inoculation

with Arbuscular Mycorrhizae (AM) on Root Colonization, Fruit Yield, and Shoot Nutrient Contents for Tomatoes Irrigated with Nonsaline or Saline Water

Very small amounts of inoculum were added to the potting mix in seedling trays. Mycorrhizal inoculation increased all parameters, but the greatest benefits of AM accrued under saline conditions. AM-inoculated plants under saline conditions yielded 5.3 kg fruit m^{-2}, not statistically different from the 5.8 kg fruit m^{-2} yield of noninoculated plants under nonsaline conditions.

Irrigation water treatment	AM root colonization	Fruit Yield	Nutrient content of plant shoot					
			Increase from AM inoculation, %					
			P	K	Na	Cu	Fe	Zn
Nonsaline (EC$_w$ = 0.5)	166	29	44	33	21	93	33	51
Saline (EC$_w$ = 2.4)	293	60	192	138	7	193	165	120

Data selected from Al-Karaki (2006)

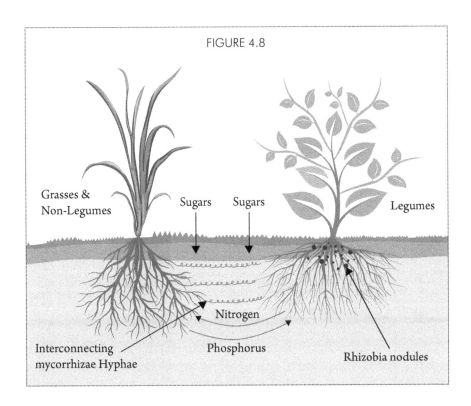

FIGURE 4.8

Grasses & Non-Legumes

Sugars   Sugars

Legumes

Nitrogen

Phosphorus

Interconnecting mycorrhizae Hyphae

Rhizobia nodules

that plants can eavesdrop or "wiretap" other plants via the "fungal internet" and generate an induced systemic resistance to diseases and insects. Equally encouraging is that different plant species can utilize this common internet to get a heads-up of what challenges lie ahead. In other words, the mycorrhizae fungi provide a security service for the entire plant community.

Both legumes and non-legumes become inoculated with shared mycorrhizae, but non-legumes, such as grasses, have a more fibrous root system, thus a larger mycorrhizal hypae network. They are more efficient in extracting phosphorus than the legumes, which are also feeding their rhizobial colonies with their photosynthate carbon compounds. In return, the legumes can more readily transfer nitrate to the non-legumes through the mycorrhizal network. These relationships are another reason why it is necessary to get as much perennial biodiversity on the farm or ranch as well as diverse, mixed cropping systems (cover crops, companion crops) when planting annuals.

In 1996, USDA researcher Sara Wright discovered perhaps one of the most important carbon treasures in our soils, named glomalin after its genus,

Glomus. It is known that AM-inoculated roots can transfer up to fifteen times more carbon to soil as the same species devoid of AM inoculation. Analyzed cucumber roots showed that a high AM-inoculated plant consisted of 20 percent of its root mass as mycorrhizae versus only 10 percent on a low inoculated root ball. In the high AM root ball, 43 percent of the photosynthesis produced above was found in the mycorrhizae hyphae. In the non-mycorrhizal roots less than half the amount of those photosynthates was found.[*] What has been discovered about this glycoprotein carbon is that it's very stable. It doesn't dissolve in water. It's resistant to decay and estimated to persist in soils for ten to fifty years. It has 25 percent more weight than humic acid and constitutes up to 30 percent of the organic soil carbon (compared to less than 10 percent being humic acid). It synthesizes soil aggregates with this glue, providing crumb structure, porosity for air, and water movement. Hundreds of meters of mycorrhizal hyphae in a mere teaspoon of soil equals large amounts of glomalin because this substance is secreted by the fungi to insulate the AM from nutrient and moisture loss as well as to protect the plant's roots from fungal, bacterial, and nematode pathogens.[†]

Another compelling revelation about AM fungi is their ability to suppress weed growth. Experiments conducted by researchers Rinaudo, Bàrberi, Giovanetti, and van der Heijden demonstrated some very encouraging conclusions, at least with sunflowers.[‡] In weedy plots where sunflowers were inoculated with AM, the total weed biomass was an average 47 percent lower than in weedy plots of sunflowers not inoculated by AM. Six weed species were used, and the biomass of two species were reduced by 66 percent and 59 percent (*Chenopodium album*, or common lambsquarters, and *Echinochloa crus-galli*, or barnyard grass) while four other weed species were reduced by 20 percent to 37 percent. Where only weeds were grown (no sunflowers), weed biomass was reduced by 25 percent due to the presence of mycorrhizae. This could be because many agricultural weeds are non-mycorrhizal dependent and those AM mutualistic crops which benefit from AM colonization of roots are better equipped to harvest more nutrients from the soil, thus outcompeting the weeds for minerals. In fact, inoculated sunflowers obtained 48 percent more phosphorus than non-inoculated.

---

[*] Jerry Brunetti, "Unseen Ecology of Soil Biology" Acres U.S.A. Conference, December 2011 (PowerPoint Presentation).
[†] I. Jakobsen and L. Rosendahl, "Carbon Flow into Soil and External Hyphae from Roots of Mycorrhizal Cucumber Plants," *New Phytol* 115 (1990): 77–83; A. H. Fitter, "Costs and Benefits of Mycorrhizas: Implications for Functioning Under Natural Conditions," *Experientia* 47 (1991): 350–55.
[‡] Valeria Rinaudo, Paolo Bàrberi, Manuela Giovanetti, and Marcel G. A. van der Heijden, "Mycorrhizal Fungi Suppress Aggressive Agricultural Weeds," *Plant and Soil* 333 nos. 1–2 (August 2010): 7–20.

Mycorrhiza on fine root system (beech), via Wikimedia Commons

Another trial challenging the theory that plants can only take up nitrogen as an ion and not as organic nitrogen, such as an amino acid, was published in 2009 by Whiteside, Treseder, and Atsatt. The amino acid glycine was detected within four hours of introduction in the AM hyphae, plant root cells, and plant shoot cells and within twenty-four hours in the AM vacuoles, the root vascular tissue and in the chloroplasts in the short cells. These observations were done on *Poa annua*, or annual bluegrass.[*]

Thus, mutualistic relationships between plants and microbes prove that organic nitrogen (e.g., glycine, an amino acid), which of course is the form in which most of our nitrogen is created in our humus-rich organic soils, can be taken up by plants.

The most damaging ways to reduce or eliminate mycorrhizae populations, and thus the glycoprotein glomalin, are a) tillage/soil disturbance, which destroys the fungi's hyphae; b) no cover crops because bare soils have no root systems for the mycorrhizae to inoculate; and c) highly soluble sources of phosphate. Plants don't need to invest photosynthetic carbon to the fungi because they're getting flooded with it. Monoammonium phosphate (MAP), diammonium phosphate (DAP), super phosphate, and even too much (especially slurry) manure can create this problem; d) anhydrous ammonia and high amounts of soluble salt nitrogen fertilizers; e) fungicides and to some extent certain insecticides and herbicides.

Tight rotations; cover crops; minimum tillage; no excess phosphate fertilizer, or if phosphorus is necessary preferably a slower-release P_2O_5 such as compost, soft rock phosphate, bone meal, and super phosphate (0-20-0) or MAP (11-52-0) that are treated with humic acids; using green manures, legumes, manure from nitrogen, or UAN-28 or 32 treated with humic acid to complex the nitrogen; and avoiding fungicides (using instead biological fungicides like terpenoids, organic acids, etc.): All of these practices will encourage mycorrhizal populations to remain stable and even grow in

[*] Matthew Whiteside, Kathleen Treseder, and Peter Atsatt, "The Brighter Side of Soils: Quantum Dots Track Organic Nitrogen through Fungi and Plants," *Ecology* 90, no. 1 (2009): 100–108.

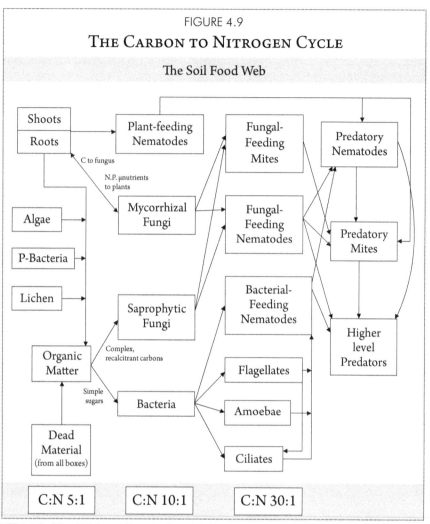

FIGURE 4.9

THE CARBON TO NITROGEN CYCLE

The Soil Food Web

Shoots / Roots	Plant-feeding Nematodes	Fungal-Feeding Mites	Predatory Nematodes
C to fungus	N.P. μnutrients to plants		
Algae	Mycorrhizal Fungi	Fungal-Feeding Nematodes	Predatory Mites
P-Bacteria			
Lichen	Saprophytic Fungi	Bacterial-Feeding Nematodes	Higher level Predators
Organic Matter	Complex, recalcitrant carbons	Flagellates	
	Simple sugars	Bacteria	Amoebae
Dead Material (from all boxes)		Ciliates	

| C:N 5:1 | C:N 10:1 | C:N 30:1 |

USDA & Soil Food Web and Elaine Ingham, NRCS.

number. You cannot afford to lose mycorrhizal numbers. They are a huge resource to increase plant-available phosphorus, necessary to produce the "energy currency" of life for plants and animals, called adenosine triphosphate, or ATP; the fungi are also hydraulic pumps for additional water and they produce powerful enzymes to extract critically important trace elements like zinc. Inoculating seed and annual transplants with mycorrhizae is a very good investment that will translate into measurable returns the very year of planting.

An important predatory microbe in this vast Serengeti landscape is the protozoa, consisting of amoebas, ciliates (having hairs), and flagellates (having whips). They dwell in the water film that lines the pores of soil. Estimates that 10 billion protozoa could live in the top six inches of soil in a square meter of a pasture are realistic. The primary food of protozoa is bacteria, and it is estimated that 90 percent of bacteria consumed are eaten by protozoa, the other 10 percent by nematodes.

In this regard, protozoa provide a significant conversion of organic nitrogen into ammonium (NH_4^+) and nitrate (NO_3^-). The mineralization of nitrogen is derived from protozoa eating bacteria. Because bacteria are rich in protein (nitrogen) there is a lot of protozoa waste (protozoa poo) generated, which can account for 70–80 percent of the plant's nitrogen. Protozoa in turn are food for nematodes, earthworms, and microarthropods. These predator-prey relationships are how terrestrial ecosystems are able to extract nitrogen gas (N_2) at over 30,000 tons hovering over each acre, combine it with water (H_2O) and the exhalation of plants and microbes (CO_2), and via the alchemy of photosynthesis convert all this "nothing" into plant-available foods like nitrate (NO_3^-) and ammonium (NH_4^+) while building humus, or soil carbon.

In figure 4.9, the soil food web is assembled relative to the "Carbon to Nitrogen Cycle." The nitrogen-rich organisms such as bacteria, fungi, and plant-feeding nematodes have a carbon-to-nitrogen (C:N) ration of only 5:1. These are consumed by protozoa, nematodes and mites, which have a C:N ration of 10:1. These predators are in turn consumed by still other predators that possess a C:N ratio of 30:1.

The huge significance of this is that as the high-nitrogen creatures are consumed, they provide raw materials in their predators' excrement, rich in nitrogen for plant use. As their populations explode, they attract greater

TABLE 4.7

• Protoplasm	• Epidermis
• Chlorophyll	• Seed coats
• Oils	• Pigments (e.g., carotenoids)
• Carbohydrates	• Cuticles
• Starches	• Spore and pollen exines
• Cellulose	• Waxes
• Lignin	• Resins

S. A. Waksman and K. R. Stevens, "The Role of Microorganisms in Peat Formation of Decomposition" *Soil Science* 28 (1929): 315–40.

numbers of carbon-rich predators, increasing their populations with this food supply and consequently enhancing the carbon content (humus) of that soil as they either die off or are consumed. This is not some neo-Darwinian, the-strong-eat-the-weak arrangement, but rather a food chain that is cooperative and reciprocal, providing collective benefits for all members of the plant and soil community. Carbon compounds are very diverse in their biochemical construction and thus vary considerably in their rate of breakdown and their conversion to various humic and non-humic compounds.

Table 4.7 provides examples of some of the miscellaneous plant compounds in their order of increasing resistance to attack by biological factors. This is significant to a farmer, gardener, rancher, or naturalist because each genus/species of plant uniquely comprises many thousands of primary compounds and secondary compounds. All of these raw materials are foods or substrates for many numerous species within the ecosystem of the soil food web. Needless to say, the more substrates (from plant biodiversity) there are, the more soil livestock species appear to feed on them, and the more predators that feed on them, and so on. The resulting matrix is thus composed of untold numbers of substances that create vitality, productivity, and resilience in the system.

Nematodes are another important part of this recycling-of-nutrients "dance" that occurs in this biosphere. There's an estimated 500,000 species of nematodes out there. We've only discovered 15,000 of them, less than 3 percent. There are basically three types of nematodes: a) the parasitic nematodes that attack plant roots and crowns; b) the bacteriovores that feed on actinomycetes and bacteria; and c) the "carnivorous," the largest of them all, that eat protozoa, rotifers, algae, soil grubs, weevils, slugs, and other nematodes. Nematodes search for their prey via biochemical scents that their victims emit, or they hunt in specific climatic zones or habitats where their prey proliferates.

It's not rocket science to understand that soils devoid of an ecological balance of soil food web denizens are plagued with parasitic nematodes. Pathogenic nematodes abound on soils that have low organic matter, a lot of soil disturbance via tillage, or are compacted and have little biodiversity. Golf course greens, for example, have many challenges because of this imbalance. The greens are a monoculture of bent grass grown on 90 percent sand with a lot of nitrogen, herbicides, insecticides, and fungicides.

The same kind of sterile environments occur in the plantation-mentality fields of strawberries, fruit trees, and produce, while the growers and chemical

FIGURE 4.10

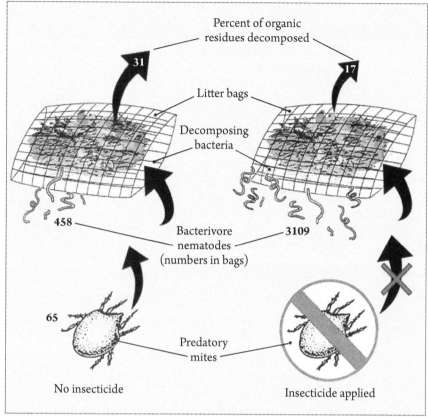

Nyle Brady and Ray Weil, *The Nature and Properties of Soil* (Upper Saddle River, NJ: Prentice Hall, 1996), 490.

manufacturers cry foul at the EPA for removing very toxic nematicides that should have been prohibited years before. Using soil ecology principles would have prevented these epidemics of nematode infestations, fungal diseases, and insect plagues beforehand; and in the event that sporadic outbreaks occur, utilizing natural alternatives such as terpenoid/phenolic extracts, neem tree oil cake and iodophor-based iodines, to name a few, can effectively arrest the outbreak.

To illustrate how interactively complex this food web is, an experiment was done in which chlordane, an insecticide, was used to kill off predatory mites (see figure 4.10). One of the foods of these mites is the bacteriovore (bacteria-eating) nematodes. Litter bags were stuffed with the same amount of creosote bush so that it could be weighed before and after the insecticide was applied. Researchers discovered that killing the predators (mites) of predators (bacteriavore nematodes) caused the population of their prey, the bacteriovore nematodes, to skyrocket from 458 in the unsprayed litter bag to 3,109 in the treated bag. Because of the high number of bacteriovore nematodes, there was a population crash of the nematodes' prey, the decomposing bacteria. The percent of organic residues that decomposed in the unsprayed control was 31 percent versus only a 17 percent decomposition in the insecticide-sprayed group. Thus, killing the mites dramatically altered (increased) the populations of their prey, the nematodes, and decreased the nematodes' prey, the bacteria, resulting in a negative impact on the creation of humus for all of the plants and soil food web members that would benefit from such. The law of unintended consequences reigns supreme.

LOOKING FOR MR. GOODBUG

A very exciting biological determinant is now available from Ward Laboratories in Kearny, Nebraska (www.wardlab.com). Ward Laboratories can provide in-depth biological information, what they call green chemistry.

The Haney Test (named after Rick Haney of USDA Agricultural Resource Service) incorporates several tests that ultimately translate into a soil health score. Part of the test includes the Solvita 24-hour CO_2 Burst Test to evaluate the respiration of the soil's microbes by measuring the carbon dioxide released in the soil sample (see www.solvita.com). The Solvita number (in ppm) is the amount of CO_2-C released in twenty-four hours from soil microbes. The higher the ppm, the better.

Then a water extract of the soil is taken to determine the water-extractable organic carbon and water-extractable organic nitrogen. The organic carbon measures the quality of your carbon, or the energy source that feeds soil microbes. Total organic matter tests are a measure of the quantity of carbon in the soil, but typically the organic pool of carbon is roughly eighty times smaller than the total carbon amount.

The water extract of the soil also determines total nitrogen, inorganic nitrogen, and organic nitrogen. The inorganic nitrogens consist of NO_3-N (nitrate) and NH_4-N (ammonium). Both of these inorganic nitrogen's are leachable, especially NO_3-N (nitrate), which will be higher in excessively tilled soils or soils heavily fertilized with nitrogen/manure. The organic nitrogen is that fraction in a form that I would call "protoplasm" because it consists of amino acids, peptides, nucleotides, and others that could be the remains of bacteria, fungi, protozoa, algae, nematodes, and plant cells. It can easily be digested by living microbes and released to growing plants while not at risk to leaching or volatilization. In other words, it is a pool of nitrogen ready to be mineralized as the crop needs it. To compute the organic nitrogen, the inorganic NO_3-N and NH_4-N are subtracted from the total nitrogen.

The H3A extraction also uses three weak organic acids and measures nitrate and ammonium nitrogen as well as orthophosphate (PO_4), aluminum, iron, calcium, potassium, magnesium, and sodium.

An organic carbon-to-nitrogen ratio is then determined using the water extracts of each (carbon and nitrogen). A soil C:N ratio above 20:1 generally indicates that no net nitrogen or phosphorous mineralization will occur, meaning the nitrogen and phosphorous are "tied up" within the microbial biomass until the ratio falls below 20:1. In such an instance, bringing in legumes (nitrogen fixers) would be a sound idea. In order for the nitrogen and phosphorous to be readily released to the growing plant, a C:N ratio of between 8:1 and 15:1 would be preferred.

The Soil Health Score is determined thusly: the Solvita score ÷ the C:N ratio, (+) the water soluble organic carbon extract ÷ 100, (+) the water soluble organic nitrogen extract ÷ 10. The score results from combining five independent measurements of the soil's biological properties. A calculation for soil health can range from zero to fifty, and numbers in the high teens to twenties are considered to be very good to excellent.

Ward Laboratories also runs a very interesting analysis called the phospholipid fatty acid (PLFA) analysis, which actually measures functional groups of microbes and their contribution to the total biomass in the soil, both in weight and percentage. Total biomass scores (in ng/g) range from <500 (very poor); 500–1,000 (poor); 1,000–1,500 (below average); 1,500–2,500 (average); 2,500–3,000 (above average); 3,000–3,500 (good); 3,500–4,000 (very good); to >4,000 (excellent). Alongside these measurements of biomass are measurements of diversity, ranging from a 1.0 (very poor) to >1.6 (excellent).

In the Functional Group column are biomass and PLFA ng/gm measurements (and their percentages of the total biomass) of: total bacteria, gram (+)/ actinomycetes, gram (-)/ rhizobia, total fungi, Arbuscular mycorrhizal, saprophytic fungi, protozoa, and the undifferentiated or nonspecific microbes.

Additionally, community composition ratios are evaluated for fungi-to-bacteria ratios, scaled from very poor (<0.05) to excellent (>0.35).While bacteria are important, fungi populations are considered indicators of soil health. A reasonable target ratio is 0.25–0.30. Predator-to-prey ratios (protozoa:bacteria) are scaled from very poor (<0.002) to excellent (>0.02).

Predator:Prey relationships are important for the release of nutrients contained within bacteria, especially nitrogen. A reasonable target ratio is 0.20. Gram+-to-gram- ratios are the measure of amount of actinomycetes (gram+) and rhizobia (gram-) in the soil. The scale ranges from (gram-) dominated (<0.5) to balanced bacterial community (1.0–2.0) to very (gram+) dominated (>4.0). These ratios are indicative of organisms that may reflect aerobic or anaerobic conditions; high (gram-) numbers may suggest stressors such as pesticides/heavy metals. A target ratio is 1.65.

Even though these ratios can be looked at separately, they need to be taken into consideration with one another to reconcile the soil ecology's "big picture." Soil types, climates, and the conditions at sampling time should be noted (e.g., "cool, wet spring; sandy loam; previously wheat; pH of 6.0; psi of 200 at eight-inch depth; medium calcium/low P_2O_5/ low sulfur, etc., etc.")

PARASITIC NEMATODES: AN INDICATOR OF SOIL SICKNESS

The group of invertebrates known as nematodes are estimated to number at a million species, but only about fifteen thousand species have been identified and described. Nematodes are actually aquatic animals; thus they need moisture to be able to migrate, including the animal parasites that are more prevalent in moist pastures.

Pathogenic varieties include the 15 percent described as plant pathogens and the 10 percent of species that parasitize animals, and they can range in size from one hundred micrometers to over thirty feet in length, these larger species being nematodes that parasitize whales.

The majority of plant pathogenic nematodes, however, are only 0.5 to 4.0 millimeters in length, and their diameter being narrower than a human hair. Nematodes can be found parasitizing all parts of a plant: root, stems, leaves, or flowers, depending on the species. They do so by utilizing an organ called a stylet, which is a protractible spear in their head that is either hollow or grooved and which they use to puncture plant tissue and withdraw the liquid contents.

In the soil, where the primary plant nematode parasites dwell, including the major crop-damaging species, there are two primary groups: ectoparasites and endoparasites. Ectoparasites remain outside of the plant tissue. Some have short stylets and thus can only feed on the epidermal tissue of the roots; others that have longer stylets are able to feed more deeply in the root tissue. Endoparasites dwell inside the root mass and thus can cause more damage to the plant. Some of the endoparasites are sedentary; that is, they remain stationary inside the root. Others are migratory, traveling throughout the root ball.

The incidence of nematode infestation in agricultural soils is directly correlated to the health and complexity of the soil's ecological community. Soils that do not contain a vibrant, diverse population in the food web are very susceptible to parasitic nematodes. This is typical when practices such as excess tillage, compaction, salt precipitation from fertilizers and irrigation water, pesticides, and a loss of organic matter can upset the balance of this soil ecosystem. Anything that compromises the size of the root mass amplifies the negative effects of nematode infestation. Sandy or sandy loam soils low in humus and subjected to repeated doses of salt fertilizers, pesticides, and irrigation water containing elevated amounts of mineral salts are an ideal environment for parasitic nematodes. Not surprisingly, golf course greens— which can be 80–90 percent sand and are constantly irrigated and subjected to soluble fertilizers, fungicides, insecticides, and herbicides—can have large populations of parasitic nematodes, as can sandy/low humus agricultural soils that are subjected to similar "chemo therapeutic" treatment.

Signs of nematode dominance in the rhizosphere may be patches of wilting, dying, chlorosis, early senescence, stunted growth, and thinning (e.g., hay, pastures). To really get a handle on what you are up against however, one needs to get an accurate assessment of the nematode problem that can only be determined by a nematode laboratory assay, to provide identification of the species, and the numbers present because the symptoms produced by nematode infestation can also be the same as those caused by other pathogens, as well as poor soil nutrition and extremes in soil moisture content.

Some crops are more tolerant than others, but other biological factors such as pathogenic bacteria or fungi may even amplify nematode damage. Some nematode species can also transmit viruses, namely the dagger (Xiphinema), needle (Longidorus), and stubby-root (Trichodorus) species, all ectoparasites. Other ectoparasitic nematodes include: ring (Criconemella spp., et al.), sheath (Hemicycliophora spp.), pin (Tylenchus spp.), spiral (Rotylenchus spp. and Helicotylenchus spp.), stunt (Merlinius spp., Amplimerlinius spp., Gracilacus spp., Tylenchorhynchus spp.), and sting (Belonolaimus spp.).

By far the most damaging nematodes are the endoparasites, which include the root knot (Meloidogyne spp.), cyst (Heterodera spp.), and root lesion (Pratylenchus spp.). The lance (Hoplolaimus spp.) nematode can behave either as an endo- or ectoparasite.

If a nematode infestation becomes apparent, what can one do ecologically to reverse the problem? Some important cultural practices should include:

1. Crop rotation, ideally not returning a crop to the same plot of ground for at least three years.
2. Cover crops, especially "cocktails" of at least four to six species.
3. Vegetative fumigants such as plants of the mustard family (crucifers). The compounds found in these plants (which also include brassicas like kale, cabbage, collards, broccoli, and brussels sprouts) and crucifers like turnips, radishes, etc., contain sulfur compounds called isothiocyanates, which also produce cyanide, a biodegradable, biological toxin that "fumigates" the soil of both bacterial and fungal diseases. These isothiocyanates are particularly toxic to root knot and root lesion nematodes, but the cover crop must be tilled under because the isothiocyanates are predominantly in the foliage, not the roots. Mustards (such as cutlass and forge), oilseed radish (such as adagio and kernel), and rapeseed produce more isothiocyantes than other crucifers. Note: when using crucifers to fumigate soils, ensure that a non-cruciferous crop is planted afterward and properly inoculated with mycorrhizae as well as rhizobium (if it's a legume). Crucifers are not host plants for mycorrhizae, and their isothiocyantes can be also suppressive to beneficial biology if overused. Marigolds (African, or *Tagetes erecta*, and French, or *Tagetes patula*) are also inhibitory to nematodes because they produce biofumigants called polythienyls and thiophenes. Marigolds need to be growing in the ground for at least two months at a high density to produce concentrations of the fumigants lethal to nematodes. Additionally, there is evidence that certain bacterial associations with marigold roots have a suppressive effect on nematodes.
4. Quality compost, to introduce a plethora of healthy bacterial, fungal, and predatory nematode species into the soil, as well as the pest-suppressing metabolites that are found in compost. It's critical to increase the organic matter content of these troubled soils.

Around the year 2000, I investigated some patent applications on iodine and discovered that iodine was used quite extensively to treat soils as well as bulbs, seeds, trees, and vegetables for disease and nematode infestation. Back in the 1950s California citrus trees infested with nematodes were successfully treated with a mixture of water and a tincture of iodine solution. The only problem was that tincture of iodine is made with alcohol, which can be phytotoxic, and thus the solution needs to be diluted enough to not create problems. That means that more repeated doses have to be applied to get results. But the results were still very encouraging. The problem called "quick decline" included symptoms of loss in yield, yellowing and falling of foliage, lack of new growth, drying out/dying of branches, and eventual tree death. Dying citrus trees were rapidly restored by first creating a six-foot diameter basin around each tree, then adding ten gallons of water to hydrate the soil (unless it already is saturated). A twenty-gallon dilute iodine solution is applied to the basin, followed by a watering in of two and a half gallons of water. In every instance, nematodes were eliminated and the trees restored, often with one treatment if caught early enough.

Consequently, Agri-Dynamics became the creator of a formula that used a cold-processed iodophor, proprietary surfactants, humectants, and organic acids in order not to risk any phytotoxicity with the alcohol. The only trial conducted was on ginger seed, which apparently harbors nematodes that stunt growth and germination. The ginger treated with the iodine product we called Eco-Dyne/Bio-Dyne demonstrated a higher percentage of germination, earlier germination, and taller growth. What I question is, "Was this primarily a result of iodine affecting the nematode population, or was the iodine a bio-stumulant?" Based on other arcane literature (*Iodine and Plant Life: Annotated Bibliography, 1813–1949*), I read that iodine was recognized as a bacterial enhancer, especially of nitrogen-fixing bacteria such as rhizobia and azotobacter. Some of the compounds used for biostimulants at that time were innocuous enough; some that were used for pests were quite toxic, such as iodoformaldehyde and ethyl mercury iodide. The good news is that I also found research on various "tamed" iodine formulas that suggested treating bulbs of daffodils against "eelworms" (nematodes) and Fusarium with buffered, tamed iodine provided the *best* protection against these pests.

On turfgrasses, a biological pesticide Agri-Dynamics christened Phyto-San was applied on patches of bentgrass showing signs of decline. Sampling prior to such indicated a certain amount of nematode pressure, according to golf course superintendants. Phyto-San, however, is not iodine, but a blend of terpenes or terpenoids, which are plant secondary metabolites that perform as insecticides, fungicides, and, in this case, a nematacide.

A recovery formula was also put together to create a vibrant biological substrate, or terrain, conducive to organism needed for healthy plant growth. This liquid recovery formula consists of worm tea, liquid kelp, humic acid, fish hydrolysate, molasses, and Sea-Crop.

Results were very satisfactory. Moreover, the therapeutic treatment (Phyto-San) seemed to be effective with only one treatment. The recovery formula was used repeatedly, every seven to fourteen days, which not only deterred nematodes from returning but also invigorated the roots of the plants and the biosphere of the soil.

Not surprisingly to ecological farmers, it is clear that nematode challenges are primarily induced by human activities. The good news is that there are very effective practices that prevent them from becoming a plague. Moreover, for both the conventional and ecological practitioner, there are really cost-effective remedies that are ecologically sound and that don't require the use of highly toxic nematicides, or methyl bromide fumigants.

5

Compost and Compost Teas

A thing is right when it tends to preserve the integrity, stability and beauty of the biotic community. It is wrong when it tends otherwise.

—Aldo Leopold

T HERE are now volumes on the alchemical wonders associated with compost, so I won't belabor those attributes in detail here, except to encourage those growing *anything* to consider compost as the touchstone for firing biological systems.

Many compost systems are sophisticated, using turners, inoculants, covers, and meters to test gases, moisture, and temperature. As a rule if you are in manufacturing compost for sale, it's business savvy to be able to produce a quality-controlled product that can perform for your customer, as he is depending on and paying the manufacturer to provide a consistent product that performs in a way that is predictable.

Home gardeners can turn piles fairly easily. Those with livestock need either machinery to do so or can keep livestock like pigs or chickens confined to the pile, where they can scratch and root for insects, food scraps, earthworms, and such. Another way to passively make compost is using a static pile that allows it to ferment. Rather than producing a finished product in weeks, it could take six months to a year—depending on the weather—before the pile is ready. Adding some amendments to a pile can really help. Clay is critical because it absorbs excess moisture and volatile gases, has a buffering effect for pH, and provides a surface area or habitat for microbes. Biochar is yet another amazing amendment that enhances the habitat for compost microbe populations.

For those using a bedding pack for livestock I recommend that about a quarter of an ounce (or seven to eight grams) each of the following be dusted daily for every thousand pounds of livestock weight: clay (or soft-rock phosphate clay if there are phosphorus needs in the soil), gypsum, and humates or leonardite. The soft-rock phosphate will scavenge ammonia (NH_3^+) and make monoammonium (MAP) or diammonium phosphate (DAP), a stable form of nitrogen. The gypsum will cause a reaction between ammonia (NH_3^+) and sulfate, creating ammonium sulfate, another stable form of nitrogen. Both clay (like Dyna-Min) and humates have sequestering properties of attracting many volatiles—including ammonia, indoles, skatoles, mercaptans, etc.—and allowing microbes to stabilize them as microbial proteins and carbohydrates to build humus.

The ideal compost on larger-scale landscapes must also integrate cover cropping and tight rotations in order to achieve what is known as sheet composting, where plant residues or fresh vegetative portions of a crop are shallowly mixed with topsoil to rapidly break down as a food source prior to planting a successive crop. I would enthusiastically recommend that everyone read the books written by Louis Bromfield, a Pulitzer Prize–winning author and ecological farmer who successfully reclaimed one thousand acres of damaged farmland in Richland County, Ohio, in the forties and fifties. The books that cover this extraordinary agrarian's accomplishments are *Malabar Farm, Pleasant Valley, Out of the Earth,* and *From My Experience.*

When making compost (or topsoil, as well) there are two pathways to consider: mineralization and humification. Mineralization is the process of liberating minerals from organic carbon compounds. Minerals may either be complexed in stable humus (humified) or be in a free form (mineralized). The difference is that the carbon compounds are either integrated within the humus, or if liberated, become CO_2 gas.

Where do elements end up after crop decomposition in the soil or when making compost? They are either minerals at 80 percent liberated (mineralized) and with 20 percent complexed in the humus (humified). Or the carbon from the carbohydrates (cellulose, hemicellulose, pectins, sugars, etc.) end up as 80 percent degrading into CO_2 gas, and 20 percent of it goes into humus formation. Another possibility lies in heavier carbons like lignin, aromatic amino acids (like tyrosine, tryptophan, etc.), and other compounds (fats, waxes, hydrocarbons, etc.), where 25 percent evolves into CO_2 gas and 75 percent contributes to humus (humified). Thus there needs to be a proper balance of the mineralization and humificiation, which requires a buffet of feedstocks because ultimately those raw materials have to be acted upon by microorganisms, especially fungi and actinomycetes.

The clay (calcium-rich) addition accelerates the production of calcium humates, which is a prerequisite of a stable humus formation, by creating the clay-humus complex. Basically, there are two main groups of humates when producing compost. The red-brown humic acids are more mobile, readily complex minerals and are foliar responsive. The red-brown humic fractions produced in the compost will then form into the black-gray stable humic complexes if the soils are properly balanced. Using these kinds of humates alone on poor soils could actually aggravate a problem, especially if there is little to no organic matter, low pH, or low cations (Ca, Mg, K).

A favorite compost activator and actual raw material for compost is the comfrey plant. Having a massive tuberous root system, comfrey produces a great deal of biomass. Its leaves are rich in both nitrogen and carbon, the latter in a form of polysaccharides that are medicinally used as demulcents to aid in tissue repair, including bone-knitting. The equivalent fifty to one hundred wet tons per acre can be produced by comfrey, and I would encourage people to grow it on the perimeter of gardens, cropland, hedgerows, and such, or on ground that isn't suitable for tillage because it's too rocky or too steep a grade. Comfrey is a wonderful plant to grow around trees, cutting the foliage several times a year and letting it lie on the soil's surface to decompose as fertilizer.

DIGESTION AS A FACTOR IN DISEASE

The proper feeding, respiration, toxin removal, and ability of all cells to reproduce is dependent on the organism's ability to convert crude raw materials into sustenance. The word for this alchemical phenomenon is digestion.

The protection of plants is expressed in the integrity of the rhizosphere of plants. Apparently a vigorous population of microbes in the rhizosphere translates into a balanced soil food web, which translates into a protective substrate to fortify phyllosphere microbes that occupy the leaf surface.

COMPOST TEA TRIALS

At Agri-Dynamics, we developed a compost tea kit and brewer, initially for use on golf courses—especially greens and tees—and also for the wine grape vineyards established primarily in the northeastern United States. We conducted research trials at Rutgers University in New Jersey and field trials at an assortment of locations representing various crops (turf, grapes, vegetables, and flowers). The 2002 Rutgers trials, although encouraging in wine grapes, were inconclusive because that year was one of the driest on record, so there was little disease pressure for the incidence of downy and powdery mildew. Furthermore, there was an unusually late killing frost that destroyed 90 percent of the fruit, so we were not able to get adequate data on fruit-related diseases such as Botrytis and black rot. Our in-vitro studies, however, suggested that both our tea and compost made from the tea were very disease suppressive.

Table 5.1 shows the analysis of the compost used to ultimately brew the compost tea. This compost comprised three separate kinds of compost blended together, including dairy and turkey manure, forest litter, and highly aerated horse manure–based mushroom compost. The soil food web lab analysis indicates a healthy population of bacteria, as well as encouraging numbers of fungi. Protozoa populations were also quite strong.

TABLE 5.1

COMPOST ANALYSIS: THE EARTHWORKS COMPOST TEA KIT

Sample received 04/11/01
Compost type: Forest litter/mushroom compost/manure

Sample #	Treatment	Dry Weight of 1 gram Fresh Material	Active Bacterial Biomass (ug/g)	Total Bacterial Biomass (ug/g)
87985	EarthWorks Compost	0.50	34.8	38.3
		OK	Excellent	Excellent
Desired Range			15–30	150–300+

Active Fungal Biomass (ug/g)	Total Fungal Biomass (ug/g)	Hyphal Dameter (um)	Protozoa Numbers/g			Total Nematodae Numbers
			Flagellates	Amoebae	Ciliates	
12.3	453	2.5	27,692	11,494	144	NR
Excellent	Excellent	OK	Excellent	Good	A Touch High	
2–10+	150–200+	2–3+	10,000+	10,000+	20–50	

Agri-Dynamics

TABLE 5.2
COMPOST SPECIES DIVERSITY

Parameters	Normal Ranges	Enumeration	Species Richness Diversity (SRD)[1]	SRD Moderate Levels
Heterotrophic Plate Count (Aerobic)	10^8–10^{10}	3.8 x 10^9 CFU/dgw 10^9	2.0	1.6
Anaerobic Bacteria	10:1 A:AN	1.6 x 10^9 CFU/gdw 10^9	0.9	0.8
Yeasts and Molds	10^3–10^5	1.2 x 10^5 CFU/gdw 10^5	2.8	0.8
Actinomycetes	10^6–10^8	1.5 x 10^6 CFU/gdw 10^6	1.5	0.9
Pseudomonads	10^3–10^6	1.7 x 10^7 CFU/gdw 10^7	1.1	0.5
Nitrogen-Fixing Bacteria	10^3–10^6	5.6 x 10^4 CFU/gdw 10^4	0.6	0.3
% Moisture (dw)	40–50%	71%	---	---
Total Species Richness Diversity	----	----	8.9	3 – 6.5 + 6.5 = high

Agri-Dynamics

Table 5.2 discloses the amount of species diversity in this blend of the three composts, as well as the population of the selected groups. It is evident that this compost is rich in species diversity and fairly balanced in terms of the percentages of each functional group. There is room for improvement on the aerobic:anaerobic ratio; and the level of pseudomonads is slightly elevated. Being that the moisture is higher than optimum, this may be a factor affecting the levels of anaerobes.

The following tables are measures of the individual composts composing the finished blend used to make the tea. The measurements taken include those parameters related to compost maturity; including: germination rate, phytotoxicity, and conductivity. These evaluations were obtained by making a water extract of the compost (not quite a brewed tea) and measuring the full strength and diluted leachate's effects. We discovered that the highly aerated dairy and turkey manure compost showed the best quality in terms of its effect on germination, phytotoxicity and conductivity. Not surprisingly, the compost with the least maturity was the aerated mushroom soil compost. This compost was turned fifty times and inoculated with biostimulants each time. Spent mushroom soil removed from the mushroom houses typically requires a lot of aging to allow for a reduction in salts, ammonia, and sulfides, all of which can be phytotoxic and detrimental to microbes in the rhizosphere. Our interest in considering this compost (only as a product that would have to be reconditioned) was because of its availability, cost, and the additional diversity it could provide.

Table 5.4 again gives a variety of parameters more representative of the chemistry of compost than its biology. These chemical indicators are associated with compost maturity and potential toxicity to the roots and organisms in the rhizosphere. The tests indicate that, ideally, this compost needs to be aged further in order to decrease excessive salts and to balance the

TABLE 5.3
COMPOST MATURITY REPORT
(DAIRY/TURKEY – LUEBKE)

Compost Maturity*	Result	Ideal	Method
Germination Rate	Full Strength Extract – 68% 1/3 Strength Extract – 92%	> 85%	Journal of Environmental Quality, 23:1177–1183 (1994)
Maturity Index (Phytotoxicity)	Full Strength Extract – 37% 1/3 Strength Extract – 82%	> 50%	Journal of Environmental Quality, 23:1177–1183 (1994)
Conductivity	Full Strength Extract – 6.69 dS 1/3 Strength Extract – 2.86 dS	< 6 Hort. < 10 Agric.	MoSA 10-3.3, Saturated Paste
pH	8.2	6.5 – 8.5	MoSA 12-2.6

Agri-Dynamics

TABLE 5.4

COMPOST MATURITY REPORT
(AERATED, INOCULATED MUSHROOM)

Compost Maturity*	Result	Ideal	Method
Germination Rate*	Full Strength Extract – 5% 1/3 Strength Extract – 72%	> 85%	Journal of Environmental Quality, 23:1177–183 (1994)
Maturity Index* (Phytotoxicity)	Full Strength Extract – 0.20% 1/3 Strength Extract – 40%	> 50%	Journal of Environmental Quality, 23:1177–183 (1994)
Conductivity	Full Strength Extract – 17.9 dS 1/3 Strength Extract – 5.97 dS	< 6 Hort. < 10 Agric.	MoSA 10-3.3, Saturated Paste
pH	7.8	6.5–8.5	MoSA 12-2.6

Agri-Dynamics   *Problem Parameters

COMPOST MATURITY REPORT
(AERATED FOREST LITTER)

TABLE 5.5

Compost Maturity*	Result	Ideal	Method
Germination Rate*	Full Strength Extract – 24% 1/3 Strength Extract – 84%	> 85%	Journal of Environmental Quality, 23:1177–183 (1994)
Maturity Index* (Phytotoxicity)	Full Strength Extract – 4% 1/3 Strength Extract – 58%	> 50%	Journal of Environmental Quality, 23:1177–183 (1994)
Conductivity	Full Strength Extract – 17.6 dS 1/3 Strength Extract – 6.05 dS	< 6 Hort. < 10 Agric.	MoSA 10-3.3, Saturated Paste
pH	7.3	6.5–8.5	MoSA 12-2.6

Agri-Dynamics

TABLE 5.6
COMPOST ANALYSIS REPORT

Sample ID	Nitrogen Tests (ppm)			Sodium (ppm)	Sulfur Tests		Seed Germ & Vigor Tests		Humus
	Ammonia NH$_3$ →	Nitrites NO$_2$ →	Nitrates NO$_3$		Sulfate S (ppm) (level)	Sulfides H$_2$S	7 day Germ (%)	14 day Vigor (%)	
Blend 1	93	1	824	74	99 √	0	95 √		100
Blend 2	190	0	844	870	888	0	60		58
Blend 3	137	0	835	713	216 √	0	50		72
Blend 1,2,3	346	2	825 √	868	752	0	75		84 √
Desired Level	<50	0	700–800	90–200	100–500	0	>80	>70	50–80

Table 5A

Sample ID	Water Soluble Tests			Moisture (%)	C:N Ratio
	pH	Conductivity (Ergs)	Redox Potential		
Blend 1	7.8	3450	25.8	62.2	25.3
Blend 2	7.6	6000	25.4	50.0	15.5
Blend 3	7.5	4100	25.1	22.5	9.9
Blend 1,2,3	7.8	4160	25.5	39.1	17.2 √
Desired Level	7.0–8.1	2–3000	26.5–29	40–50	15–20

Agri-Dynamics   Table 5B

nitrogen and sulfur. Again, the biggest challenges apparently are originating from the mushroom soil compost.

Table 5.7 illustrates the degree of stability based upon the respiration rates. All aerobic organisms inhale O$_2$ and exhale CO$_2$, and so this rate of respiration measurement is an indication of additional digestion needed in order for the compost to stabilize.

FROM COMPOST TO TEA

After concluding that we had a compost that met a majority of the prerequisites to make a tea, we then brewed a batch of compost tea in our own Earthworks compost tea brewing machine, consisting of ten pounds of equal parts of the three composts. These individual composts were mixed

TABLE 5.7

COMPOST STABILITY

Client Sample ID	Lab ID	Respiration Rate
Blend 1	10412	39 mg O$_2$/Kg compost ds-h
Blend 2	10413	34 mg O$_2$/Kg compost ds-h
Blend 3	10414	6 mg O$_2$/Kg compost ds-h

Interpretation of Respiration rate:
Respiration rate of < 100 mg O$_2$/kg compost dry solids – hour acceptable for field applications.
Respiration rate of < 20 mg O$_2$/kg compost dry solids – hour acceptable for horticultural applications.

Agri-Dynamics

together in a compost pile and then thoroughly aerated again as if it were one compost.

Table 5.8 provides an analysis of a tea made with this same compost, brewing it for twenty-two hours at 70°F and adding three pounds of foods to the solution (thirty-five gallons) prior to brewing. These foods consisted of simple sugars, starches, cellulose, humic acids, seaweed extracts, herbs, vitamins, and minerals. The ratio of bacteria to fungi would not normally be considered ideal because the level of bacteria is so high, over fifty times higher than the expected range. However, both the total and the active fungal biomass are more than twice the maximum of what is usually expected. It is unusual to get the active fungal biomass this high for two reasons: 1) the compost quality is not rich in adequate fungal populations, and 2) during the brewing process, not enough fungal foods are supplied to grow these organisms. The importance of having active fungal growth is associated with the fact that many disease-suppressive exudates (antibiotics) are produced by beneficial fungal organisms.

Table 5.9 provides the results of pathogen inhibition assays, used to determine the degree of disease suppression the tea had on selected organisms in vitro. The pathogen was challenged in twelve trials with the control being twelve trials of sterile water. The diseases selected were primarily those affecting wine grapes, turf, and vegetables (to a lesser degree). Trials scored as "strong" inhibition are those in which there was little or no expansion of the initial pathogen sample. Trials scored as "partial" inhibition are those in which there was significant growth of the pathogen in the presence of the

TABLE 5.8

Compost Tea Analysis

Sample received 04/11/01
Compost type: Forest litter/mushroom compost/manure

Sample #	Treatment	Tea Volume (mL)	Active Bacterial Biomass (µg/mL)	Total Bacterial Biomass (µg/mL)
92034	EarthWorks	1.00	579 Excellent	15744 Excellent
Desired Range		1	10-150	150-300

Active Fungal Biomass (µg/mL)	Total Fungal Biomass (µg/mL)	Hyphal Diameter (µm)	Protozoa Numbers/mL Flagellates	Amoebae	Ciliates	Total Nematodae Numbers
22.7 Excellent	42.8 Excellent	2.5 OK	NR	NR	NR	NR
2-10	2-20	(A)	1,000	1,000	20-50	2-10

(A) Hyphal diameter of 2.0 indicates mostly actinomycete hyphae; 2.5 indicates community is mainly ascomycete, typical soil fungi for grasslands; diameters of 3.0 of higher indicate community is dominated by highly beneficial fungi, a Basidiomycete community.
Temperature for brewing, type of water (chlorine will kill organisms), type of compost, and type of brewer used must be considered in determining the set of organisms in the tea.
Tea assessment should be accompanied by leaf organism assessment to see if there were effects of spraying or diluting in the sprayer. Pesticide use, fertilizer use, tillage, irrigation, etc., affect soil and foliar effectiveness.

Twenty-two-hour brew with one-third each Leubke compost (dairy/chicken/hay/straw), deciduous tree trimming compost, and aerated mushroom compost; and well water reached 70°F.

Agri-Dynamics

product, but the pathogen colony was unable to reach the product samples. The tea was not used full strength but diluted to 25 percent strength. The diseases selected were Botrytis, *Colletotrichum graminicola* (anthracnose), *Helminthosporium solani* (leaf spot), *Phaeoacremonium inflatipes* (grape vine decline), *Phaeomoniella chlamydospora* (slow decline, grapes), *Phytophthora*

TABLE 5.9
Pathogen Inhibition Assay Compost Tea

Pathogen Challenged	Inhibition to Pathogen Growth
Botrytis cinerea	Partial Inhibition – 100 Trials (12/12)
Colletotrichum graminicola	Partial Inhibition – 75% Trials (9/12)
	No Inhibition – 25% Trials (3/12)
Helminthosporium solani	Strong Inhibition – 100% Trials (12/12)
Phaeoacremonium inflatipes	Strong Inhibition 75% Trials 9/12
	No Inhibition – 25% Trials (3/12)
Pheaomoniella chlamydospora	Strong Inhibition 67% Trials 8/12
	Partial Inhibition – 33% Trials (4/12)
Phytophthora cinnamomi	Partial Inhibition – 100% Trials (12/12)
Phytophthora infestans	Partial Inhibition – 100% Trials (12/12)
Pythium ultimum	Partial Inhibition – 92% Trials (11/12)
	No Inhibition – 8% Trials (1/12)

Agri-Dynamics

cinnamomi (blight, grapes and misc.), *Phytophthora infestans* (late blight), *Pythium ultimum*, *Rhizoctonia solani* (root rot), *Sclerotium rolfsii* (white rot), and *Sclerotinia sclerotiorum* (white mold). In seven of the eleven pathogen trials there were partial inhibitions ranging from 75–100 percent of the twelve repetitions. In four of the eleven pathogen trials there were strong inhibitions ranging from 67–100 percent of the twelve repetitions.

FROM LABORATORY TO LANDSCAPE
We discovered that when the tea was made properly (temperature, amount of time brewed, proper amount of foods, etc.), there was an impact on disease suppression, despite the climate issues that plagued the northeastern United States in 2002 that hindered our research. Greens keepers who injected our compost tea into their fertigation systems saw positive effects on root diseases such as Pythium. Those who applied the product on trees and greens as a spray were surveyed about their results. Generally speaking, those who applied the tea every five days, especially when disease pressure was highest (humidity, temperature, traffic stress, rains, etc.), appeared to get disease suppression on

anthracnose, fairy ring, leaf spot, summer patch, dollar spot, and Pythium. Those who waited until diseases showed up and then attempted to use the tea as a fungicide were not successful. It appears that incorporating compost tea as part of a total soils and horticultural systems approach shows much promise, especially with high-value crops.

VERMICOMPOST: HI TEST WORM JUICE

The vermicastings from either native earthworms such as *Lumbricus terrestris* (the night crawler) or compost worms like *Eisenia fetida* (red wigglers) can be an amazing contribution to soil fertility, but the value of vermicastings from a fertility point of view is many times what the surrounding soil indicates. Ranges of nitrogen in vermicastings are 1.5–2.2 percent, of phosphorus 1.8– 2.2 percent, and of potassium 1.0–1.5 percent, not to mention trace elements, microbes, enzymes, metabolites, vitamins, calcium, etc. This accounts for five times the nitrogen, seven times the phosphorus, eleven times the potash, and three times the magnesium than that in soil: all free!

Making a vermicompost tea is quite simple and consists of merely adding eight ounces of worm castings to one gallon of water to soak for one to three days. I've kept worm tea packaged in five-gallon pails for three years without any spoilage! The worm tea I had made was done via a centrifuge compost tea extractor. The worm castings themselves can be used in potting mixes (less than 25 percent of the mix, though; it can become plant suppressive).

The take-home lesson here is that biological systems cannot be left out of the equation if a regeneration of soil productivity is to be accomplished. Moreover, biological systems need to be continually encouraged and enhanced if the landscape is to become robust and resilient.

INDUSTRIAL YOGURT

Back in 2000, I codeveloped a liquid plant protectant with my French Canadian friend Jean Brunet. This product, which I initially called Bio-Net, was an industrial yogurt. Whey was first pasteurized and then inoculated with three proprietary cultures known for their ability to produce high amounts of specific bacteriocins, or antibiotics that could effectively suppress bacterial and fungal pathogens. The yogurt was then fed with nutritional amendments during the fermentation process.

Initially, the product was sprayed on commercial fertilizer (N-P-K) at the rate of one-half to one gallon per ton. The fertilizer was broadcast on wheat, soybeans, potatoes, and corn with a reduction of nitrogen by 25 percent. We observed both earlier germination and a higher percentage of germination. The farmers were so pleased with the results that the next year they demanded to be able to purchase the "fertilizer that smelled good" (Bio-Net imparted a sweet, lactic acid aroma to fertilizers, which typically have an acrid, caustic odor). Unfortunately, the fertilizer elevator that oversaw the trial was a franchised subsidiary of a multinational corporation. The agents of this cartel became concerned that they might lose some N-P-K business (they would!), so they prohibited the franchisee from using the product and confiscated the research trial data.

Not to be thwarted, Bio-Net morphed into a plant protection spray for diseases, and trials were conducted at both academic research facilities and with independent consultants with very encouraging results on diseases such as the mildews, Botrytis, etc. Application rates as a fungicide were done at 4 percent, 8 percent, and 12 percent, and 8 percent seemed to make the most sense from an economic and effective prospective.

Lebanese cucumbers, wine grapes, strawberries, and cranberries all appeared to benefit from a series of multiple spray applications. Experiments included controls, treated controls (fungicides), and various concentrations of Lacto-San, as Bio-Net was now called. From a preventative perspective, Lacto-San made the largest impression, even outcompeting the fungicide. The questions that remain are: Were the results due to bactericidal activity, induced systemic resistance, or a biological mode of action? Disc assay sensitivity tests strongly suggest that this "yogurt" contains bacteriocidins that act as growth inhibitors.

The resistance to disease when sprayed preventatively suggests that there may be metabolites in this "yogurt" that perform as signaling mechanisms to stimulate an immune response, or induced systemic resistance (ISR).

The increase in yield, solids, and sugars suggests that there is a biological mode of action that enhances the crops' physiology to take in nutrients and increase photosynthesis. I'm convinced that this formulation substrate could demonstrate great promise as a plant biostimulant, plant protectant, seed inoculant, and root dip, especially if it were fortified with other cofactors following the fermentation, such as minerals, vitamins, fatty acids, amino acids, worm tea, compost tea, and such. When putting together biological formulations as I'm presenting, it behooves both the "alchemist" making such products and the farmer using them to understand what is actually contributing to the end result. And though a researcher or analytical scientist could spend untold numbers of hours finding and isolating what may be called active ingredients, the fact is that in concert not only is *everything* "active," but it's all a moving target. Biology is a rhythm of energies and substances coming into view only to recede and be displaced by yet more energies and substances. This is especially true with compounds that can have synergistic properties, meaning their susceptibility to react with other compounds increases exponentially as the mix becomes more complex and as time passes.

Based on observing livestock for over three decades, I can say with some confidence that the ground rules apply across nature. We need to encourage as much as we can the three-legged stool of geology/chemistry (minerals), biology (the soil web of life), and the physical structure of soils, while encouraging diversity ("all our relations"), if we want to increase our opportunities for healthy, profitable, toxic-free production to happen on our landscapes.

Industrial yogurt is basically made through a lacto-fermentation process, whereby a nutrient-rich media like whey, rich in lactose, is consumed via an anaerobic fermentation (little oxygen).

Feeding the microbes some minerals, complex proteins, and specific amounts of certain vitamins after a couple of days of them dining on the whey and buffering the solution to above 6.0 will extend the fermentation and cause the critters to synthesize additional kinds and quantities of metabolites. The waste products (bacterial excrement) are the metabolites that perform as growth inhibitors, biostimulants, and ISR immune activators. It's not the bugs, but their by-products. In fact, once the pH stabilizes at 3.8–4.0, the product is dormant. Not only that, it's stable. I have had buckets of the stuff hanging around for two years at room temperature with no spoilage.

Contrary to what some may proclaim, a type of fermentation has been developed in Korea and Japan called Nature Farming in which the inoculant is obtained from native soil in the forest or grassland and blended with a substrate like wheat bran on molasses, and the subsequent culture is then inoculated upon rice and so forth in order to produce metabolites that can be used for plant growth, plant protection, odor control, livestock health, and other uses. A commercial product originating in Japan called Effective Microorganisms (EM) is now available in the United States. The mesophyllic strains are homofermentive; that is, they ferment sugars predominantly into lactic acid and grow rapidly under a wide range of moisture conditions and temperatures. One of the objectives of Nature Farming is to wild-craft indigenous microorganisms (IM) from assorted local and regional soils to produce various fermented products, thereby increasing the natural diversity of microbial populations through the farm's ecosystem, including the digestive system and manures of livestock and humans.

Because milk is highly perishable, prior to refrigeration the only way to preserve it was to ferment it, yielding yogurt, kefir, clabbered milk, and similar edibles. Predictably fermenting dairy products, however, requires the incorporation of thermophyllic organisms, which ferment the substrate in a healthy environment under controlled temperatures, producing biologically useful metabolites for both plants and animals. Anaerobic manures in a lagoon can become septic and putrefy. It is my belief that the metabolites or unidentified growth factors (UGFs) are what orchestrate healthy behavior with the native indigenous microflora on the leaf surface (phyllosphere) and in the root ball (rhizosphere). This is not any different than humans consuming fermented foods like lacto-fermented kimchi, sauerkraut, kefir, yogurt, kvass, miso, and so many other foods that fortify the native gut flora with nutrients and metabolites.

The bacterial or fermentation "soups" contain goodies like lactic acid, lactoperoxidase, acidolin, nicin, hydrogen peroxide, lactoferrin, and innumberable bacteriocidins.

When fermenting a substrate there are two main groups of fermenters: mesophyllic and thermophyllic. The mesophyllic fermenters operate at ambient temperatures and are the catalysts associated with the fermentation

TABLE 5.10
PATHOGEN INHIBITION ASSAY LACTO-SAN 4

Pathogen Challenged	Inhibition to Pathogen Growth
Alternaria alternata	88% reduction in pathogen growth, relative to control
Botrytis cinerea	52% reduction in pathogen growth, relative to control

Agri-Dynamics

TABLE 5.11
PATHOGEN INHIBITION ASSAY
LACTO-SAN 3 AND 4

Pathogen Challenged	Inhibition to Pathogen Growth
Alternaria alternata	85% reduction in pathogen growth, relative to control
Botrytis cinerea	71% reduction in pathogen growth, relative to control
Phytophthora infestans	100% reduction in pathogen growth, relative to control

Agri-Dynamics

of silage, sauerkraut, kimchi, etc. Thermophyllic fermenters are only effective in controlled temperature, usually around 95°F–105° F and are what I experimented with in fermenting milk and whey. Curiously, specific cultures have specific preferences for temperatures and nutrients, thus all ferments are hardly the same. Making the maximum conversion of lactose (milk sugar) into lactic acid requires that specific adequate pH ranges, particularly appropriate for the chosen innoculant, are maintained; otherwise the lactic acid production can drop the pH sooner than desired and fermentation ceases. Using different cultures, Jean Brunet and I concocted four variations of Lacto-San and conducted greenhouse trials. The lab's findings on an in-vitro pathogen assay were very encouraging. Lacto-San 4 inhibited *Alternaria alternata* by 88 percent relative to controls. It inhibited *Botrytis cinerea* 52 percent relative to controls. When Lacto-San 3 and 4 were blended, the mix reduced growth on the two pathogens by 85 percent and 71 percent respectively. Trialed on late blight, *Phytophthora infestans*, the effect was an astonishing 100 percent reduction relative to controls! These trials were conducted using an 8 percent solution of Lacto-San.

6

Foliar Nutrition

The doctor of the future will no longer treat the human frame with
drugs, but rather will cure and prevent disease with nutrition.

—Thomas Edison

THE idea of feeding plants nutritional ingredients is hardly a new one, and mixed results have rendered it a controversial methodology. The key to consistent outcomes is predicated on a number of ground rules, which if adhered to can provide remarkable responses in any crop.

The uptake of nutrition via foliage can be ten to twenty times more efficient than what plants can take in the root. However, soil amendments and soil-applied plant foods are needed to not only feed the plant but also support the entire soil ecosystem of the plant.

There are five primary advantages to foliar feeding.

1. Rapid and efficient uptake of nutrients.
2. Provides nutrients in problem soils where there is limited biology, which inhibits the uptake of soil nutrients into the plant. Examples are compacted soil, waterlogged soil nutrients, or excess leaching of soil nutrients (sandy soils).
3. Minimizes the stress of weather extremes (drought, cold, wet, cloudy weather).
4. Incites induced activated resistance (IAR), which is a grower's way of stimulating a protective response similar to what a healthy plant does when challenged by a pest, which is called systemic acquired

FIGURE 6.1

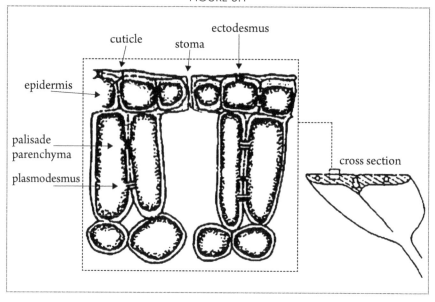

resistance (SAR). Plants under attack release compounds called phytoalexins, which perform as deterrents or toxins to adversarial challenges.

5. Manipulates the metabolism of plants so that the growth or vegetative phase can be morphed into a reproductive phase, where fruit or seed is desired.

As one can see from the figure 6.1, there are a number of portals for foliar substances to enter the cytoplasm of a leaf's cell. The cuticle is a waxy layer covering the leaves, and its primary function is to prevent moisture loss and plant tissue injury. The cuticle is a triple-layer covering consisting of cutin—the lowest or first layer—covered by a wax layer in the middle, covered by a wax rodlet on top. Cracks in the cuticle occur and can serve as a port of entry for foliar sprays. The stomata are located almost exclusively on leaves and are only a few millionths of an inch in diameter. They are breathing holes, allowing CO_2 gas to enter so that plants can photosynthesize it into sugar in the chloroplast while emitting oxygen into the atmosphere. They are also thermo-regulators allowing a plant to transpire, that is, getting rid of water vapor to cool the plant. The stomata are closed at night and the hottest part of the day. Broadleaf plants and trees have the vast majority of their stomata on the bottom of the leaf. Grasses can have the same number of stomata on both surfaces. For example, a bean plant can have 40,000 stomata on the underside of the leaf and only 3,000 on the upper side, while a sorghum plant can have 16,000 on the lower surface and 11,000 on top. Also, grass stomata can be several times the diameter of dicots/broadleaf stomata. Because younger plants have so much thinner a cuticle than older plants, they readily respond to foliar feeding as they are much more efficient in absorbing nutrients.

Foliar nutrients have to be in an ionic or colloidal presentation in order for plants to be able to take in the nutrients. An example of an anionic solution is salt water; an example of a colloidal liquid is whole, homogenized milk. Some foliar products may be finely ground rock materials but are still too large. Particle size matters! Most growers are unaware that the uptake and utilization of foliars is quite inefficient because of the difficulty the applied substance has penetrating the waxy cuticle. That may mean that only 10–20 percent of nutrients applied are taken in, the remaining being washed off into the soil. Particle sizes are usually measured in microns, 0.001 meter or 0.00004 inch. Many commercial products may average forty to fifty microns, quite small if it gets into the soil, but the leaf stoma are only five microns. Five pounds of a fifty-micron product has a surface area of about seven hundred square feet. The same amount at one micron has a surface area of 27,000 square feet! Entry points for foliar-applied materials are the stomata, the ectodesmus, and the cuticle, with the cuticle offering the largest surface area but the smallest entry point into the vascular organs in the plant. Also, many of these micronized compounds are complex compounds such as carbonates (limestone) and phosphates (tri-calcium phosphates like rock phosphate), which are not likely to be assimilated and transported throughout the plant's vascular system because substances that enhance movement within the plant are usually ion specific. Their advantage would be in a soil drench/fertigation system to be assimilated more efficiently by the roots.

As the old adage states, "Timing is everything." As it pertains to foliar application, timing is not only important, it can be critical. Early morning or dusk are the opportune times to apply foliars because the stomata are more likely to be open when temperatures are lower, humidity is high, and dew is on the leaves. Ideally, temperatures below 80°F are preferred. In midday, hot temperatures will cause the stomata to close off to entry of even carbon dioxide gas, which is necessary for photosynthesis. Apparently, higher temperatures increase carbon dioxide concentrations inside the leaf, which acts as a trigger to close the stomata. For every 10°C (50°F) increase in temperature, the rate of water evaporation doubles. Stomata actually close when air temperatures

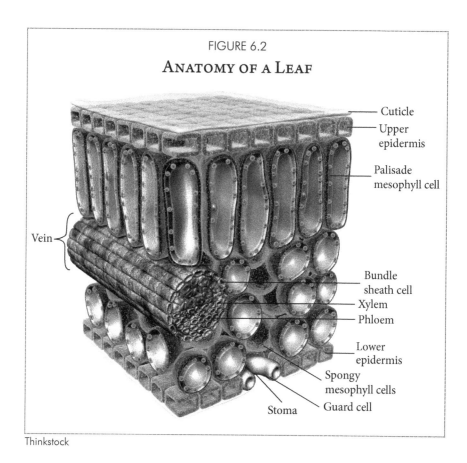

FIGURE 6.2

ANATOMY OF A LEAF

Cuticle

Upper epidermis

Palisade mesophyll cell

Vein

Bundle sheath cell

Xylem

Phloem

Lower epidermis

Spongy mesophyll cells

Stoma

Guard cell

Thinkstock

exceed 85°F, and plants give up moisture above those temperatures through a process called transpiration. Also, elevated temperatures remove the water carrying the nutrients, which allows the nutrients to stay in a water capsule until the plant is ready to take them in.

It isn't a good idea to foliar spray when too cool (less than 50°F), either, because plant physiological functions are not optimum. Don't spray the same day rain is forecast, as the combination of precipitation (runoff) and cloudy weather (compromised photosynthesis) is objectionable to the goal of foliar feeding: leaf absorption. The intervals in the crop growth cycle are also important. Typically, for row crops and produce, foliars should be applied at the third to sixth or seventh leaf stage, as young plant tissue is quite responsive because it needs to synthesize those protective plant secondary metabolites. And another spray could be done ten to fourteen days later. For high-value crops such as produce, fruit, berries, vines, and brambles, a schedule of every ten to fourteen days throughout the season until harvest

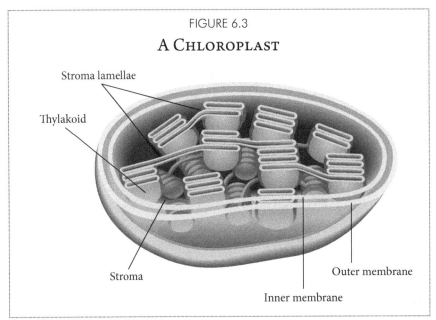

FIGURE 6.3

A CHLOROPLAST

Stroma lamellae

Thylakoid

Stroma

Outer membrane

Inner membrane

Thinkstock

can produce gratifying dividends. For those high-value crops, petiole and tissue tests throughout the season, as recommended by the standards set within the industry, are a good idea. For forage and row crops (cereals, corn, beans), at least one and preferably two sprays would be recommended.

Established tissue guidelines are typically utilized to find the ranges of elements within the variety of crop. What is typically seen is that as the plant matures and therefore creates more biomass, the desired nutrient levels in percentages or parts per million decline. Early sampling can be important because some crops like cereals, forages, and corn determine the number of ears, pods, grain, and seed at early growth phases; for example corn determines the number of ears it will produce at the fifth or sixth collar stage. Essentially, the tissue test is the report card for your soil test. To have a stronger hand on the pulse of your growing endeavor, you need "real time" information to ascertain if what's in the soil is manifesting in your crop, and if not, how to make adjustments.

According to Bill McKibben, author of *The Art of Balancing Soil Nutrients*, you have to adjust the samples based on weight because the heaviest plants do not have the highest nutrient values. "Therefore comparing all the samples in an equal basis without adjusting for the weight for the whole plant samples is like comparing a 300 pound mini-horse to a 2,000 pound draft horse. The horses' blood analysis would be very comparable, but the level of work that could be done by each horse would be vastly different." Well said, but the adjustment for weight can only be practically accomplished for crops and plants on an individual basis (e.g., corn, tomatoes, etc.), not for cereals (which are community crops like wheat or oats). Thus, tissue tests give answers where soil tests leave us with questions, such as why a crop growing in an "ideal" soil, fertility-wise, is not performing. Obviously, something else isn't ideal, like soil compaction, insects, disease, nematodes, dryness, wetness, etc.

Visual surveillance is certainly a key tool for growers, as it is something one can do oneself at any time. It also allows a grower to notice a problem as soon as it develops. The text *What's Wrong with My Plant? (And How Do I Fix It?)* by David Deardorff and Kathryn Wadsworth is a highly recommended reference to reconcile what one sees in the field and what one reads in the text.

Reference manuals with photographs of plants afflicted with nutritional deficiencies and/or insects, diseases, or pests, available from the Cooperative Extension Service or land-grant universities, are useful, if for no other reason than to troubleshoot the origin of any such problem.

Spraying equipment is best if the droplet size is minimized. Mist sprayers, used by commercial orchardists because they provide very complete foliar coverage (top and bottom of leaves) with the least amount of water, surfactants, and chemicals, are obviously the best appliances to get the job done. Any spray nozzle that is designed to create a cone shaped spray pattern, causing the spray to spin as it departs from the nozzle tip, is also an advantage over the "flat" spray design. There are now magnetic devices to be attached to spray nozzles, and the feedback from even very large commercial operators is encouraging. Apparently the magnetic influence in the water molecule causes them to de-cluster from larger aggregates into a structured spray of many smaller clusters of water molecules. This makes the water "wetter" and charged, encouraging more thorough coverage in the leaf and better assimilation into the plant with these compounds in the mix.

Nutritional spraying is not necessarily compatible with chemical spraying because spraying pesticides encourages a larger particle size to minimize drift, and the combination of pesticides with plant foods can have dire consequences, causing the mixture to react and precipitate in the tank and plugging up in-line screens and nozzles. Always bench test first!

Adding a wetting agent is quite essential in my experience. It breaks apart the water tension, allowing a more uniform film to spread out evenly on the leaf. An organic product that my company Agri-Dynamics utilizes in miscellaneous mixes is called Dyna-Sol. These surfactants are critical to

The Secrets of Foliar Spraying
by Roland Evans

Your tomato plants look limp and sickly. Their lower leaves have turned a nasty yellow between the veins. You need to do something quickly. Searching the web, you discover your tomatoes have magnesium deficiency. Under the bathroom sink, you find an old bag of Epsom salts and an empty spray bottle. Dissolving a tablespoon of the salts in a couple of pints of warm water, you spray the leaves of the tomato plants all over. A couple of days later, the plants are bright green and healthy again.

From this example, it looks like foliar spraying could be the magic bullet we are all looking for. Within one hour, according to the scientists, a plant can transport minerals from its leaves all the way down to its roots. Compared to root feeding, this looks like the fast track. However, foliar spraying is not an alternative to good growing methods. It is best seen as a powerful addition that has its own secrets for success.

MINERAL DEFICIENCY SPRAYING

Spraying for mineral deficiencies can be particularly effective: magnesium for tomatoes, zinc for grapes, boron for many vegetables; the list is long and complex. Plants signal their need for help by exhibiting distress in leaf, bud, and flower. As the plant's "primary care person," your task is to diagnose the problem and provide corrective procedures. Mineral spraying acts rather like an injection; it gets the medicine into the plant's system as quickly and efficiently as possible.

The main stumbling block is our limited diagnostic skills. Each species of plant has both general and specific mineral needs. When these minerals are missing from the soil or hydroponic solution, a range of confusing symptoms appear. We may not discover the specific reason quickly enough to prevent plant collapse. Even when we do, that plant will take time to recover and may never reach optimum productivity.

Spraying for mineral deficiencies is emergency medicine—fast and efficient. To be successful, we need to know which element is missing and have the cure ready at hand. This is not always possible, so, in general, it is better to think in terms of prevention rather than cure. We do not wait until sick to take vitamins (a contraction of "vital minerals"). Just so, rather than spraying when a deficiency appears, put in place a program of foliar fertilization to increase plant health and resilience. If deficiency spraying is specific first aid, foliar fertilization is preventative health care.

FOLIAR FERTILIZATION

We all have had the basic course in fertilization: plants need NPK—nitrogen, phosphorous, and potassium. This is like saying humans need carbohydrates, fats, and protein. It tells us the basics but certainly does not say how to eat well. We need a balanced diet with nourishing foods—and plants are similar. They prefer nutrients in which the complex chemicals are bound organically. Rather than a dose of chemical nitrates, plants thrive best on organic products that provide not only the NPK but also a range of trace elements.

Vegetation evolved in the oceans, bathed in a solution containing every imaginable mineral. Seaweed takes food directly from seawater. Land plants, like their marine ancestors, can take in nourishment through the pores or stomata on their leaf surfaces. Stomata are tiny mouths that breathe in CO_2 and exhale water and oxygen. They also transport nutrients up to ten times more efficiently that root systems. Foliar feeding bolsters the nutrients available to each plant, like a regular dose of vitamins and supplements.

Most vegetation requires a minimum of sixteen, but probably more like fifty, essential minerals and trace elements. Is it just coincidence that some of the best providers of these elements come from the ocean? Fish products are high in organic nitrogen; kelp is a wonderful source of minerals, particularly potassium; while algae have a range of trace elements and hormones beneficial for cellular development. Research suggests that natural sea salt contains a vast range of trace elements. When sprayed in a very diluted form, sea minerals provide most elements needed to prevent deficiencies.

Foliar fertilization is fast becoming an essential addition to standard cultivation techniques. For many growers who have grown up with chemicals, it is a small step to organic fertilization—the NPK is just packaged differently. However, there is another, less well-known aspect to plant cultivation based on biology rather than chemistry—the realm of the microbes.

SPRAYING WITH COMPOST TEA

When plants evolved on land, they formed an alliance with the microbial life in the soil and air. Certain species of bacteria and fungi became the chefs that prepared the plant's food, the medics that helped them fight disease. Plants like to dine on biologically predigested nutrients; it is easier for them to assimilate. Healthy plants have a strong immune system that includes a "bio-film" of microbial life on the roots, stems, and leaves. To make use of these biological principles to feed and protect our plants, we can spray with compost tea.

Compost tea is "brewed" by aerating a mixture of water, compost (sometimes humus or worm castings), and organic nutrients such as molasses, kelp, fish emulsion, and yucca. This produces a nutrient-rich solution containing vast colonies of beneficial bacteria and fungi. The microbes digest the nutrients into organic compounds that can be easily taken in by the plant. These same microbes colonize the surface of the leaves to help fight off disease.

When you spray with compost tea, you envelope the plant with living organisms—and you enhance the web of life of which the plant is a part. The results can be astounding: large, mineral-rich vegetation with clear, glossy leaves, decreased disease, and even lessened insect attacks. Plants treated with foliar fertilization and especially compost tea have higher "Brix" levels—a measure of the carbohydrates and mineral density in the sap. High Brix is said to make the plants less attractive to pests and more resilient to stress. If they are vegetables, they even taste better!

Compost tea, unlike mineral sprays and foliar fertilization, cannot be over-applied and does not burn leaves. The microbe-rich droplets drip off the leaves to improve soil and growing solutions. Those same microbes can clean up toxic chemicals and turn them into nutrients. For growers who regularly use compost tea, there is nothing better. The main drawback is that brewed compost tea is not always available and, being alive, has a limited shelf life. If you brew your own compost tea, it needs to have the best ingredients and proven test results.

Whether you apply a mineral solution to deficient plants, have a regular foliar fertilization program, or go the distance with compost tea, foliar spraying benefits your plant quickly and profoundly. Find that old spray bottle, hook up your hose-end sprayer, and invest in a commercial spray pack. Once you see the results, you will never neglect this method of plant care again.

Tips on Spraying

Below are guidelines for foliar spraying:

1. When mixing up your formulation, whether mineral, organic fertilization, or compost tea, use non-chlorinated, well-oxygenated water. Bubble air through chlorinated water or leave it to off-gas overnight. You can try using seltzer in your foliar spray to give plants an added CO_2 boost.

2. Make sure mineral ingredients are dissolved and the solution is very diluted. Chemicals in high concentration tend to "burn" foliage and leave a salt residue. Compost teas need to be diluted 10–1.

3. Add a natural surfactant or wetting agent to help the solution flow over and stick to foliage. Yucca is a natural surfactant and is often a component of compost teas. Use true organic soaps such as Dr. Bronner's, Tom's, or Pangea. The great majority or other soaps contain detergents that do not break down easily.

4. Young transplants prefer a more alkaline solution (pH 7.0) while older growth like a somewhat more acid (pH 6.2) spray. Use baking soda to raise pH and apple cider vinegar to lower the pH of your spray.

5. Spray with a fine sprayer for foliar fertilization and a coarser, low-pressure sprayer for compost tea. The microbes in compost tea need large protective water droplets. Apply

in the early morning or evening when the stomata are open. Do not spray if the temperature is over 80°F or in the bright sun. Harsh ultraviolet rays can kill microbes in compost tea.

6. Cover at least 70 percent of the foliage, paying particular attention to the underneath of the leaf surfaces.

Apply foliar fertilization or sprayed compost tea every two to three weeks during the growing season.

Originally published by Organic Bountea at www.bountea.com. Reprinted by permission.

add to the mix if one is using any kind of oil—like neem, karanja, essential oils, fish emulsion, or soybean oils—as an encapsulator of foliar nutrients or pesticides so that they don't readily wash off or volatilize from UV radiation or temperature.

Another emulsifier and sticker we've had a great luck with is a product called X-tend, a terpene derived from pine oil resin. It acts as a "saran-wrap," holding nutrients or biocides (organic or conventional) in place until they are ready to be delivered into the stomata. This product used with liquid potassium (0-0-25) and a mix of zinc, manganese, and copper will help prevent frost damage if applied just prior to an anticipated freeze. Typically two quarts per acre of the nutrients along with the X-tend can really help.

Don't forget water pH! Many growers have hard water (more than ten grains), many have very hard water (more than twenty-five grains), and out West too many have "impossible" hard water (more than fifty grains). Hardness is a result of the carbonates of calcium and magnesium. And if the hard water contains elevated levels of iron and/or manganese it can be very difficult to use in foliar applications.

The finished pH of the tank mix ready to spray on the crop needs to be on the acidic side, at least between 5.0 and 6.0. The reason for such is because most plants' sap pH is in that range. Actual plant sap is considered "neutral" at 5.6. Damage can occur if the spray's pH is too high or low, especially with younger plants or fruits and berries.

The only way to acidify the tank water is with an organic acid (acetic or citric) or phosphoric acid. With acetic acid, a fifty-gallon tank probably needs a pint, maybe more; with citric acid, one needs six to eight ounces or so. With phosphoric acid it may only take a few ounces. Measure the pH of the water with either a pH meter or litmus paper and *slowly* adjust the acid additions to the tank mix accordingly.

Some years ago, I was privileged to get to know Doug Murray, an entomologist from Michigan who was consulting with ecological growers around the country. Fruit was his specialty, and he told me that one of the ways he addressed tree diseases organically was to alternate weekly between spraying an acidic solution (pH at 5 or below) and an alkaline solution (pH at 8 or above) because different diseases thrived in different acidic/alkaline terrains. Constantly alternating the environment made it difficult for any pest to get a foothold. The only suggestions I would add is to put a pH-neutral (that is, something not contributing to pH) fungicide, like essential oil extracts, emulsified neem, and trace elements—like boron, copper, and zinc—at a couple of ounce of each. Sadly, Doug Murray departed this life in April 2009, a big loss to the family of eco-agriculture.

Some aficionados of foliar nutrition feel that electrical conductivity of the spray solution is important. I would agree; if the conductivity becomes too elevated, you may singe the foliage. Start with measuring the conductivity of your tank water. As you add more ingredients, it will only get higher! Electrical conductivity (EC) is measured in one of the following: siemens per meter S/m); microsiemens per centimeter (μS/cm); or millisiemens per centimeter (mS/cm). What one is actually measuring is the electrolyte or salt concentration in the mix. The EC is a moving target that can also be influenced by temperature, as much as 2 percent for every 35°F difference in temperature.

A target for EC is 1.5–3.0 mS/cm. Less than 1.2 EC (mS/cm) can be too dilute to achieve the maximum response and greater than 7.0 EC (mS/cm) may cause a salt burn.

That all being said, there are "buffers" to high salt indexes in the tank mix. One of my favorites is humic acid, and the one I prefer is a wettable powder that can be used in water of any pH (between 1 and 14). Humic acids such as this one (Huma-Dyne) are great in encapsulating liquid nitrogen, or UAN (urea/ammonium nitrate). For conventional farmers, urea as a foliar is quite sensational as a quick protein-building molecule as it is already in the amine form (NH_2), as urea is chemically $NH_2\text{-}CO\text{-}NH_2$. Buffering it with humic acid provides a carbon-based delivery system that enhances uptake and lowers the chances of phytotoxicity. Other buffers that can insulate elements from "antagonizing" one another, as well as insulating the leaf from phytotoxicity, are fulvic acid, blackstrap molasses, fish hydrolysate, and seaweed extracts.

These can even perform as chelators of sorts by creating a polysaccharide wrap around the mineral elements, thus sequestering them in the solution. There is a livestock mineral manufacturer that accomplishes such a feat by coating trace mineral sulfates with polysaccharides derived from kelp and enhancing the absorption of these minerals into livestock.

A caveat on tissue testing: always sample tissue *prior* to spraying a foliar amendment or corrective. A higher reading may sometimes be because of residues on the *outside* of the leaf, not the inside. Sometimes, nutrient levels in the leaf will *decrease* following a foliar application because the spray accelerated the growth of the plant, which has caused a dilution of the nutrients in the leaf, called the Steenbjerg Effect.

Another phenomenon is that following a foliar spray application, nutrients may have been mobilized and transported to parts of the plant other than the leaf, such as roots, buds, fruits, and others. So, even though tissue analysis from the laboratory is a monitoring system that is in my opinion necessary for keeping an eye on a moving target, it ultimately is the *response* that one is getting from the foliar application that is the "proof of the pudding": resistance to stress, vigor, yield, and quality are the goals of the inputs, be they soil amendments or foliar correctives.

Spray oils can help with both the adherence of foliar amendments and their ability to readily remain on the cuticle surface of the leaf. Oils in liquid fish products contribute to this objective. Another option is a refined mineral oil called PureSpray Green, which is organically acceptable. These oils can help reduce evaporation, rain runoff, and spreading capacity over the waxy surface of the cuticle by encapsulating the foliage with a layer of lipids, which interferes with evaporation and repels rainwater.

When sampling plant tissue, choose a mature but not aged leaf. Sample at least seven to ten days following a foliar application and wear latex gloves to avoid contamination. If there are isolated problem areas, sample those separately. If abnormal leaf aberrations are spotty, it may be one of the challenges with soil-borne diseases or insect attacks due to plant trophobiosis (the imbalance or deficiency of nutrients leading to a flush of excess amino acids or simple sugars attracting pests).

APPLIANCES TO MONITOR PROGRESS

Some growers and consultants are using real-time utensils in the field to get a handle on changes that may be rapidly occurring due to weather events, like flooding, heat/drought, insects and disease outbreaks, and so on. (See chapter 12 for an in-depth look at field diagnostic devices).

One tool easily used is a Brix refractometer, an instrument that measures dissolved solids in the plant sap as functions of the covalent bonds on the sugar molecules. It's a tool widely utilized in the wine grape industry to ascertain the caliber of grapes—the higher the Brix value, the better the wine. Higher Brix crops typically have higher carbohydrates as saccharides, higher-quality proteins, and a greater specific gravity (density or test weight). As a general rule of thumb, high Brix crops have more resistance to insects and disease, are tastier, and have better shelf life (lower water/nitrate content).

Higher sugars in the sap mean more antifreeze, thus frost resistance, and it usually means that soils are fertile, both biologically (microorganisms) and geologically (minerals), as the uptake of especially calcium, phosphate, magnesium, boron, and sulfur are needed to raise Brix levels. My French Canadian friend Jean Brunet has demonstrated that certain plant diseases like downy mildew can actually raise plant sap pH.

Some caveats: Brix in plant sap is a moving target. Taking a Brix reading following five days of rainy, cloudy weather in good soils will likely give you a lower reading than the same species of plants growing on poor soil following a week of sunny weather. Remember, sugar production is a function of photosynthesis!

Also, some forage plants may not direct their metabolism to produce as much sugar because they are orienting some of their photosynthetic energy to produce non-sugar carbohydrates, like cellulose, hemicellulose, pectins, glucans, fatty acids, oils, resins, carotenes, and such. These are energy compounds as well, especially for ruminants, but won't necessarily show up in a high Brix test, even though the plant is nutrient-dense and loaded with carbohydrates and carbon compounds. Many broad leaf forbs are in this category, like dandelion, burdock, and plantain.

Another example of this testing distortion is that those who test their milk with a refractometer may not realize that animal breeds with a higher butterfat content will actually have a lower Brix reading on the refractometer than they "should" because their higher butterfat content interferes with the true or actual reading of the lactose, sucrose, and other sugars that are in the milk.

According to Don Schriefer (*From the Soil Up* and *Agriculture in Transition*), one does not want to see elevated Brix readings early in the morning. Plants need to shuttle 30–50 percent of their sugars down into the root ball overnight, where it is needed as nutrients for the microbial community living in the rhizosphere.

In calcium-loving plants like alfalfa, foliar applying a calcium/boron mix can really kick up the Brix. I've seen alfalfa as low as 4 Brix and as high as 29

Brix. The Brix refractive index ranges from 0 to 32 Brix. One organic alfalfa producer using a lime dust slurry mixture with boron increased his Brix levels into the upper twenties.

Plant sap pH meters are now being used by growers to ascertain the health of their plants. Allegedly, too low a pH indicates a cation deficiency, leading to fungal opportunism. Plant sap with too high a pH renders the plant more susceptible to insect attack. What is the "ideal" plant sap pH? According to microbiologist and agricultural consultant Bruce Tainio, it is 6.4. According to other plant pathologists and agronomists, the normal plant sap pH approximates 5.6–5.70—a big difference.

There is no question that applying a foliar product, whether it is nutritional or remedial (for diseases or insects), always elicits a response in plant sap pH, and usually Brix as well.

Plant sap conductivity meters are used to reconcile the electrical conductivity with those electrolytes like nitrogen, potassium, and calcium ions in order to determine if there is an excessive amount or an imbalanced ratio of these electrolytes that could lead to plant stress, and thus crop failure or setbacks.

Even a chlorophyll meter is now available to determine how healthy your photosynthesis index is. If chlorophyll readings are less than optimum, it may be time to consider catalysts that contribute to chlorophyll production, such as magnesium, nitrogen, sulfur, and phosphate, as well as biostimulants that can amp up chlorophyll production.

A balanced leaf analysis may or may not mirror a soil analysis because uptakes of nutrients are predicated so much on biology and weather. For example, potassium, being a cation with a single positive charge (K^+), is much less attached to a negatively charged soil particle compared to cations with double positive charges, like calcium and magnesium (Ca^{++}, Mg^{++}), and are thus more bound to not only soil (clay) particles, but also other negatively charged anions like phosphate $P_2O_5^=$) or sulfate ($SO_4^=$). Thus, in this example, potassium is *always* likely to get into the plant more easily than calcium or magnesium, even though the soil test may suggest that there is adequate calcium and magnesium in the soil.

Foliar feeding the deficient nutrients; or spraying compounds that could suppress excess solutes in the tissue with other nutrients; or catalysts, such as plant hormones, or catalysts that act like plant hormones—humic acids, fulvic acids, gibberellins, seaweed extract (especially the fresh juice), fish hydrolysate, etc.—can often save the day, especially if you know what you're up against.

TABLE 6.1

Plant Therapy™

Date: xx-xx-xx
Name: Mr. Sample
Address:

Land Use: Broccoli
Paddock: Block 1
Sample Rec:
Contact Fax:

Element or Category	Your Level	Acceptable Range	Deficient	Acceptable	Excessive or Toxic
N - Nitrogen	4.12%	3.2-6.1%			
P - Phosphorus	0.58%	0.3-0.7%			
K - Potassium	3.65%	3.5-4.2%			
S - Sulfur	2.19%	1.9%			
Ca - Calcium	1%	1.2-2.5%			
Mg - Magnesium	0.3%	0.23-0.40%			
Na - Sodium	0.1%	<1.0%			
Cu - Copper	4 ppm	1-5 ppm			
Zn - Zinc	23 ppm	45-95 ppm			
Mn - Manganese	197 ppm	25-150 ppm			
Fe - Iron	98 ppm	50-150 ppm			
B - Boron	34 ppm	30-100 ppm			
Si - Silicon	213 ppm	N/A	N/A		

Nutri-tech Solutions, *Plant and Pest Management*, 30.

When looking at tissue/leaf analysis, the levels are important, but equally and perhaps more important are the *ratios*, such as were exemplified in the section on trace minerals.

SOME FOLIARS AND NON-FOLIARS TO CONSIDER

Seaweed Extracts

Seaweed extract is a fabulous biostimulant for all crops. Because seaweed grows in ocean waters, it's a reservoir for numerous mineral elements. Additionally, it's a great source of plant hormones/catalysts like auxins and cytokinins. Alginic acid is an amazing soil conditioner and actually chelates metals in the soil. Alginates are even used as heavy metal chelators for humans.

Studies at Clemson University in South Carolina on seed soaking demonstrated that seed emergence dramatically increased, especially at seaweed concentrations of 0.50 percent. Tremendous amounts of data can be gleaned from the accomplishments of academic and field researchers on how seaweed can make such a difference in yield, quality, disease, and insect resistance.

Trials were done in the 1960s on peaches on which one quart of seaweed extract (in one hundred gallons of water, 0.25 percent) was sprayed four times. Both treated and untreated peaches were first put in refrigerated storage for one to two weeks, depending on the time of harvest, and then placed in a shed at ambient temperature (in September) for about one week. The seaweed parcels had 14.6 percent rot; the untreated controls had 32.6 percent.

Seaweed extract also affects plants' resistance to pests like spider mites and aphids, perhaps because it produces a thicker leaf cuticle, perhaps because it changes the flavor of the sap, perhaps because it is so loaded with nutrition (see table 6.2), or perhaps because it acts as a triggering mechanism to create an induced systemic resistance (ISR) reaction. But it clearly has an ancient and very long history of multiple uses in agriculture.

Cucumbers treated with seaweed versus those treated with a conventional insecticide produced a 14 percent heavier crop with a measurable improvement over the treated controls regarding plant damage from spider mites.

A biological farming enthusiast can learn a great deal from T. L. Senn's seminal 1987 publication *Seaweed and Plant Growth*, based on studies at Clemson University. Another treatise on such is *Seaweed in Agriculture and Horticulture* by W. A. Stephenson.

Seaweeds are found in many sizes and shapes. A good text on such is *Seaweed: A User's Guide*, by Sonia Surey-Gent and Gordon Morris. There are the families of green seaweeds, or the Chlorphyceae family, like sea lettuce; the brown seaweeds, or the Phaeophyceae family, like *Ascophyllum nodosum*, Fucus (bladderwrack), Laminaria (oarweed), and sugar kelp; and the red seaweeds, or the Rhodophyceae family, consisting of Irish moss and dulse. There are more of course, especially when perusing the innumerable sea vegetables eaten, especially in the Orient.

Gibberellic acid, yet another compound found in kelp, apparently afflicts the maturity of insects like red spider mites. All three plant hormones, normally auxins, gibberellins and cytokinins, affect the senescence of plants, in other words, the length of their lives, and the keeping quality of the harvest (in some instances shelf life two to three times longer). I like to see liquid kelp used at a rate of at least one pint to two quarts per acre. Fresh liquid kelp juice, such as the North American Kelp's Nitrozyme, is a registered plant growth regulator. Another such product from South Africa, made using bull kelp, is called Ocean Glow and apparently has a very high level of those plant hormones.

TABLE 6.2
ANALYSIS OF *ASCOPHYLLUM NODOSUM* BY
NORWEGIAN INSTITUTE OF SEAWEED RESEARCH

COMPONENTS	%	CARBOHYDRATES	%
Proteins	5.7	Mannitol	4.2
Fat	2.6	Alginic acid	26.7
Fiber	7.0	Methylpentosans	7.0
Nitrogen-free extracts	58.6	Laminarin	9.3
Moisture	10.7	Undefined sugars	14.4
Ash	15.4		
	100	Methylpentosans are complex polysaccharides	

(Nitrogen-free extracts are made up of non-protein material such as sugars)

ELEMENTS

	%		%
Silver	.000004	Nitrogen	.062400
Aluminum	.193000	Sodium	4.180000
Gold	.000006	Nickel	.003500
Boron	.019400	Oxygen	Undeclared
Barium	.001276	Osmium	Trace
Carbon	Undeclared	Phosphorus	.211000
Calcium	1.904000	Lead	.000014
Chlorine	3.680000	Rubidium	.000005
Cobalt	.001227	Sulfur	1.564200
Copper	.000635	Antimony	.000142
Fluorine	.032650	Silicon	.164200
Iron	.089560	Tin	.000006
Germanium	.000005	Strontium	.074876
Hydrogen	Undeclared	Tellurium	Trace
Mercury	.000190	Titanium	.000012
Iodine	.062400	Thallium	.000293
Potassium	1.280000	Vanadium	.000531
Lanthanum	.000019	Tungsten	.000033
Lithium	.000007	Zinc	.003516
Magnesium	.213000	Zirconium	.000001
Manganese	.123500	Selenium	.000043
Molybdenum	.001592	Uranium	.000004

OTHER ELEMENTS PRESENT

Bismuth	Chromium	Iridium	Radium
Beryllium	Cesium	Palladium	Bromine
Nionium	Gallium	Platinum	Cerium
Cadmium	Indium	Thorium	Rhodium

William Anthony Stephenson, *Seaweed in Agriculture and Horticulture* (Wakefield: E. P. Pub., 1973), 32.

I use a wettable powder, spray dried at low temperatures so as to not denature the amino acids, carbohydrates, and plant hormones. About twelve to sixteen ounces mixed with one gallon of water would constitute a liquid kelp concentrate, which then would be added to a tank mix at one pint to two quarts per forty to fifty gallons of spray tank or seed soak.

Humic Acids and Humates

Humic acids and humates are perhaps the most mysterious compounds now in common use in agriculture both with conventional and organic practitioners. Originally derived from prehistoric vegetation, humic acids and humates arise not only from the degradation of this biomass; they are also the end products of a secondary synthesis reaction, which is a complex degradation or digestion of carbon-rich substances into geologically compounded organic substances that are an amalgamation of minerals, organic acids, inert carbons, volatile hydrocarbons, phenols, flavonoids, etc. As they are the end product of microbiological activity, they are thus extremely resistant to further microbial breakdown.

Humic substances, being the largest sink of sequestered carbon, are deemed the most abundant organic material on our planetcontaining an estimated one thousand times more carbon than what is growing above the ground.

Humic substances enhance microbial activity, but, contrary to some assumptions, they are not microbial foods, like sugars, proteins, cellulose, or lignin. They chelate cations and stabilize anions in the soil, thus not only releasing complexed or tied-up minerals but preventing any leaching. They have water-holding attributes, can help buffer pH, and have an antitoxin characteristic as well.

On sandy soils, adding humates as a dry soil amendment, namely as leonardite or lignite, can provide a higher cation exchange capacity (CEC) around the seed and root ball, thus increasing the opportunity for plants to have access to more exchangeable nutrients and moisture. Adding a wettable powder to a tank mix can do wonders in stabilizing liquid urea, or UAN, by complexing the nitrogen with carbon and allowing the urea to not volatilize. Additionally, stabilizing UAN not only provides more NH_2 (an amide) to the plant to build protein, it also helps stabilize the carbon compounds within urea, allowing them to be more plant available. Humic acids are effective chelators of calcium as well; in the case of a tissue deficiency the only way to quickly increase calcium levels is with a soluble foliar calcium, as soil availability and uptake from the roots are poor at that time.

Humic acids have been found to contribute to reducing herbicide applications by 20–30 percent, and this research was conducted by a major herbicide manufacturing corporation (results were made available by the American Colloid Co. in Skokie, Illinois, back in the 1980s). Perhaps this is because humic acids are recognized in increasing cell membrane permeability by up to 30 percent.

The chelating effects of humates like leonardite were originally found to be effective in the oil fields, where drilling bits encountering salt domes were thwarted in their ability to efficiently punch holes in the rock strata due to the corrosiveness of the salt. Humates were poured down the well shafts along with bentonite clay (to act as a lubricant), and the humates sequestered the salts, thereby aggregating them and allowing the bits to drill deeper without as much friction or corrosive action. Such findings led to multiple investigations of humates being used to help recover sodic soils, which have toxic levels of salts, and soils too high in bicarbonates, which elevate soil pH so high that certain minerals, especially trace minerals, become unavailable.

In Florida, it was discovered that adding dry humates to limestone allowed the calcium to migrate into the lower soil horizons in citrus groves, thereby providing the root systems with access to more calcium and other nutrients while also opening up the clay compaction. Mixing humates with limestone, gypsum, and other soil amendments (such as rock phosphate, carbonotite, nitrogen fertilizers, and trace elements) can enhance their bioavailability and thus their uptake.

Humates are quite useful as vehicles to shuttle other nutritional compounds throughout the vascular system of plants to roots, leaves, flowers, and fruit and also shuttle nutrients for biologically based substances like calcium humate or humate-clay complexes that can be utilized for crop decomposition, especially stubble digestion at the end of the growing season.

Humic acids are simplistically defined as being the humic fraction that is not soluble in acids and is soluble in alkali, which is quite erroneous. Humic fractions can be of various pHs, therefore there is no single pH below which humic acids are not soluble.

Fulvic Acids

Fulvic acids are the very low molecular weight fractions of humates or humic substances that are typically referred to as the acid soluble fraction. They contain more oxygen and less carbon then humic materials. These acids are recognized to behave like a "growth hormone" for plants, apparently affecting transpiration and the opening of the stomata. Like humic acids, they are recognized to increase the permeability of plant cell membranes and perform as an effective chelating agent.

Fulvic acids are especially important because of their ability to interact with silica, and they have a strong affinity for reaction with iron. The fulvic solution I've used is a liquid concentrate called Fusion™. It is not made with an acid-alkaline extraction process. Rather, it is a leachate from a stacked humate-clay deposit that contains over seventy elements as well as fulvic acids. This leachate is also very rich in tannins or tannic acid, residues of prehistoric vegetation that made up tropical forests during the Cretaceous period. Because of its very complex constitution (fulvic acid, minerals, tannins, phenols, etc.), Fusion™ acts both as a synergist and plant food provider.

The nature of this product is that it has a catalytic benefit; one can blend antagonistic ingredients—such as calcium and phosphorus or calcium and boron—without reactions, while supplying an array of naturally occurring elements.

Fusion™ has been analyzed to contain over 350,000 milligrams per liter (350,000 ppm) of dissolved colloidal solids. Colloidal particles range in size from 2.0 microns down to 0.0001 microns. The humic clay deposit's liquid leachate allegedly has colloidal particles at sizes of 0.005 microns or less. The mineral and tannin levels are so concentrated it can even be utilized as a livestock remedy for miscellaneous challenges, such as scours. Only one pint to one quart per acre is used, preferably with humic acid and other foliar or soil drench materials like fish hydrolysate, liquid seaweed, and molasses.

Sea-Crop

Dr. Maynard Murray made famous the near-miraculous agricultural properties of ocean water, which were detailed in his book *Sea Energy Agriculture* and Charles Walters's *Fertility from the Ocean Deep*. Using a sea salt deposit in Baja, Mexico, Murray utilized these "sea solids" as fertilizers for just about everything, with very encouraging results. The only obstacle for a number of growers is the eventual accumulation of both chloride and sodium in the soil.

The organic fertilizer Sea-Crop was developed by Arthur Zeigler, a mining and mineral consultant/metallurgist who ran with Dr. Murray's research and produced a seawater concentrate that is essentially sea water with most of the sodium and chloride removed. Typical ocean water contains 38 percent sodium and 55 percent chlorine, whereas Sea-Crop contains 0.85 percent sodium and 7.5 percent chloride. The liquid is 20 percent solids, with elements from the ocean broth as well as other macroelements like magnesium, trace elements like zinc, and ultratrace elements like vanadium.

According to its inventor, Sea-Crop has up to 1 billion bacteria and 10 billion beneficial viruses and virus-like particles per tablespoon. Very substantiated results, especially on vegetables and fruits but also on row crops and livestock, have been documented. The typical rate of application is about four gallons per acre per year and on specialty, highest-value crops, six gallons per year. Sea-Crop is recommended as both a soil drench and foliar spray.

Blackstrap Molasses

Blackstrap molasses, the viscous syrup left over after sugar is extracted from raw sugarcane, has a variety of attributes that make it an excellent addition to foliar sprays or soil drenches. For one, it is a fast-acting supply of energy as invert sugar. This energy can take the form of one of many varieties of carbon to feed microbes either in the root ball or on the stubble. The molasses is a warehouse of many trace minerals like iron, zinc, copper, and chromium. It's a good sticker for other materials in the tank mix. It also has mild buffering properties that help insulate antagonistic elements from reacting with one another.

Blackstrap molasses makes a great companion ("go food," or energy) for nitrogen ("grow food," or protein), but there is a need to err on the side of caution. Plant residues are typically mostly carbohydrates, cellulose and hemicellulose, and small amounts of sugars (in young, succulent green plants). Too much sugar applied to a low organic matter soil will increase the populations of the zymogenous organisms (fermentation bacteria that could encourage certain disease organisms) over the native flora, called autochthonous (meaning indigenous or native) organisms. The native flora in healthy soil have ecological importance because they are symbionts, or partners, with the other microflora and plant roots to provide optimal plant health and productivity. Excess sugar by itself can also stimulate certain pathogens like Pythium. When applying molasses, consider mixing it with more complex carbohydrates as well, found in seaweed extract, fish hydrolysates, and compost teas. Also, add humic and fulvic acids as buffers and chelators.

Fish Hydrolysates

Fish hydrolysates are liquid fish fertilizers that are produced via a cold (ambient, or mesophilic) process whereby the native enzymes found in the digestive tract digest the non-marketable parts of the high-value fish and the entire carcass of noncommercial fish (e.g., carp). This process apparently

Chicken Soup for the Soil

The following is a recipe I concocted beginning in the mid 1980s, when I was consulting for over four dozen farms on various subjects, including soil health and fertility, forage production and quality, and livestock health. I recommend using the following recipe approximately ten days following a grazing or cutting or for row crops and vegetables: An eighty to one hundred gallon mix to cover two acres contained:

1. Calcium nitrate 9-0-0-11 Ca at 2 gallons. For organic growers, use dry Chilean nitrate,16-0-0, but this soluble product needs to be added to water over 100°F first or it won't dissolve.
2. Blackstrap molasses: 2 gallons.
3. Humic acid: 2 quarts (preferably use a wettable powder that is pH compatible at acid and alkaline pHs).
4. Liquid seaweed: 2 quarts.
5. Liquid fish: 2 gallons/acre.
6. Boric acid (17% B): 1 pound.
7. Fusion™ (fulvic acid/leachate/catalyst): 1 pint.
8. Epsom salts: 5–8 lbs.
9. Citric acid: 1.5 lbs.
10. Trace minerals (as per tissue test), if needed:
    a. Iron sulfate (20% Fe): 2–4 oz
    b. Zinc sulfate (36% Zn): 2–4 oz
    c. Copper sulfate (25% Cu): 2–4 oz
    d. Manganese sulfate (28% Mn): 2–4 oz
11. Sodium molybdenate (39% Mo): 1–2 oz.
12. Cobalt sulfate (20% Co): 1–2 oz.
13. Dyna-Sol™ (wetting agent): 4–6 oz.
14. Hydrated lime: 3–4 lbs/50 gallons tank mix to buffer the pH from a 4.0 to a 5.0 (excess acidity may come from Fusion).

The protocol is as follows:

Acidify the water with either: a) phosphoric acid at 2–3 oz per tank; b) acetic acid/vinegar at 1 pint per tank; or c) citric acid at 8 oz per tank. The purpose of these organic acids is to drop the tank water pH down to pH of 5–6. The harder the water, the more acid required. Keep tank mix agitated while adding ingredients.

Add Dyna-Sol™ at 4–6 oz/tank
Add calcium nitrate or Chilean nitrate
Add Fusion™
Add citric acid
Add molasses
Add fish
Add humic acid
Add molybdenum
Add cobalt
Add Epsom salts
Add boric acid
Add appropriate trace elements, as per tissue tests (e.g., iron, zinc, copper, manganese, etc.)
Test pH and add hydrated lime if necessary to adjust pH

These ingredients need to be added while the tank water is being agitated. Ideally, warm water (at least room temperature) would help. Spray this eighty- to hundred-gallon mixture on two acres, and photosynthesis will really kick in. In the late 1980s this soup mix was part of a fertility program for a client who also utilized a soils program that incorporated cement kiln dust (for calcium, sulfur, and potash), monoammonium phosphate, manure, rock phosphate, boron, zinc, and copper. Though not organic, this client took first place in Penn State University's Alfalfa Regional Competition with over eight tons per acre of dry matter (the state average is three and a half tons). And no leap hoppers or weevils, thus no poisons.

Additionally, this was a year of a major heat wave and a drought, and in early August his alfalfa measured over three feet tall while still in the vegetative stage; his neighbors across the lane who grew alfalfa conventionally had plants about one foot tall that were lignified and in heavy blossom. The following year was an extremely wet year, and he was the only grower of green pack tomatoes that did not lose a crop, nor did he use fungicides.

Ecological farming is a bottom-line profit maker because it's congruent with nature's laws of chemistry, biology, and physics. It's not a religion or ideology— it's a scientific system that works with the "nature of nature."

leaves intact the enzymes, amino acids, hormones, fats, vitamins, etc., as there is no high heat to denature them. The products are typically stabilized with phosphoric acid to drop the pH low enough to prevent further fermentation/putrefaction. The N-P-K analysis is typically 2–3 percent nitrogen, 3–5 percent phosphorus, and 1–2 percent potassium. Companies that produce fish hydrolysates include Brown's, Organic Gem, Dramm, Neptune's Harvest, Schafer Fisheries, and Omega.

Liquid fish is a very bioavailable plant food, a great soil biostimulant, a sticker for other liquids, and a chelator of elements because of the free amino acids that envelop the minerals. It should be part of a base mix for other foliars and soil drenches.

SOME HOMEMADE FOLIARS

- Comfrey tea foliar can be produced by harvesting about twenty pounds of fresh leaves per fifty five gallons of water. Add ten pounds of compost or worm castings, four ounces of Epsom salts, ten pounds of molasses, one ounce of sea salt, and five gallons of milk. Let ferment in a vented container, stirring and shaking at least every couple of days for three weeks. Comfrey is very high in nitrogen because it's 25(+) protein. It's loaded with macro- and microelements as well as polysaccharides (long chain sugars) as a source of carbon. Strain and use as a soil drench or foliar at three to four ounces per gallon of water or 2–3 percent dilution.
- Nettle tea makes another potent plant-based ferment. The recipe is the same as above. Nettle is not only high in nitrogen, but very high in organically bound iron as well as a suite of other minerals.
- Alfalfa is not only a rich reservoir of calcium, potassium, nitrogen magnesium, phosphorus, and minor elements, but it is also a storehouse of a plant stimulant called triacontanol, which influences photosynthesis, thus contributing to larger root systems, yield increases, more flowering, better water uptake, mineral absorption, and even earlier maturity. Fresh-harvested alfalfa or alfalfa meal can be used in the spray mix. Prepare like comfrey.

- Japanese knotweed is considered an invasive streamside plant in my parts and is growing on stretches of the stream on my property. I'm grateful for its presence as it has kept those parts of the bank from eroding. Additionally, knotweed is revered in Japan as a powerful healing plant. And it's no wonder; *Polygonum cuspidatum* is the largest reservoir of the potent and highly researched stilbene known as resveratrol. Highly anti-inflammatory and anticancer, it's one of the most medicinally researched plants around. New Zealand researchers using Effective Microorganisms in fermentation noted that fermented Japanese knotweed gave the best crop response when used as a foliar compared to other fermented botanicals. Prepare like comfrey. A commercially available plant protectant called Regalia is produced from Japanese knotweed and works by stimulating induced systemic resistance against plant diseases.

I would consider using all the recipes included. For those growers already utilizing other commercially available products, adding liquid fish, seaweed extract, and humic acid to the liquid after fermentation would be a good contributing resource of other growth factors found in those products. Blending the above recipes after fermentation may be most beneficial, especially if one's ferment isn't doing as much as one hoped for.

The Eternal Earthworm

*Everything is the product of one universal creative effort. There is
nothing dead in Nature. Everything is organic and living, and therefore
the whole world appears to be a living organism.*

—Seneca

I use the word *eternal* to describe the earthworm because of the never-ending work in which this remarkable creature of the earth is engaged. Even though this book has showcased much of the microbial soil food web, I wanted to devote some specific space to earthworms because they can readily be observed and counted, yet most lovers of the soil actually know little of them.

Charles Darwin's seminal work *The Formation of Vegetable Mould, Through the Action of Worms, with Observations on Their Habitats*, published in 1881, was perhaps as important a journal of nature as his account of his global expedition on the HMS *Beagle*. This book, finally published one year before Darwin's death, summarizes more than thirty-nine years of observations. No scientist prior to Darwin had taken such an interest in this creature. In fact, many believed earthworms to be vegetable pests that attacked plant roots as do parasitic nematodes. Darwin, on the other hand, was fascinated by the behavior and beneficial effects of the unjustly maligned creature. In chapter 4, Darwin discusses how he placed stones on pastures and observed how those stones eventually "sank" into the soil. What actually occurred, as Darwin discovered, was that the earthworm castings, or feces, in the pasture increased the layer of topsoil by seven inches over twenty-nine years, or a quarter of an inch per year, and buried the stones. Darwin learned that worms are also calculating engineers, as they know that dragging pine needles or fallen leaves into their burrows by their base prevents them from getting lodged in the burrow. The fact that a creature so small can literally move the earth, aerate it, and fertilize it, thus creating habitat for microbes, channels for water to percolate, and conduits for roots to extend themselves, makes this creature a wonder of the visible world.

I have thought of earthworms as kind of a tiny hybrid between a chicken and a cow. Not having teeth, like birds, they use a gizzard, or a pre-stomach filled with grit, to grind up lignified material such as leaves. Then, like a ruminant, they regurgitate this digesta and slime the walls of their burrows with it, allowing temperature and time to work its magic on this petri dish of nutrients. The burrow is then colonized by bacteria and yeasts rich in protein not found in the original plant debris, which are grazed by the earthworm. This process is very similar to a ruminant growing a large mass of bacteria, protozoa, and fungi in its rumen and synthesizing large amounts of microbial protein from an indigestible source of fiber such as cellulose or lignin.

Other times, I have thought of earthworms as the whales of the soil; they are certainly one of the largest creatures swimming in the deeps of our earth, ingesting untold quantities of bacteria, protozoa, nematodes, and fungi, just as our mammalian behemoths inhale tons of zoo plankton, like krill.

Earthworms can also be seen as massive herds of ungulates, like antelope or bison, tiny herbivores that continually graze the plankton of the earth, aerifying the soil so that plants and their microbial symbionts can thrive, creating more soil carbon (humus/topsoil) to serve as a sponge to hold more water and cleanse the waters that fill the aquifers and our streams.

Earthworm gut bacteria number more than four dozen species. Protozoa, predators of bacteria, are important fare for earthworms, and some species survive digestion by earthworms, thus enriching the worm castings. And though earthworms literally dwell in a soup of microbes internally and externally, their health is apparently not affected by the legion of bacteria, fungi, protozoa, nematodes, springtails, mites, and the other denizens of topsoil. Meanwhile, earthworms have provided some evidence of being able to "clean" an infested soil of such undesirable plant pathogens as take-all fungus (*Gaeumannomyces graminis*) by spreading its antagonist *Pseudomonas corrugata* around, especially if the latter bacteria was first added to animal dung then spread on a wheat field where earthworms could ingest it. Apple scab, too, appears to be less of a challenge if the orchard is populated with high amounts of night crawlers able to devour the fallen infected leaves.

The dark side of nonnative worms, those that came here from Europe during the colonial settlement period (especially in the eighteenth and nineteenth centuries), is that deciduous forests are at risk of being radically altered by the deep-burrowing anecic varieties, like night crawlers (*Lumbricus terrestris*). Anecic worms rapidly convert leaf mold, or duff (leaves at various stages of decomposition), into bare soil, which discourages the survival of native plants dependent on the duff. In many cases native plants decline at a rate of 80–90 percent without the duff necessary for their growth. Even some deciduous trees dependent on duff for seed germination can't hold on without it. Native plants are thus replaced by invasive species. The microbial landscape also changes, going from a fungal-dominated ecosystem to a bacterial one because fungi grow on forest litter better than on soil (fungal-dominated ecosystems are more conducive to certain native species such as wild orchid). Voles and shrews, which prey on insects more prevalent in forest litter than in soil alone, are replaced by mice. Plants that survive this ecological tectonic plate shift are more vulnerable to being eaten by the deer population.

But another report, in the USDA Yearbook of Agriculture for 1930, found that "mulls," granular mixes of organic matter and minerals created by earthworms, are a forest's best friend. Additionally, Svend Heiberg, associate professor of silviculture of the New York State College of Forestry, wrote an article on the importance of mull production by earthworms as a critical factor for tree productivity.* Could it be that invasive anecic worm species occupying our woodlands today far outnumber the native species prevalent a century ago? As I've stated above, the species suspected of being mostly responsible for the decline of native plants are the deep-burrowing anecic worms, like *Lumbricus terrestris*. Apparently, it is the horizontal burrowers like the "red worm" (*Lumbricus rubellus*, an epigenic burrower) that manufacture those fertile "mulls" beneficial to trees up to a point. Because if all three functional groups of worms are in the forest, it will have a major impact on converting fallen leaf duff into soil. Earthworms are thus labeled ecosystem engineers because their burrowing not only churns the soil but also modifies the habitat of microbes, plants, and animals, for better or worse. The bottom line is that many of the worms now invading our forests are exotic species.

---

* Svend Heiberg , "Forest Soil in Relation to Silviculture," *Journal of Forestry* 37, no. 1 (January 1939): 42–46.

The northern latitude deciduous forests actually evolved by creating this layer of duff, which is habitat to native species like wild ginger, trillium, false Solomon's Seal, trout lilies, bellwort, and many others. Duff is also home to amphibians such as newts, salamanders, and frogs as well as ground-nesting warblers like the oven bird. The forest is a fungal-dominated ecosystem. Cropland is bacterial-dominated ecosystem. Worms, in general, encourage bacterial-dominated ecosystems.

Earthworms can have an even more profound effect on ecosystems than a legion of beavers. The only thing to do to help these declining forests and mitigate effects of the night crawlers is to: 1) stop fragmenting them with lawns, golf courses, and tilled farm ground; 2) don't use live bait when fishing because the night crawlers are discarded into the forests afterward; 3) control the deer population via fences and hunting to prevent them from consuming the native understory and native seedlings that are struggling to remain healthy and well-established; 4) invite and encourage worm predators like moles and worm-eating birds. It's a tall order, with an unprecedented challenge that has rarely been undertaken.

But let's focus on the bright side of the farmer's friend. Jim Kinsella, a no-till farmer in Lexington, Illinois, has stated that "ten large worm holes and a hundred small holes per square foot means over 330 miles per acre of pencil thickness holes and over 800 miles per acre of small holes" That's saying a lot for water infiltration (four times higher than comparable fields without worms); soil aeration; hardpan penetration; reduced soil compaction; surface residue digested into the soil; release of crop growth stimulants, like auxins and cytokinins; minerals transferred up from the subsoil; neutralization of soil pH due to the worm's calciferous glands; a rapid growth of soil microbes, especially because earthworm dung is so rich in them; improved soil tilth from the exudates, polysaccharides, and enzymes; better parasitic nematode control (because earthworms eat them); and a higher bioavailability of trace elements to crops.

Now do some math: Having twenty-five earthworms per cubic foot of soil (12"x12"x12") means one ton of worms per acre, which some estimate equals 1 million worms per acre. That acre will receive thirty to one hundred tons of casting per year! That's an additional plant-available source of nitrate, phosphorous, potash, magnesium, and five hundred pounds of actual, elemental calcium, which is three-fourths of a ton of limestone. Additionally, once earthworms die, their bodies provide another 50–990 pounds of nitrogen per acre. Clearly, pastures harbor the mother lode of earthworm population.

Ken Lee of South Australia's Commonwealth Scientific and Industrial

Research Organisation released data showing that French pastures had eight hundred burrows per square meter. Orchards in the Netherlands had a range of seventeen to thirty-three burrows per square meter. Cropland that was not tilled for four years ranged from 117 burrows per square meter in the United States to 305 in Germany.

To condense all of this info, one acre of U.S. topsoil contains between 250,000 to 2.5 million earthworms weighing between 500–5,000 pounds. Every twenty-four hours the body weight of soil passes through these creatures, amounting to one-quarter to two and a half tons per acre *per day*. Without earthworms, generating one inch of topsoil requires five hundred to a thousand years. With ample amounts of earthworms, an inch can be made in five years!

Investigations conducted by the British government in the Valley of the White Nile in Sudan indicate a great deal of the soil fertility there is attributed to earthworms.[*] Earthworm castings were estimated to amount to 239,580 pounds, or 119.79 tons per acre, during the six months of active growing season. The two sources of the Nile are the Blue Nile and the White Nile. The Blue Nile begins in Abyssinia at nine thousand feet of elevation. During the hundred-day rainy season, it is laden with 17 percent silt, half organic matter and half minerals. The Blue Nile meets the White Nile at the confluence called Khartoum, the midway point of this four-thousand-mile-long river system. Above Khartoum is a triangular expanse of land called Gezira, which lies between the Blue and White Nile Rivers, amounting to 5 million acres, roughly 250 miles long and 100 miles wide at the base of the triangle, the apex being Khartoum.

Gezira has been riddled with billions of earthworm tunnels to a depth of several feet, creating a honeycomb of cavities that become infused with the fertile silt carried by the three-month rainy season. Up until the early twentieth century tillage wasn't done, as earthworms were the plows. Seeding and harvesting were the primary labor inputs. When conversing with a local chef here in the United States, originally from Egypt, he told me that the Sudan region (Gezira) is so fertile it could feed the entire Middle East.

Other amazing examples of earthworms influencing soil fertility abound. Research by Patrick Lavelle and Beto Pashanasi showed that adding mulch and inoculating the soil with earthworms increased maize (corn) yields the first season by 23–60 percent.[†] In New Zealand, from 1925 to 1945, a farmer

---

[*] USDA archives, Experiment Station Record 27, no. 6, from Thomas J. Barrett, *Harnessing the Earthworm* (Eagle River, WI: Shields Publications, 1947), 25.
[†] Patrick Lavelle et al., "Soil Macrofauna and Land Management in Peruvian Amazonia," *Pedobiologia* 33 (1989): 283–91.

transplanted chunks of earthworm-inoculated fertile bottomland to pastures with a low earthworm population. He grew twenty times more ryegrass and doubled his breeding ewe flock, generating an additional four thousand pounds of wool. He credits the increase to the 8 million extra worms per acre in those pastures. Additional New Zealand research by K. E. Lee, author *Earthworms: Their Ecology and Relationships with Soils and Land Use* (1985), resulted in similar findings. Inoculating pastures devoid of earthworms created within five years a population of 1,150 worms per square meter, or 5 million per acre.

TABLE 7.1

IMPROVEMENTS IN SOIL QUALITY OF RESTORED COAL MINE LAND BY INOCULATING WITH EARTHWORMS

	Earthworm population 6 years after inoculation		Soil properties 9 years after earthworm inoculation	
	Number/ m^2	Carbohydrate[a] content in soil (g/100 g soil)	Clay dispersed upon wetting (susceptibility to erosion) (g/100 g soil)	Respiration per g of microbial biomass (metabolic quotient, of CO_2[b]), mg CO_2-$Cg^{-1}h^{-1}$
No earthworms added	8	0.90	23.7	15.3
Earthworms added 70/m^2	106	1.28	16.9	10.9
Percent difference	+1200	+42	-29	-29

a Mainly polysaccharides produced by earthworms themselves or by bacteria stimulated by the earthworms.

b A higher value indicates a stressed ecosystem in which microorganisms must devote increased energy to survival rather than growth.

J. Scullion and A. Malik, "Earthworm activity affecting Organic Matter, Aggregation and Microbial Activity in Soils Restored after Opencast Mining for Coal," *Soil Biology and Biochemistry* 32, no. 1 (2000): 119–26.

Table 7.1 shows some very encouraging results in coal mine reclamation, a stupendous accomplishment in light of the fact that strip-mined land is often quite damaged.

Noteworthy observations include: an increase of earthworms from the seventy per square meter (334,000 worms per acre) to 106 per square meter (505,000 worms per acre) six years later. Consequently, carbohydrates found in the inoculated soil amounted to a greater than 42 percent increase. Nine years following reclamation, the clay in the earthworm plots was 29 percent less susceptible to erosion than the non-inoculated. There was also a reduction of respiration, suggesting less soil microbial energy was required for survival and so more was available for growth.

Table 7.2 demonstrates the soil-remediating properties of these passive plows on tropical regrowth forest soils are nothing less than remarkable.

TABLE 7.2

COMPARATIVE CHARACTERISTICS OF EARTHWORM CASTS AND SOILS

Characteristic (Macro-aggregates cover 50–60 percent of soil surface)	Earthworm Casts	Soils
Silt and Clay, %	38.8	22.2
Bulk density, Mg/m³	1.11	1.28
Structural stability[a]	849	65
Cation exchange capacity, cmol/kg	13.8	3.5
Exchangeable Ca2+, cmol/kg	8.9	2.0
Exchangeable K+, cmol/kg	0.6	0.2
Soluble P, ppm	17.8	6.1
Total N, %	0.33	0.12

a Numbers of raindrops required to destroy structural aggregates.

D. de Vleeschauwer and R. Lal, "Properties of Worm Casts under Secondary Tropical Forest Regrowth," Soil Science 132 (1981): 175–81.

The earthworm castings and native soils were compared using both chemical and physical determinants. The bulk density (compaction) decreased by 13 percent; cation exchange capacity increased by 500 percent; potassium increased by 300 percent; soluble phosphorous increased by

300 percent; total soil nitrogen increased by nearly 300 percent. Structural stability was determined by counting the number of raindrops required to destroy the structural aggregates. The native soils succumbed to 65 drops, whereas the earthworm castings required 849, an improvement of 1,300 percent.

A fascinating study by plant pathologist Wade H. Elmer at the Department of Plant Pathology and Ecology, the Connecticut Agricultural Experiment

TABLE 7.3
Eggplant
INFLUENCE OF EARTHWORMS (*LUMBRICUS TERRESTRIS*)
ON EGGPLANT GROWTH AND DISEASE SEVERITY OF VERTICILLIUM
WILT IN GREENHOUSE STUDIES

Treatment	Dry plant weight (g)	AUDPC^y	Earthworms Recovered
Manure alone	3.8 a^z	117 a	0
Manure-earthworms	4.0 a	91 b	5.57
Fertilized (20-10-20)	10.3 b	163 a	0
Autoclaved-Fertilized	8.2 b	91 b	0

Wade Elmer, "Influence of Earthworm Activity on Soil Microbes and Soilborne Diseases of Vegetables," *Plant Diseases* 93, no. 2 (2009): 175–79.

TABLE 7.4
Tomatoes:
2X NUMBER OF FRUIT; PLANTS 78 PERCENT LARGER; FRUIT 3X WEIGHT

Influence of earthworms (*Lumbricus terrestris*) on tomato growth and severity of *Fusarium* wilt in greenhouse studies

Treatment	Plant weight (g)	No. Fruit	Fruit weight (g)	Vas. Discoloration	AUDPC^y	Earthworms Recovered
Control	20.6	0.6	9.2	51.2	60.1	0
Earthworms	36.7	1.3	25.4	30.8	19.5	3.80

Wade Elmer, "Influence of Earthworm Activity on Soil Microbes and Soilborne Diseases of Vegetables," *Plant Diseases* 93, no. 2 (2009): 175–79.

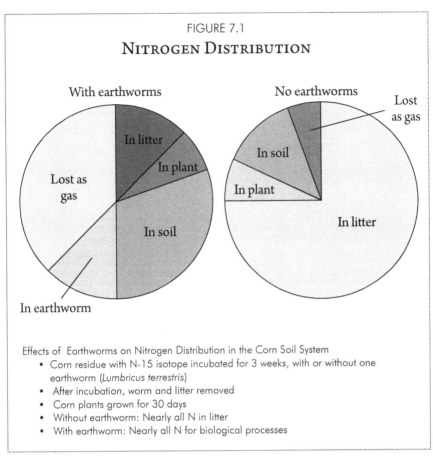

FIGURE 7.1

NITROGEN DISTRIBUTION

With earthworms

In litter
In plant
Lost as gas
In soil
In earthworm

No earthworms

Lost as gas
In soil
In plant
In litter

Effects of Earthworms on Nitrogen Distribution in the Corn Soil System
- Corn residue with N-15 isotope incubated for 3 weeks, with or without one earthworm (*Lumbricus terrestris*)
- After incubation, worm and litter removed
- Corn plants grown for 30 days
- Without earthworm: Nearly all N in litter
- With earthworm: Nearly all N for biological processes

José Amador and Josef Görres, "Role of the Anecic Earthworm Lumbricus terrestris in the Distribution of Plant Residue Nitrogen in a Corn Soil System," *Applied Soil Ecology* 30, no. 3 (November 2005): 203–14.

Station, in New Haven, Connecticut, proves that earthworms contribute to plant's resistance to diseases.[*] Elmer also conducted the studies depicted in tables 7.3 and 7.4 at the Connecticut Agricultural Experimental Station in New Haven, Connecticut. Earthworms have long been recognized as able to modify soil structure and enhance soil fertility, but their role in suppression of plant diseases has not been widely recognized. Several greenhouse studies were conducted to ascertain whether soils infested with plant diseases and inoculated with earthworms (*Lumbricus terrestris*) could positively impact cultivars of asparagus, eggplant, and tomato. In general, plant weights

* Wade H. Elmer, "Influence of Earthworm Activity on Soil Microbes and Soilborne Diseases of Vegetables," *American Phytopathological Society* 93, no. 2 (February 2009): 175–79.

increased 60–80 percent, and disease pressure as measured by root lesions decreased 50–70 percent, suggesting that increasing earthworm populations in the soil will likely suppress soil-borne diseases. The eggplant trial in table 7.3 shows that disease pressure was as low as it was in sterile (autoclaved) soil.

The tomato trial as illustrated in table 7.4 shows that *Lumbricus terrestris*–inoculated pots had twice the number of fruit, plants that were 78 percent larger, fruit that weighed 300 percent more, and an 80 percent reduction in disease pressure (area under the disease pressure curve, or AUDPC) of Fusarium.

The two pie charts in figure 7.1 explain how earthworms help soils and thus plants retain and recycle crop residues (as nitrogen distribution) for future crop production.[*] Without earthworms, nearly all the nitrogen was in the litter. With earthworms consuming and physically moving the litter, it was transformed and distributed throughout the soil to the advantage of the earthworm itself, the soil solution, and the corn plant.

The seven thousand species of earthworms, divided into over seven hundred genera and twenty-three families, may be a bit overwhelming to contemplate. Worm species are best categorized according to habitats and burrowing habits. Worms exist in nearly all the earth's environments—including oceans, lakes, ponds, forests, grasslands, and mountains—anywhere there is a ready supply of decaying organic matter. They're not typically found in deep deserts or in permafrost. There are three primary kinds of earthworms farmers and ranchers need to know about.

Epigeic earthworms are those dwelling in surface soils that are organically rich. This type includes the compost worm *Eisenia fetida*, or the red wiggler. They are not burrowers and are the choice for vermicomposting. Endogeic worms are those that create and dwell in shallow (four- to twelve-inch) horizontal burrows and are often found in a root ball or the rhizosphere. Such a specimen is *Allolobophora caliginosa*, a pale, pink, shiny, active worm, commonly known as the red worm. Last are the anecic worms, or the deep burrowers, the most popular of which is the infamous night crawler, capable of creating cavities six to ten feet deep. This variety can live as long as six to eight years, and they cover their burrow entrances with middens, a granular "door" of plant and soil debris.

---

* José Amador and Josef Görres, "Role of the Anecic Earthworm *Lumbricus terrestris* L. in the Distribution of Plant Residue Nitrogen in a Corn Soil System," *Applied Soil Ecology* 30, no. 3 (November 2005): 203–14 (2005).

Earthworms need an aerobic, cool, moist environment with adequate organic materials to flourish. They don't thrive in coarse sands (abrasive) and prefer a pH that ranges from 5.5 to 8.5 that preferably has adequate calcium levels, which are necessary for their mucus excretions. Direct contact with ammonia fertilizers, (including slurry manure), exposure to certain insecticides (e.g., carbamates like Sevin, etc.), and tillage are hazardous to earthworms.

In a rural area of Florida, near the 600,000 acre Apalachicola National Forest and Tate's Hell State Forest southwest of Tallahassee, some folks like Gary and Audrey Revell make their living "harvesting" earthworms. They don't do it the hard way, turning over spades of earth; rather, they coax them out of the soil using a fear tactic that tricks the worms into believing they are in danger of being consumed by their most feared predator: moles.

The "grunting" technique, as it's called locally, consists of pounding a two-foot wooden stake in the ground, leaving about eight to nine inches above ground. Then, taking a ten-pound piece of flat iron, the grunter rubs the iron on top of the stake back and forth, like a cello, sending sound and vibrations into the ground. The result is that scores of worms begin scurrying out of the soil in an area of fifty to one hundred square feet around the grunter and are then picked up and sold for fish bait.

Researchers like Ken Catania of Vanderbilt University believe this technique is effective because the sound and vibrations of the stake mimic that of a mole digging. The two noises were compared using a microphone to record both the grunting and mole digging sounds, which are strikingly similar. Perhaps if one wants to inoculate a piece of real estate that may need a higher population of worms, this process could be used to recruit some from a very fertile pasture or woodland and inoculate one's soils with a larger number of earthworms in a reasonably short period of time. Apparently, a good grunt session could coax hundreds of worms out of the ground.

There are a number of how-to books on raising composting worms, such as *Recycle with Earthworms* by Shelley Grossman and Toby Weitzel and *Harnessing the Earthworm* by Thomas Barrett. A favorite scientific investigative work is *The Biology of Earthworms* by Clive Edwards and J. R. Lofty of Ohio State University. The USDA North Appalachian Experimental Watershed Ag Research facility in Coshocton, Ohio, is also a great resource, and where a lot of data on increases in organic matter, water infiltration, eliminating erosion, and reducing fertilizer costs was acquired due to the growth of no-till farming practices over the last half century. Other "think tanks" on earthworm enhancement in the landscape are the Leopold Center for Sustainable Agriculture at Iowa State University (*www.leopold.iastate.edu*) and the Natural Resource Ecology Laboratory at Colorado State University (*www.nrel.colostate.edu*).

In reflecting back on Darwin, it's fascinating to note that he was traveling on the HMS *Beagle* for five years beginning at the age of thirty. He returned to England with 1,500 preserved specimens and over two thousand pages of journal notes. A leviathan amount of work lay before him to organize all of his findings, and yet the final book written before his life would pass was on the earthworm in his own backyard, which he spent a tremendous amount of time meticulously studying.

"The plow is one of the most ancient and most valuable of man's inventions; but long before he existed, the land was in fact regularly plowed and still continues to be thus plowed by earthworms." Yes, plowed indeed, but instead of plowing that incites erosion, it is the earthworm plowing that grows topsoil.

"It may be doubted whether there are many other animals which have played so important a part in the history of the world, as have these lowly organized creatures." The above two quotes by Darwin, taken from his *The Formation of Vegetable Mould, Through the Action of Worms, with Observations on Their Habitats*, strongly suggest that earthworms may provide answers for many of our challenges associated with topsoil conservation, feeding the hungry, recycling all of our biological wastes, preserving our watersheds, decontaminating toxins, restoring damaged landscapes, and providing a low-cost feed for poultry (worms are rich in quality amino acids, fats, vitamins, and minerals). And there's even the potential for cottage industries that can sell fish worms, compost worms, worm castings, and vermitea. Long live the earthworm.

Water

A Medium for Metamorphosis

Water flows and streams on the earth as ceaselessly as the
stream of time itself. It is the fundamental melody that forever
accompanies life in all its variations.

—Theodor Schwenk

A LTHOUGH water quality is obviously a huge consideration for livestock health and production, the following comments are focused
more on its effect on soil and plant health and productivity than its
significance to animal and human vitality. The following information pertain-
ing to water vitalization, or enlivening, is relevant to soils, plants, animals, and
other bodies of water. Usually when one considers water as a critical factor
in irrigation, water is laboratory-analyzed for its mineral levels and the ratios
of these minerals. Thus, irrigation water can dramatically affect soil mineral
availability, especially if that water is the primary or only source of water for
the crop. This is the case when there is little or no rainfall available, such as in
arid environments, greenhouses, and high tunnels.

Water that is "hard"—grains above ten—may carry with it high levels of
carbonates and bicarbonates, which can raise pH above desired levels. High
pH and bicarbonates can reduce the solubility of phosphorous, boron, and
iron, compromising plant uptake. In arid environments and greenhouses,
soils are not flushed by rainwater, which is in essence "distilled" water that
can help remove the build-up of sulfates, sodium, bicarbonates, and salts
of calcium and magnesium. Thus, it's important to deal with the water that
causes these accumulations of deleterious salts by accommodating the plants'

needs according to tissue analysis. Drip or foliar supplements of various plant foods that become complexed (i.e., "tied up" with other elements) might be necessary to overcome water-induced deficiencies. Also, salts can increase to such an extent that plants consume more of their energy reservoir to bring in water and nutrients against the salt concentration gradient.

One solution to problematic water—recycled waste water, overly mineralized well waters, and surface waters (stream, rivers, etc.)—is to first have it thoroughly analyzed at an agricultural laboratory that provides the following:

- pH
- hardness (grains and parts per million)
- conductivity as millimhos per centimeter
- sodium absorption ratio
- cation levels and balance of Ca, Mg, K, Na, and Fe in
    a. parts per million
    b. milliequivalents per liter
    c. pounds per acre inch
    d. base saturation percent

- total alkalinity
- carbonates
- bicarbonates
- chlorides
- sulfates
- salt concentration
- boron
- cation/anion ratio
- nitrates

Work with a lab technician who understands adequate water chemistry, soil mineral balance, and specific crop requirements as can be addressed with foliar or drip supplementation. For example, high salts in the water could be helped by adding humic acids, citric acid (for high pH and bicarbonates), sulfur burners (which produce weak sulfuric acid to perform like citric acid on high pH and high-carbonate and bicarbonate soils), and soluble gypsum or calcium sulfate (to displace high sodium in soils). Obviously, one needs to know what else is going on in the soil. Sulfur levels in greenhouse soils often can become very elevated if the well water is high in sulfates, so using a sulfur burner or gypsum would be counterproductive.

Humic acids are often a normalizing substance that can help sequester various salt build-ups while increasing the cation exchange capacity (CEC) of the soil, thus improving water holding capability and providing a carbon-based buffer. Using both dry humates and liquid humic acids can provide a range of carbon compounds to buffer the rhizosphere against salt stress.

TABLE 8.1

Desirable Ranges for Irrigation Water

Parameter	
Potassium	1.5–10 ppm
Calcium	40–120 ppm
Magnesium	6–24 ppm
Manganese	0.5–2 ppm
Iron	2–5 ppm
Boron	0.2–0.8 ppm
Copper	0–0.2 ppm
Sulfates	0–400 ppm
Electrical Conductivity	0–1.5 mmhos
Zinc	1–5 ppm
Sodium	0–50 ppm
Chloride	0–140 ppm
Alkalinity	1–100 ppm
Bicarbonate	0–120 ppm
SAR	0–4

Logan Labs Soil Testing Services, General Guidelines, 2013, http://www.loganlabs.com/customer-tools.html.

Adding soluble silica as potassium silicate can assist in high sodic soils by reducing the negative effect sodium has on soil biology and plant roots. Last but not least are high-quality compost and vigorous cover crops, both of which can sequester salts through microbiological ingestion and the carbon exudates (like mucilage and glomalin) they excrete.

Some growers have found that adding hydrogen peroxide (H_2O_2) to the irrigation drip can help by oxidizing some of the reduced metals like manganese and iron. The H_2O_2 can also supply some readily available oxygen to the rhizosphere, which can enhance the population and health of the microbes in the root ball, provided that the H_2O_2 concentration isn't too elevated, thus behaving as a sanitizer. The recommended application amount can vary considerably because of the numerous variables that are found in the soil's biology and chemistry. With livestock drinking water, for example, 20–30 ppm of H_2O_2 is the goal to improve herd health; anything above 30 ppm has been shown to suppress rumen microbes over time. Much higher doses have been used therapeutically in livestock for an acute situation or illness. And perhaps an elevated dose would be warranted with plant diseases in the root and using H_2O_2 as a foliar disease suppressant. The most economical way to administer H_2O_2 in the water is by using a technical or food-grade 35 percent or 50 percent H_2O_2. It must be handled with extreme caution as it can be quite caustic when undiluted.

There is another component of water purification that is just beginning to be recognized as an effective, scientific method to improve water quality. The technology is hardly new; it was demonstrated to be successful back in the early part of the twentieth century. Rudolf Steiner, the founder of biodynamic agriculture, stated that the role of water in agriculture is as a medium to transfer information to biological systems for their growth, development, and vitality, and for them to be connected to the whole, the earth as an organism. Theodor Schwenk (1910–1986), a follower of Steiner's work, investigated how flow and rhythm found throughout all natural processes are mirrored in water and founded the Institute for Flow Sciences in Germany. He developed the Drop Picture Method, which could reveal the health of water by allowing it to express its innate vitality. This process involved dripping steam-distilled water, one drop at a time (up to thirty drops), on a water specimen contained in a thin layer to which glycerin is added. As each drop is introduced to the water film, a flow pattern develops in which currents are set into motion. The patterns formed were rendered visible by an optical device developed by Schwenk and then photographically recorded. When looking at the rosette architecture of the drop, Schwenk noticed how well the rosette was developed and how separate, distinct, and robust were the petals or leaves of the rosette. The accompanying photographs show examples of living water from a mountain spring, from a mountain brook in the Black Forest, and the same mountain brook water at a point downstream following the entrance of domestic sewage/industrial effluents. It's not too difficult to see how the architecture of the rosette changes from a very clear, defined, and sculptured image to one that is more blurred and, without question, less attractive. More about this method can be found online at the Institute of Flow Sciences www.stroemungsinstitut.de/tbs.htm.

Schwenk's seminal work *Sensitive Chaos* shows water's influence in all of nature's architecture: the spiral or vortex. Other examples of this architecture include beach sand vortices below a submerged stone, the spirals found in seashells, the cochlea of the human ear, the design of jellyfish, horns on an African kudu antelope, the wood grain in a tree trunk, intestinal convolutions in animals, and on and on.

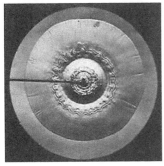

The Drop Picture Method
1). A sample of water from a mountain spring. 2). A sample of water from a mountain brook in Germany, taken below the source. 3). A sample of water from the same brook, but contaminated by sewage and industrial waste. Theodor Schwenk and Wolfram Schwenk, *Water: The Element of Life* (Gt. Barrington, MA: Anthroposophic Press, 1989). Courtesy Steiner Books.

Water is the universal solvent, able to dissolve the hardest rocks that would normally require immeasurable amounts of horsepower and hardened steel to fracture and grind. Some years ago, I purchased some large riprap from a quarry mining bluestone dolomite, a very hard rock used for road base and aggregate to make ready-mix concrete. Drilling a hole into a concrete foundation impregnated with this aggregate would be a slow, tedious, drill bit–dulling process. I deposited this rock on the eroding banks of a stream, and of course some of it spilled into the creek. A number of years later, I found some of these rocks in the creek bed and discovered that the outer skin had softened. Merely hitting this rock with a cobblestone would cause it to shatter. It now was a soft dolomite. Why?

Water is always permeated with air and gases. In the autumn, the leaves have fallen off the trees, so they are not only *not* taking in CO_2, the leaf debris in the creek water is also generating CO_2. Water (H_2O) plus carbon dioxide (CO_2) creates H_2CO_3, or carbonic acid, which can readily attack carbonate rocks like calcite or dolomite (calcium and magnesium carbonates). Over eons of time, carbonic acid also breaks down the silica-rich slates and shale that line the creek banks as well, slowly turning rock into sand with the help of the perpetual abrasive movement of the stream, even grinding larger rock into pebbles in the process.

Air and water constantly mingle in order to cocreate other manifestations of themselves. Waterfalls create water vapor, a source of moisture to nearby plants, while the air from the falls dissolved in the water is a source of oxygen for fish and macroinvertebrates. Water evaporates into air, and just as rocks in streams create stationary wave forms, the water vapor within the flowing air when it collides with a mountain range separates out in the form of clouds, one lying behind the other, wave crest after wave crest with a wave trough in between.

There is a rhythm of air and water that becomes the climate. Day and night are microcosms of summer and winter seasons, the former being when warm summer air (daytime) rises over the continents and falls over the oceans. In winter (night) the opposite occurs. What is actually happening is a fractal foundation of air/water vortices spiraling around the globe based on oceanic and continental influences, which are larger "organs" consisting of many smaller "organelles" of spirals that are created by the effects of air and water doing their dance everywhere—over deciduous forests, evergreen forests, meadows, pastures, lakes, rivers, alpine peaks, tropical lowlands, swamps, etc. All of the "organelles" are connected to one another within this great framework of the Earth as one organism constantly adjusting from chaos to order and back again

Then, factor in the moon's influence! Tree sap changes its flow based on the phases of the moon, influencing those who are attuned to such as to when to cut timber, when to plant fence posts, when to dig a well, when to plant seeds or transplants, and when to cut thistles. The moon's influence is so profound that all water bodies are affected—the seas, lakes, ponds, rivers, water-laden air, and even the water in the earth's crust. In fact, because of lunar influences, land surfaces rise and fall an average of twelve inches daily! Lunar forces even influence the bodily fluids and the endocrine or hormonal tides like ovulation and menstruation.

The sensitivity of water and its propensity to be a mediator between all of life and the cosmos in which we are immersed can be recognized, as Schwenk tells it, in the fascinating story of the California smelt, a relative of the salmon. Once yearly, smelt approach the California coast in May, awaiting the May full moon. When the tide reaches its apex on the third day following the full moon, they allow themselves to be carried to shore on the highest wave. There, females lay their eggs while males fertilize them, returning out to sea in the next receding wave. High tide reappears fourteen days later, and the smelt spawn will hatch literally minutes before being carried out to sea. They will return some years later as adults to spawn once again, three days after the full moon in May. A ritual of fertilization and procreation literally occurs at the same time within minutes every year because of lunar influence.

Even though it could be argued that water itself is not alive as it doesn't grow, digest, excrete waste, reproduce, and perform the metabolic processes of microbes, plants, and animals, it can readily be considered an organ of nature. Essentially, water is assembled in layers; that is, it's laminated and thus it possesses membranes. As water moves by flowing, these membranes expand, contract, and eventually fold over, creating vortices that vibrate rhythmically, collecting and passing on information. This then stimulates the phenomena of structured water, which is now forming and reforming, giving water the potential of having "memory." What water records is the resonance of its environment, the local topography, geology, electromagnetic influences, its pH, velocity, temperature, the electromagnetic influences, its BOD (biological oxygen demand), its COD (chemical oxygen demand), and so forth, not memories as we define them. And according to many involved in the investigation of water, one key to this is that the hydrogen bonds *between* water molecules are only one-tenth the strength of the hydrogen-oxygen bond *within* the water molecule, enabling the structure of water to resist compression, continuously turning and folding and vibrating, thus being able to retain its energy and its innate character, what Jennifer Green of the Water Research Institute of Blue Hill, Maine, calls the "wateriness of water."

Andreas Schulz of the Hagalis AG uses water crystal analysis (the Hagalis method) to evaluate a water sample's quality without adding anything to it. The water sample is initially distilled at a relatively low temperature, 158°F–176°F (70°–80°C). A portion of the sample is dried into a powdery residue, which is then reconstituted with the distilled liquid portion, placed on a glass slide, and allowed to crystallize at room temperature. The crystals formed are then photographed at room temperature.

Crystals are evaluated for their geometry, with sixty-degree angles indicating a higher quality and a tendency toward ninety-degree angles indicating poorer quality water. The crystals are also assessed for their spread, border structures, fields of darkness, strength, etc. What is being measured is not the crystalline structure of the water based on the dissolved minerals, but the actual energy and vitality of the water, which manifests as a "water crystal." Examples of these crystals can be found at www.hagalis.de.

In the same scientific vein, David Schweitzer, a researcher of blood vitality, was utilizing a dark field microscope to reveal photonic emissions and found that his investigative methods could also disclose the vitality of water. Photons were researched and recognized by German biophysicist Fritz-Albert Popp, who found that biological systems emit light. Photons are fundamental particles or waves, of electromagnetic radiation and are utilized by researchers to measure vitality in a biological system or organism, that emits photons of varying intensity in a continuous sequence. Schweitzer treated tap water with a vortex energizer and then photographed both the untreated and treated water through a polarizing filter at a magnification of 4,000x. His photographs showed a remarkable difference in the photonic crystalline design of the water after it was energized and structured.

Paolo Consigli, MD, author of *Water, Pure and Simple*, states, "Like all living things, water is a self-organizing system: a drop of water is a universe unto itself, containing substances and living creatures, generating and responding to vibrations, perpetuating the same patterns and sequences that we find on a larger scale in our own bodies, in the Earth, indeed throughout the entire universe."

Alick Bartholomew, in his prescient work *The Spiritual Life of Water: Its Power and Purpose*, proposes that water can store information because

FIGURE 8.3

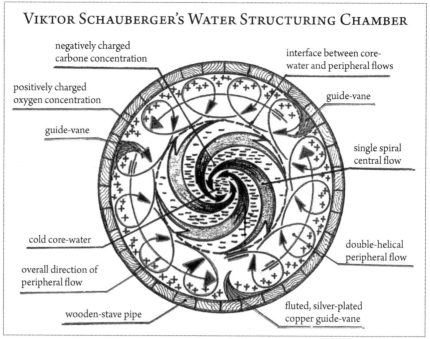

Alick Bartholomew, *The Spiritual Life of Water* (Rochester, VT: Park Street Press, 2010). Copyright Callum Coats.

as water naturally flows in spirals and vortices, its molecules organize themselves into the structures necessary for it to carry constructive information. These microclusters of vibrating dynamic energy centers are constantly receiving and transmitting energy from every contact the water body makes. The vertical movement creates polymer liquid crystalline chains, and the laminar structure that generates dynamic energy from the interaction of their plane surfaces against each other. The more powerful the vertical action, the greater the storage capacity of information (like adding "memory" to a computer).... The clusters have the ability to store vibrational impressions or imprints. If these are beneficial, they may be able to restore healthy resonance. ... If they are the imprints of toxins or pollutants ... they may be carriers of disharmony and disease.

So, this water molecule is restless, asymmetrical, and unstable, which compels it to search for order and organized symmetries. Perhaps the grandfather of Western water wizards, Viktor Schauberger was born June 30, 1885, in Ulrichsberg, Austria. Schauberger became intrigued with the characteristics of water movement as a youngster, and he eventually grasped enough understanding about water dynamics to devise an ingenious system for floating logs upstream, not unlike how fish can remain motionless in the middle of a swift current and then effortlessly and rapidly swim upstream against the strong rapids. Schauberger concluded that water has a spiral design, allowing it to generate energy at its center. The combination of the spiral vortex and the centripetal concentration formed a natural source of collecting energy, allowing fish to remain still in a current or to use that energy to effectively swim seemingly effortlessly against the current, even jump a six-foot waterfall!

So what does all of this have to do with ecological and profitable agriculture? Agriculture overuses and abuses much of our most precious resource. The amount of water on Earth hasn't changed since the dinosaurs drank it millions of years ago. Although we live on a watery blue planet, 97 percent of our water is salty and 2 percent is locked up in ice caps and glaciers. That leaves less than 1 percent to grow our crops, supply drinking and bathing water, and cool our power plants. Two-thirds of our freshwater is used to grow food, and with 83 million extra people appearing each year upon the earth, we will have to find much better ways to improve our irrigation techniques and even the quality of our water.

Naturally occurring mineral salts include carbonates, bicarbonates, calcium, magnesium, selenium, boron, sulfur, iron, and manganese, a short list of what can be found in irrigation water. It can be challenging to grow a crop adequately with irrigated water without stressing the plants or creating excessive mineral salt precipitates in the soil that discourage the soil's biology or adversely affect its physical structure (density, pore space, aggregates). In fact, a lot of arable land has been rendered unproductive due to a build-up of irrigation water salts.

Clearly, soil management strategies are the primary key here to avoiding mineral salt build-ups, which means improving the organic content of soils as well as the infiltration rate through conservation farming strategies that include cover crops, tight rotations, residue management, and soil aerification. Other activities include less wasteful irrigation methods such as micro-irrigation, whereby only a small portion of the soil is wetted, precisely where the plants are growing. Also known as drip or trickle irrigation, water is supplied at a low rate but a higher frequency. For trees, this method can be modified to use "spitters" (microsprayers) or "bubblers" (small vertical standpipes), both of which usually require a small, level basin in the soil under each tree. Benefits to this practice include less mineral salt build-up in the soil and less water waste.

Where enlivened water strategies might help is because even though water waste can be reduced via smarter irrigation techniques and equipment, the lack of *quality* of that water could still be of paramount importance to crop yields or crop stress reduction.

Certain devices attached to water systems have proven to be of real value in making water much more efficient in irrigation and decontamination, and in improving odors and flavors, not creating scale or slag on heating elements and in appliances, holding tanks, cooling towers, and the plumbing systems. The premise of these devices—be they implosion designs or magnetic or electronic frequency generators—is that their influence on the water molecule is such that the large clusters of water molecules, which are created by the magnetic attraction of water molecules to one another, can be broken. The hydrogen-oxygen bonds are the reason for this, and clusters continually form and break apart depending on what external influences they are subject to, as well as the internal forces at work.

A company in California that markets a magnetic ring design has demonstrated in a trial that with their Magnetron System monitored by tensiometers, an almond orchard showed rapid moisture gains in five feet depths. A tensiometer is typically a permanently installed device that

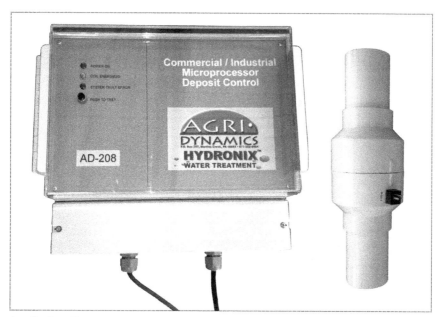

Jennifer Barnett

measures the tension by which soil holds on to water, thus disclosing the suction that occurs as the water infiltrates or doesn't.

Another device I have utilized is the Hydronix™ device, invented by Nathan Jeffries. With this device, water passes through a reaction chamber, basically a sleeve of pipe wrapped with a wire coil. The sleeve is spliced into the plumbing, and the two electrical terminals on the sleeve plug into a microprocessor that emits a pyramidal (not square) wave form of frequency and amplitude that bombards both the water molecules and the suspended minerals that readily clump together. The Hydronix units have allowed large pulp mills to continue to operate when they normally would have to shut down for thirty to sixty days for users to descale the slag on their cooling towers. It encourages mineral-rich water to percolate more readily into the greenhouse vegetable beds, which usually have poor percolation due to salt build-up. It stopped the water cups in poultry houses from dripping due to lime scale build-up, causing water loss and wet manure (odors/flies). Both the Hydronix unit and the magnetic coil reduce surface tension of the water, decluster the water molecules, and restructure the water so that it can be enlivened, or made more biologically acceptable.

In the biodynamic community, there are many farms, municipalities, parks, and waste water treatment facilities using flowforms—sculptured, cascading shelves of dual pools of water reservoirs. Flowforms cause water to circulate

Peter Bacchus, *Biodynamic Pasture Management* (Austin, TX: Acres U.S.A., 2013), 105

horizontally back and forth between the two cups as it drops down a cascading stairway. The design's purpose is to create an "organ" that is defined by Rudolf Steiner's description/definition in his August 17, 1916, lecture. Every living organism, he said, receives substances that are accepted and digested. The organism responds with certain secretive processes, is nourished, grows, and eventually reproduces itself.

The flowform is designed is to encourage the water taken in to relate to all surfaces—air, gases, other water, suspended minerals, microbes, etc.—in an intimate way so that rhythmic, pulsating movements are generated. Opening up the water to multiple forces—biological, physical, chemical, as well as cosmic forces such as the sun and moon and celestial bodies—can then be transported downstream into the environment to enhance regenerative processes.

Water from flowforms was found to enhance root length and mass more than water from aerated sources, especially if the seeds of the plants were sowed at the new moon. Other studies showed that flowform water enhanced wheat germination by 11 percent. Similar to Andreas Shulz's work as well as Theodor Schwenk's analysis on water crystallization, microscopically analyzed flowform water showed cross-like $CaCO_3$ crystals, whereas the aerated control water formed ring-like amorphous forms around centers.

Other water wizards have been developing devices based on Schauberger's implosion research and Wilhelm Reich's orgone energy research. German engineer Eckhard Weber developed a Weber-Isis Water Activator that has multiple residential industrial, and agricultural applications, including the cleansing of ponds and lakes of eutrophication.

Roland Plocher, a German mechanic, developed some rock dust remedies treated with orgone accumulators that become soil and plant biocatalysts and water purification additives. The device he designed was an energy-collecting funnel several yards tall that collects the orgone, or bioenergy, in the air, accumulating it in the funnel and making it denser. The orgone "informs" the carrier material (quartz powder), which leads to a substantial increase in oxygen where the rock dust is applied.

Hans-Helmut Preisel, a German mechanical engineer inspired by Plocher's work, founded the Alvito Company. He created a meticulously defined arrangement of permanent magnets and reacted-upon green clay that is integrated into the water vitalizer. The devices are quite popular in Europe for addressing hard water challenges.

The Elisa Energy System, invented by Gebhard Bader-Donner, uses a plumbing grid design in which the water passes through stainless-steel sheathing and then through hermetically sealed crystal chambers containing gold and precious and semi-precious gems that impart high vibrational frequencies, finally passing through a layer of pine, itself sheathed in copper, to finish the crystalline structured water. This system has received rave reviews by bakeries and physicians.

My personal belief is that these devices can be quite effective in remediating troublesome water, especially for washing and cleaning or irrigation. However, there are times when high iron or manganese loads can really get in the way of the efficiency of some of these technologies, especially for residential, barn, milkhouse, and stable applications. Under those conditions, aerification may be a preferred addition to the treatment, causing the reduced elements like iron, sulfur, and manganese to oxidize, thus encouraging them to precipitate out of the water solution prior to their arrival at the enlivening or cluster

TABLE 8.2

Comprehensive Water Analysis Parameters
Ideal Levels of the Following Contaminants should Read "Not Detected"

Analysis Performed	Max Containment Level (Mg/L)	Detection Level	Ideal Level
Total Coliform	Presence	Presence	Absence
Inorganic Chemicals:			
Metals:			
Aluminum	0.2	0.1	Not Detected
Arsenic	0.05	0.010	Not Detected
Barium	2	0.30	Not Detected
Cadmium	0.005	0.002	Not Detected
Chromium	0.1	0.010	Not Detected
Copper	1.3	0.004	Not Detected
Iron	0.3	0.020	***
Lead	0.015	0.002	Not Detected
Manganese	0.05	0.0004	***
Mercury	0.002	0.001	Not Detected
Nickel	———	0.02	Not Detected
Selenium	0.05	0.020	Not Detected
Silver	0.1	0.002	Not Detected
Sodium	———	1	***
Zinc	5	0.004	***
Other Inorganics/Physical Factors:			
Alkalinity (Total as CaCO3)	———	20	***
Chloride	250	5.0	***
Fluoride	4	0.5	Not Detected
Nitrate as N	10	0.5	Not Detected
Nitrite as N	1	0.5	Not Detected
Sulfate	250	5.0	***
Hardness	100	10	***
pH	6.5–8.5		7.0
Total Dissolved Solids	500	20	***
Turbidity	1.0	0.1	Not Detected

***Should be less than maximum contaminant level and preferable within parameter ranges closest to "Detection Levels"

National Testing Laboratories, Cleveland, Ohio.

TABLE 8.3

COMPREHENSIVE WATER ANALYSIS PARAMETERS
IDEAL LEVELS OF THE FOLLOWING CONTAMINANTS
SHOULD READ "NOT DETECTED"

Organic Chemicals/Trihalomethanes

Bromoform	1,2,3- Trichloropropane	Tetrachloroethene (PCE)
Dibromochlormethane	Methyl-Tert-Butyl-Ether	1,1,2- Trichloroethane
Vinyl Chloride	Bromodichloromethane	Toluene
Trichloroethene (TCE)	Total THMs	Chloroform
1, 1, 1,-Trichlorocthane	Carbon Tetrachloride	Benzene
Chlorobenzene	1,4-Dichlorobenzene	1,2-Dichloroethane
2-Chlorotoluene	Bromobenzene	1,1-Dichloroethene
Dibromomethane	Chloroethane	Bromomethane
Dichlorodifluoromethane	4-Chlorotoluene	Chloromethane
Cis-1,2-Dichloroethene	1,2-Dichlorobenzene	Dibromochloropropane
Trans-1,3-Dichloropropene	1,1-Dichloroethane	1,3-Dichlorobenzene
1,1-Dichloropropene	Dichloromethane	Trans-1,2-Dichloroethene
Ethylenedibromide (EDB)	Cis-1,3-Dichloropropene	1,2,4- Trichlorobenzene
1,1,2,2- Tetrachloroethane	1,3-Dichloropropane	Trichlorofluoromethane
1,2,3- Trichlorobenzene	Styrene	Xylene

Organic Chemicals, Pesticides, Herbicides, and PCBs

Alachlor	Atrazine	2,4-D
Aldrin	Dichloran	Chlordane
Endrin	Heptachlor	Dieldrin
Hexachlorobenzene	Hexachlorocyclopenta-	Heptachlor Epoxide
Methoxychlor	diene	Lindane
Silvex (2,4,5-TP)	PCBs	Pentachloronitrobenzene
Trifluralin	Simazine	Toxaphene

***Should be less than maximum contaminant level, and preferably within parameter ranges closest to "Detection Levels."

National Testing Laboratories, Cleveland, Ohio.

device. I experienced this, having had water also high in iron and manganese. The tell-tale indication that the Hydronix unit was performing was the glass door of the shower stall. Typically it accumulated a soap-mineral film that literally had to be scraped off with a scouring pad. Following the Hydronix installation there was an improvement, although I was still not completely satisfied. I then installed an oxidation system, called the Iron Genie, which removed both iron and manganese. Consequently, the film on the glass door could be rubbed off with one's hand.

Installing the oxidation appliance alone would not have addressed the calcium-magnesium deposits, causing the scale, however.

Although water softeners can readily address these issues, they are not always economically viable for irrigation systems or even livestock operations that consume large quantities of water due to the continued need for salt used in the brine tanks. That being said, water consumption for animals and humans needs to take in to consideration health-limiting factors, such as bacteria, nitrates, heavy metals like arsenic, troublesome elements like iron, manganese and sulfates, industrial/agricultural chemicals, low pH, total dissolved solids, etc. My suggestion is to first remove these contaminants, then structure the water if livestock, pets, or people are in the equation. I also believe water that's "scrubbed" first will structure more effectively in an implosion-type device. Needless to say, on farms consuming a lot of water for irrigation, utilizing both options may not be cost effective.

The water report in table 8.3 is from National Testing Laboratories, a certified laboratory that analyzes water for multiple water quality issues, and I would encourage everyone to get a comprehensive analysis in order to know what, if any, remediation is necessary to drink, bathe, and irrigate with assurance.

The bottom line, however, is that enlivened water is what nature automatically creates and what healthy biological systems apparently need.

Systemic Acquired Resistance and Induced Systemic Resistance

Plants have the ability to produce an almost endless number of chemical variations on a single chemical structure.

—David Hoffman, Phytochemistry: Molecular Veriditas

S YSTEMIC acquired resistance (SAR) is essentially an "immune response" generated by plants triggered by a stressor (called an elicitor). This trigger could be an insect bite, a fungal or bacterial disease infection, a nematode challenge, or even the overgrazing of herbivorous animals. The plant then orchestrates a gene cascade that begins the process of synthesizing defensive compounds of low molecular weight, such as chlorogenic acid, pisitan, umbelliferone, and about 350 more substances (called phytoalexins) found in thirty plant families. Phytoalexins can be found in the roots, stems, leaves, and fruit.

For example, legumes rich in isoflavones, or isoflavonoids like daidzein and genistein (also called phytoestrogens), are the raw materials of phytoalexins that deter fungi like mildews that can attack legumes.

In the "coevolutionary arms race" between plants and their adversaries, plants that are susceptible to pests may be so because the pathogen or insect apparently either has adapted to tolerate the accumulated phytoalexins, suppresses the production of them, detoxifies them, or avoids triggering or eliciting them when attacking the plant. Additionally, there are other reasons why, at times, this plant protection by phytoalexins fails. Research has found that certain compounds that suppressed the production of defensive phytoalexins were either low molecular weight polysaccharides (long chain sugars) or glycopeptides (sugar-proteins). Evidently, these suppressor compounds are associated with specific genes being expressed by the plant, creating these phytoalexin suppressors. Plant breeding, including transgenic (GMO) manipulation, may contribute to creating plant cultivars with these gene-expressing handicaps that invite the production of these suppressor polysaccharides and glycopeptides. Other defense compounds produced by plants that some scientists consider not to be phytoalexins but are nevertheless plant protectants are enzymes like chitinases, B-1-3 glucanases, and peroxidases; salicylic acid (aspirin); jasmonates (hormones); and active oxygen species (free radicals).

Other than a pest attack, many factors can elicit a phytoalexin response: ethylene, fatty acids, polypeptides, inorganic salts, low temperatures, ultraviolet radiation and even some fungicides. Additionally, plants under normal stress of drought growing in clay loam soils versus sandy loam soils had higher amounts of beta-carotene, vitamin C, folic acid, lycopene, and phenols like chlorogenic acid. Clay loam soils are higher in minerals than sandy soils. Minerals are necessary for plants to synthesize the phytoalexin compounds.

This understanding of SAR can now allow us to implement induced systemic resistance, or ISR. Just as vaccinating an animal elicits an immune reaction against a pathogen without creating the disease, ISR "tricks" the plant into sensing that it is being challenged by a pest when there is none. The signals generated by this ISR "vaccine" can initiate a gene cascade involving as many as twenty genes to produce a single phytoalexin. There are multiple substances that are used to create an ISR response: non-pathogenic bacteria (such as *Bacillus* spp.); chemicals that are produced by infected plants (such as resveratrol, a stilbene found in Japanese knotweed); certain terpenes, phenols, and alkaloids; compost teas; ionic minerals (such as Sea-Crop); kelp extracts; and humic acid extracts. Much research would be necessary to ascertain what specific substances in these many compounds cause what kinds of phytoalexin production and in what kinds of plants.

Some interesting research conducted at University of Arizona found that they could significantly increase the amounts of plant phytoalexins via "electro-elicitation," that is, subjecting plants to non-lethal levels of electric current. Pea roots that were thus electrically treated with 30–100 mA of current produced thirteen times higher amounts of (+)- pisatin phytoalexin than did the non-electrically elicited controls. Similar results were found to occur in the seedlings, roots, or cell suppression cultures of fenugreek (*Trigonella foenum-graecum*), barrel medic (*Medicago truncatula*), red clover (*Trifolium pratense*), chickpea (*Cicer arietinum*), and *Arabidopsis thaliana*, a type of mustard or cress.

My father, Aurelio Brunetti, was a master tomato grower. He always removed the suckers that would sprout out of the "crotch," or juncture between the stem and the branches. For him the advantage of this practice was not only to grow erect tomatoes on a trellis or stake; he felt that the pruning invigorated the tomatoes.

Rena and Aurelio Brunetti

Research published in *Nature* has substantiated Aurelio's "hunch." Both herbivory (insect) and mechanical wounding initiate electrical signal transmissions, mediated by two proteins. The electrical signal then spreads to neighboring organs where the biosynthesis of jasmonate hormone is induced, which in turn triggers jasmonate-dependent defense responses, namely phytoalexin production. Curiously, similar results occurred by applying electrical pulses that mimicked the plant's innate electrical signals.*

ISR treatments, however "generic" (as are the previous foliar examples), provide the advantage that they activate *multiple* mechanisms for pest resistance, rather than only a *single* mechanism for pest resistance, such as would be the case in genetic engineering research and strategies where manipulation of limited gene expression yields a narrow benefit.

The plant secondary metabolites (PSMs) referred to in chapter 3 number in the tens of thousands. These compounds include terpenes, phenols, alkaloids, sulfated amino acids, and sulfated fatty acids. Their purposes are: 1) to attract pollinators as perfume and color, 2) to create green leaf volatiles to attract predatory insects and to warn other plants about a threat in the neighborhood, 3) to act as built-in inhibitors or repellents against would-be adversaries, 4) to be converted to another class of compounds called phytoalexins—biochemicals that are synthesized as toxins or repellents—to be made by the plant quickly when that plant has been attacked, like an immune reaction, and 5) to act as a sunscreen against ultraviolet radiation.

As perfumes or green leaf volatiles, PSMs act as molecular messengers or communication molecules to other plant companions and to would-be adversaries that are warned to go elsewhere to feed. Think of this action as a Paul Revere–style sounding of the alarm to the militia of predatory insects alerting them to the presence of parasites that are prey for lady beetles, predatory wasps, hornets, ground beetles, lacewings, nematodes, mantids, or others.

Inhibitins are essentially built-in repellents that discourage a plant's enemies from taking too much. Inhibitins might explain why some plants can be only slightly damaged versus destroyed. The same is true with the phytoalexins, which are actually immune responses that cause a plant to synthesize specific PSMs based on the specific proteins encoded on the saliva of a parasitic insect.

All of these innate or synthesized PSM substances depend on a few important requirements, specifically minerals in the soil rhizosphere and

---

* Alexander Christmann and Erwin Grill, "Plant Biology: Electric Defence," *Nature* 500, no. 7463 (August 22, 2013): 404–5.

plant varieties. Minerals, and especially trace elements, are required for the plant enzyme systems to manufacture these PSMs. Through genetic selection via hybridization we have reduced our crops' ability to protect themselves in exchange for the benefit of high yields. Consequently, the genes required to put in motion a cascade of biochemical reactions that actually make a plant resistant to pests are no longer active.

An interesting research paper titled "Declining Fruit and Vegetable Nutrient Composition: What is the Evidence?" authored by Donald Davis of the Biochemical Institute, University in Wichita, Kansas, suggests strongly that as we have been manipulating our crops to be larger and to grow faster there are consistent correlations between yields and the concentration of minerals, proteins, and vitamins, with a range of 5–40 percent in declines. This is referred to as the "genetic dilution effect."

Modern crops, because they can grow larger in a shorter period of time— as well as being dependent upon higher amounts of N-P-K fertilizers and pesticides—have less time to absorb nutrients from the soil. Also, excess levels of N-P-K often interfere with a plant's ability to take up nutrients. Industrial farming practices, which have created topsoil degradation and loss, have also led to soil mineral depletion. Soils lower in humus or organic matter are less able to assist plants in taking up nutrients, primarily because humus is the digestive system of the plant, necessary for absorption of nutrients.

Another research report that verifies this nutritional evisceration of crops comes from the article "The Mineral Depletion of Foods Available to U.S. as a Nation" by David Thomas, M. Sc. D.I.C.* The report demonstrates precisely what its title suggests: the evisceration of crop minerals through modern agricultural practices.

A remarkable study on how plants must communicate with their predatory allies when challenged by a parasitic pest, titled "Restoring a Maize Root Signal that Attracts Insect Killing Nematodes to Control a Major Pest," was published in 2009 by Jörg Degenhardt et al.† Apparently, Western corn rootworm can be controlled by "entomopathogenic predatory nematodes" that infect and kill these voracious root pests. Farmers will know these beneficials as roundworms. Unfortunately, because of selected plant breeding strategies, most North American corn varieties have lost the ability to emit a specific communication molecule (a sesquiterpene called

---

* David Thomas, "The Mineral Depletion of Foods Available to U.S. as a Nation (1940–2002): A Review of the 6th Edition of McCance and Widdowson," *Nutrition and Health* 19 (2007): 21–55.
† Jörg Degenhardt et al., "Restoring a Maize Root Signal that Attracts Insect Killing Nematodes to Control a Major Pest," *PNAS* 106, no. 32 (August 11, 2009): 13213–3218.

Microbes Give Insects Resistance to Pesticides

Whether academic institutions, corporations that manufacture pesticides, government agencies like the USDA and EPA, or farmers, we are not winning the war against insects or diseases by trying to "kill the bastards" with increasingly toxic and frequent applications of biocides.

One of the reasons humans are failing to contain insects with pesticides is that insects have successfully recruited the assistance of microbes that can detoxify the poisons. The typical process of pesticide resistance takes many generations and involves the modification of the insect's genes. But ask yourself, how long is an insect generation?

Meanwhile, scientists in Japan have discovered that a bean insect, *Riptortus pedestris*, has found a quick route to becoming instantly resistant to insecticides by ingesting the right kind of bacteria. This insect and related stink bugs harbor up to 100 million mutualistic bacteria of the genus Burkholderia in their gut. These bacteria are able to degrade and thus detoxify the insecticide Fenitrothion, used regularly in sugar cane fields.

These stink bugs actually acquire the bacteria from the soil, and amazingly the population of these insecticide-detoxifying bacteria skyrockets in the field's soil from an undetectable level if Fenitrothion is not sprayed to 80 percent of the culturable bacterial counts after this insecticide has been applied. These findings strongly suggest that symbiont-mediated (via bacterial partnerships) insecticide resistance may develop even in the absence of pests, rapidly establishing itself within a single insect species and potentially migrating across other species of insects, as has occurred with antibiotic resistance between bacterial species that are shared by animals and humans.[*]

The bright side of these findings is that perhaps the most efficient and rapid way of decontaminating our soils and aquatic ecosystems of the thousands of tons of pesticides that have been applied is to ensure that we have a very strong microbial community in the soil that can "learn" from one another how to detoxify the landscape of fungicides, insecticides, herbicides, and nematacides.

---

[*] Yoshitomo Kikuchi et al., "Symbiont-Mediated Insecticide Resistance," *PNAS* 109, no. 22 (March 2012): http://dx.doi.org/10.1073/pnas.1200231109.

(E)-B-caryophyllene) that actually recruits the nematodes, thus allowing the rootworms to feed on corn roots without predation.

The report relates that attempts to control the rootworm by "seeding" the field with nematodes have been largely ineffective, and furthermore fields that grew corn varieties that were able to emit the sesquiterpene were five-fold higher in predatory nematodes than varieties unable to produce the signal.

To restore the signal to the vulnerable corn variety, it was transformed with a gene from oregano (*Origanum vulgare*), resulting in emissions of the key chemical (E)-B-caryophyllene sesquiterpene. The result was that the transformed plants suffered significantly less root damage and had 60 percent fewer adult beetles emerge than non-emitting varieties of the crop. In other words, nematodes cannot do their job of eliminating the rootworm pests until the corn sends the proper molecular signals to them via the carophyllene terpenoid.

A similar comparison pertains to resistance by crucifers—broccoli, cabbage, turnips, etc.—to downy mildew. In this case plants convert sinigrin, a glucosinolate ($C_4H_5S_2O_4N$), into the finished PSM "fungicide" called allyl isothiocyanate (C_4H_5SN). Varieties resistant to downy mildews contained 630 mcg/gram dry weight of the allyl isothiocyanate compared to susceptible varieties, which contained 21–450 mcg/gram dry weight of allyl isothiocyanate. Perhaps high levels of this key PSM explain why some cultivars bred for size or shipping advantages could be more prone to diseases than their heirloom relatives. Conversely, hybrids bred for greater disease resistance can be examples of improving genetic vigor.

Another fascinating experiment was conducted by A. Kessler and R. Haletschke of the Department of Ecology and Evolutionary Biology of Cornell University and C. Diezell and I. T. Baldwin of the Department of Molecular Ecology at the Max-Planck Institute for Chemical Ecology in Germany. The researchers conducted an experiment in which sagebrush (Artemisia) plants adjacent to native tobacco (Nicotiana) plants were mechanically clipped in order to release green leaf volatiles (GLVs) such as methyl jasmonate and a bouquet of terpenes. This is called plant priming. Such an intervention caused a release of green leaf volatiles from the sagebrush, which in turn accelerated the production of trypsin proteinase inhibitors in the tobacco plants. This resulted in reduced damage to the tobacco plants by the *Manduca sexta* caterpillars that fed on those plants previously exposed to the sagebrush volatiles, and it also contributed to a higher mortality rate on young caterpillars.[*]

---

[*] A. Kessler, R. Haletschke, C. Diezell, and I. T. Baldwin, "Priming of Plant Defense Responses in Nature by Airborne Signaling between *Artemisia tridentata* and *Nicotiana attenuate*," Oecologia 148 (2006): 280–92.

INDIRECT VERSUS DIRECT RESPONSES

The plant response in the corn plant is what is known as systemic acquired resistance, where a protein found in the saliva of the pest bite is recognized, which in turn trips a signaling molecule (called an oxylipin), such as jasmonic acid. This causes a gene cascade that then initiates an external defense system in which green leaf volatiles are emitted into the soil environment, attracting predatory nematodes to come and dine on root worm larvae.

In the second example, the systemic acquired resistance (SAR) is actually induced (induced systemic resistance, or ISR) by the volatiles emitted from the sagebrush that was clipped, causing an internal defense system, whereby a feeding and digestive compound called trypsin protease inhibitors were made by the tobacco plant, reducing feeding pressure and actually causing caterpillar mortality.

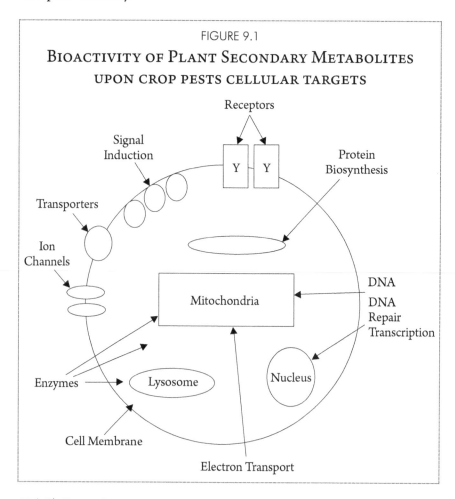

FIGURE 9.1

BIOACTIVITY OF PLANT SECONDARY METABOLITES UPON CROP PESTS CELLULAR TARGETS

There are an estimated 1,700 known volatile compounds from ninety plant families, yet these only constitute just 1 percent of the plant secondary metabolites! This may explain why "resistance is futile" when it comes to utilizing PSM's plant protectants. Not only are there very many volatile compounds, there are also the innumerable non-volatile compounds, such as the phenolic family of flavonoids, tannins, lignans, and stilbenes or the phenylpropanoids, steroids, sulfated amino acids, and sulfated fatty acids. These are all extremely complex chemical compounds, not isolates of an individual poison such as are manufactured by pesticide corporations.

As figure 9.1 illustrates, there are many different sites of potential bioactivity of PSMs upon the crop pests' cellular targets, such as the cell membrane, the mitochondria, ion channels, electron transport chains, and so on.

Moreover, the odor blends of attacked plants comprise more than two hundred separate compounds that directly influence herbivores' behavior, attract the predatory enemies of herbivore pests, cause a phytoalexin response to synthesize new biochemicals that protect the plant, and also release from the plant "pantry" its repellent substances that deter feeding.

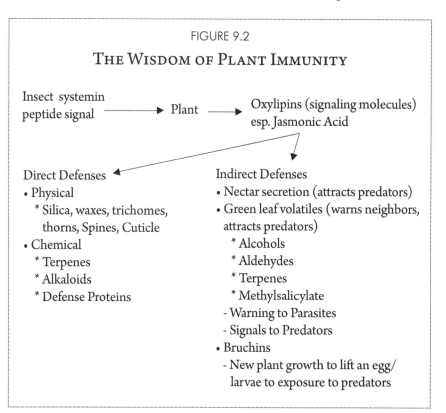

FIGURE 9.2

THE WISDOM OF PLANT IMMUNITY

Insect systemin peptide signal → Plant → Oxylipins (signaling molecules) esp. Jasmonic Acid

Direct Defenses
• Physical
  * Silica, waxes, trichomes, thorns, Spines, Cuticle
• Chemical
  * Terpenes
  * Alkaloids
  * Defense Proteins

Indirect Defenses
• Nectar secretion (attracts predators)
• Green leaf volatiles (warns neighbors, attracts predators)
  * Alcohols
  * Aldehydes
  * Terpenes
  * Methylsalicylate
  - Warning to Parasites
  - Signals to Predators
• Bruchins
  - New plant growth to lift an egg/ larvae to exposure to predators

Even browsing and grazing animals, wild and domestic, are subject to the rules of nature, such as not to overconsume plants by destructive grazing and browsing behavior.

Elephants feeding on mopane trees (*Colophospermum mopane*) and giraffes feeding on acacias are eventually discouraged from overeating because the individual trees begin to alter their chemistries as they are being browsed. Neighboring trees, which are being sent PSM information about the presence of browsers in the area, begin to alter their plant chemistry preventatively. Much of the overgrazed rangeland in the western United States is now overgrown with plants very high in secondary metabolites, such as leafy spurge, sagebrush, knapweed, etc. This is nature's method of protecting the landscape from animals reducing their favorite foods until they graze it down to bare soils.

So, both a system acquired (or internal) response generated by plants themselves and an induced (or external) response generated by human manipulation (such as a foliar spray) can incite both direct defenses, producing toxins or repellents to the pests, and indirect defenses, or a "calling to arms" of allies such as predatory nematodes or wasps.

FIGURE 9.3

AN INDIRECT DEFENSE CASCADE

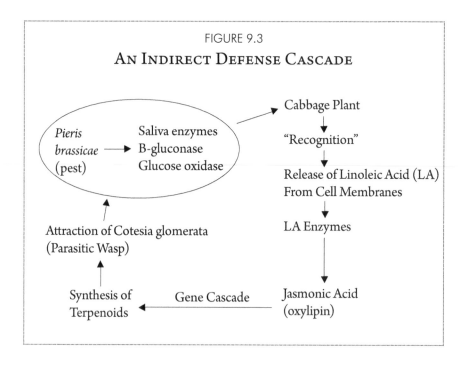

COMBINED INTERNAL/EXTERNAL RESPONSES

A defense that is both an internal/external response is what is known as Bruchin formation (see figure 9.2). This phenomenon occurs when eggs from a pest are deposited in a location on the plant that isn't very visible because the insect that laid them wants to keep them hidden from its enemies. A Bruchin formation is new plant growth that is produced specifically to lift either newly hatched larvae or the eggs themselves to exposure to sunlight, which can desiccate the eggs, or make them visible to predators to consume the eggs or the larvae. The plant actually spawns growth to repel the predator.

ESSENTIAL OILS

PSMs are powerful controllers of both insects and diseases, especially a class of compounds called applied terpenoids. A study titled "Antibiotic Properties of Essential Oils"* studied fifty essential oils and their effects on twenty-five test bacteria. The results were amazing. All fifty essential oils inhibited the growth of at least one bacterium; forty-one essential oils inhibited the growth of five or more bacteria; thirty-three essential oils inhibited ten or more bacteria; and ten oils inhibited twenty or more bacteria.

The top ten essential oils that achieved these results were:

Angelica	25 bacteria
Bay	24 bacteria
Cinnamon	23 bacteria
Clove	23 bacteria
Thyme	23 bacteria
Bitter almond	23 bacteria
Marjoram	22 bacteria
Pimento	22 bacteria
Geranium	21 bacteria
Lovage	20 bacteria

Studies conducted in Brazil and Italy confirmed these results: "Antimicrobial Activity of Secondary Metabolites and Lectins from Plants," Departmento de Bioquimica, Universidade Federal de Pernambuco, Av. Prof. Moraes Rego s/n 50670-420 Recife, Brazil; and "Antimicrobial activity of Plant Essential Oils" by B. Biavati, et al., Dept. of Agroenvironmental Science and Technology, University of Bologna, Italy. In the Italian study both bacteria and fungi (yeasts) were tested. There was a 75–100 percent inhibition of

---

* "Antibiotic Properties of Essential Oils," *International Journal of Food Microbiology* 5 (1987): 165–80.

both yeast and bacteria from Spanish oregano, oregano, rosemary, thyme, (*T. capitatus, T. vulgaris*) and savory (*S. coneifolia* and *S. hortensis*).

My own company initiated several terpenoid studies to be conducted in Canada. One was a field trial on conventionally grown greenhouse Lebanese cucumbers for the control of both two-spotted spider mites and downy mildew. This trial was overseen by an agronomic consultant, Jean Brunet. Controls on most insects, sucking and chewing, were established, namely: aphids, caterpillars, tarnished plant bug, chinch bugs, scale, thrips, flea beetles, Colorado potato beetle (except stage 3 larvae), striped cucumber beetle, and two-spotted spider mites. The cucumber trial was remarkably effective, using a 1–2 percent dilution of terpenoids and sprayed on the conventionally grown potted plants. Results were 100 percent for both pests with a residual affect for nine to ten days. In 2013 another formula was created, and this time the residual effect against mites lasted at least two and a half weeks at a time when there were heavy spider mite infestations on the controls. Also, the very same formula arrested the growth of downy and powdery mildews, suggesting that the behavior of this product was both fungicidal and insecticidal.

Magnolia trees often acquire black sooty mold, a result of sugary exudates from scale (*Neolecanium cornuparvum*). Applying the diluted terpenoids

Agri-Dynamics

only twice, about ten to fourteen days apart, yielded excellent results on both the scale and the mold. Botrytis control on peony leaves was also just as impressive.

Another set of trials were conducted in 2011, also on Lebanese cucumbers, for downy mildew and two-spotted spider mites. Tables 9.1–9.4 indicate that the terpenoid was competitive in efficacy as a conventional insecticide. Likewise, with control of downy mildew, results of efficacy were impressive, except that it was obvious that between September 27 and October there was a spike in disease incidence until spraying, at which time there was a sharp decrease as monitored on October 3. Another spray should have been applied after October 3 to keep pace with the systemic fungicide, which indicates that as a foliar product only, regular applications are warranted every seven to ten days for at least four to five sequences until the season of mildew wanes.

PLANT RESPONSES—GROW OR DEFEND

The basic distinctions between systemic acquired resistance (SAR) and induced systemic resistance (ISR) is that SAR is brought on by pathogens whereas ISR is incited by either non-pathogenic bacteria or biochemical stimula to "trick" a plant into a response, just as a vaccine initiates an immune response in animals without actually introducing the disease. ISRs can be provided from a variety of sources: compost teas, industrial yogurt, *Bacillus subtilis* species, streptomyces species, trichoderma species, terpenes, or other botanicals like neem oil, milk, etc.

TABLE 9.1

GREENHOUSE CUCUMBERS IN POTS

MEAN NO. OF SPOTS FROM POWDERY MILDEW PER LEAF, ACCORDING TO TREATMENTS, USE RATES AND DATES

Spray Dates: September 15, September 22, and October 1, 2011 (Canada)

Treatment Names and Use Rates	Sept. 19	Sept. 22	Sept. 27	Oct. 1	Oct. 3	Oct.11
Untreated Check	2.2	4.1	7.6	9.8	15.1	20.3
Phyto-Guard 1% v/v	0.8	0.1	0.6	1.5	0.4	6.2
Phyto-Guard 1% v/v & X-Tend @ 0.5% v/v	1.0	0.4	0.2	3.9	1.0	5.7
Phyto-Guard @ 2% v/v	1.2	0.5	0.5	1.4	0.3	1.0
Phyto-Plus @ 1% v/v	0.6	0.2	0.3	1.2	0.4	5.7
Phyto-Plus @ 1% v/v & X-Tend @ 0.5% v/v	0.0	0.0	0.1	0.3	0.6	6.1
NOVA @ 34 g/100 L alternating with Rhapsody 1.5L/100L	0.9	0.9	0.1	0.5	0.2	0.0

* Seven-day intervals are optimal for complete disease interruption.

A plant's potential dilemma is to "grow" or "defend." Energy is required to do both, but if plant nutrition is optimal, then plants have enough energy to both grow and defend, and thus both SAR or ISR do not thwart the plants' genetic potential to produce a flavorful, nutritious leaf; tuber; or fruit with great shelf life.

TABLE 9.2
GREENHOUSE CUCUMBERS IN POTS
MEAN NUMBER OF DEAD EGGS CM^2 PER LEAF ACCORDING TO TREATMENTS, USE RATES, AND DATES
Spray Dates: July 4, July 11, August 2011 (Canada)

Treatment Names and Use Rates	July 7	July 13	July 19	July 28	August 3
Untreated Check	0.0	0.1	0.1	0.1	0.2
Phyto-Guard @ 1% v/v & X-Tend @ 0.5% v/v	0.2	0.8	0.7	0.1	0.1
Phyto-Guard @ 1.5% v/v & X-Tend @ 0.5% v/v	0.1	0.4	0.1	0.1	0.1
Phyto-Guard @ 1.5% v/v & X-Tend @ 0.5% v/v	0.4	1.0	0.5	0.2	0.2
Phyto-Guard @ 2.0% v/v & X-Tend @ 0.5% v/v	0.3	0.7	0.2	0.1	0.1
Phyto-Plus @ 1% v/v	0.2	0.2	0.3	0.1	0.2
Forbid @ 4 fl oz/100 gallons	0.5	1.3	0.6	0.2	0.2

* First application, by reducing adults also reduced egg numbers

PSM BENEFITS

Plant secondary metabolites are always produced in surplus from healthy crops. The extras are deposited in the soil for the benefit of microbial ecosystems and to be shared by the roots of neighboring plants. The aerosols are communication molecules for the plants neighbors, pollinators, and predatory allies. And the concentrations in the leaves and fruits are made available as medicines for the animal and human community.

TABLE 9.3

GREENHOUSE CUCUMBERS IN POTS
MEAN NUMBER OF DEAD MITES CM² PER LEAF ACCORDING TO TREATMENTS, USE RATES AND DATES

Spray Dates: July 4, July 11, August 3, 2011 (Canada)

Treatment Names and Use Rates	July 7	July 13	July 19	July 28	August 3
Untreated check	0.1	0.3	0.1	0.8	0.4
Phyto-Guard @ 1% v/v & X-Tend @ 0.5% v/v	1.4	0.6	0.6	1.1	0.3
Phyto-Guard @ 1.5% v/v & X-Tend @ 0.5% v/v	0.9	0.6	0.5	1.4	0.7
Phyto-Guard @ 1.5% v/v & X-Tend @ 0.5% v/v	1.6	0.6	0.6	1.2	0.7
Phyto-Guard @ 2.0% v/v & X-Tend @ 0.5% v/v	1.0	0.6	0.6	0.9	0.4
Phyto-Plus @ 1.0% v/v	0.6	1.7	0.4	0.9	0.6
Forbid @ 4 fl. oz/100 gallons	2.9	0.8	0.2	0.8	0.4

* First application, by reducing adults also reduced egg numbers

Essentially, what these PSMs really are in the big picture are "information" and "language." Plant aromatherapy is everywhere. Evergreen forests release two trillion pounds of aerosols annually. Aromatic plants release trillions more, and these words of plant language are purposely infused into terrestrial, aquatic, and atmospheric ecosystems because they affect the respiration of plants, inhibit the growth of competitors (allelopathy), contribute to the formation of humic acids, purify the air and water (autumn leaf drop rich in tannins cleanse

TABLE 9.4

GREENHOUSE CUCUMBERS IN POTS

MEAN PERCENTAGES OF LEAVES INFECTED FROM POWDERY MILDEW ACCORDING TO TREATMENTS, USE OF RATES, AND DATES

Spray Dates: September 15, September 22, October 1, 2011 (Canada)

Treatment Names and Use Rates	Sept. 19	Sept. 22	Sept. 27	Oct. 1	Oct. 3	Oct. 11
Untreated Check	55.0%	57.5%	52.5%→50.0%		60.0%	70.0%
Phyto-Guard 1% v/v	32.5%	5.0%	12.5%→27.5%		↓12.5%	37.5%
Phyto-Guard 1% v/v & X-Tend @ 0.5% v/v	37.5%	10.0%	5.0%→22.5%		↓12.5%	30.0%
Phyto-Guard 2% v/v	32.5%	17.5%	10.0%→25.0%		↓5.0%	10.0%
Phyto-Plus 1% v/v	25.0%	5.0%	2.5%→10.0%		↓10%	40.0%
Phyto-Plus 1% v/v & X-Tend @ 0.5% v/v	0.0%	0.0%	2.5%→12.5%		↓7.5%	32.5%
NOVA @ 34 g/100 L alternating with Rhapsody 1.5 L/100 L	27.5%	25.0%	2.5%→10.0%		↓5.0%	0.0%

streams, rivers, lakes, and ponds), modulate the activity and growth of fungal communities such as mycorrhizae, attract pollinators and beneficial predators, warn pests, act as "sunscreen" to protect the chlorophyll within the chloroplast, and deter/repel both microbial and insect/nematode pests.

As a crop producer, it's always important to keep in mind that optimal plant protection comes from the three-legged stool of geology (minerals), biology (microbes and their mutualism with plants), and diversity, or avoidance of monocultures. This translates into creating "immune soils" inhabited and dominated by predatory and/or antagonistic microbes like trichoderma, pseudomonas, penicillum, aspergillus, streptomycetes, gliocladium, *bacillus subtilis/longum/megaterum*, verticillium, beauveria, metarhizum, predatory nematodes, nematophagous fungi (which trap parasitic nematodes), talaromyces fungi, and more.

These microbes play a key soil role in systemic acquired responses—remember, soils are the digestive and immune "organs" of the plant—and when applied as a foliar, via a compost tea or a ferment of plants like nettle, knotweed, comfrey, industrial yogurt, terpene sprays, etc., they can really make a difference in priming the SAR flywheel by stimulating the resistance via ISR. A pathogen or insect sends a strong signal to the plant's immune system. A plant that is properly nourished and genetically primed can then send a strong SAR response; a malnourished or genetically compromised plant can only send an inadequate, weak response. A strong signal via an ISR input can cause a plant to also send a strong response; and if used preventively and on a schedule this can send a series of weak or strong signals that allow a plant the time it needs to build an ISR reaction.

Plant secondary metabolites are the holy grail of crop vibrancy, plant protection, and botanical animal and human medicine. They are the crown jewels of a well-organized, integrated, communicative, and nourished ecosystem.

10

Our Precious Pollinators and Predators

The transactions between pollen-producing plants and pollen-moving animals make up a significant portion of what biological scientists are now calling biodiversity.

—Gary Paul Nabhan, The Forgotten Pollinators

O UR pollinators consist of a legion of animals of numerous species, including bees, ants, moths, butterflies, beetles, mosquitoes, wasps, hornets, birds, bats, lizards, flying foxes, monkeys, and opossums—literally hundreds of thousands. Only 0.6 percent or fewer species have been identified as pollinators, for example: 1,500 birds, 15,000 wasps, 40,000 bees, 20,000 butterflies, 14,000 flies, 200,000 beetles, 165 bats, and 300 miscellaneous mammals.

There are 250,000 species of flowering plants pollinated by animals. The disturbing news is that the pollinators are in trouble—which means all life-forms are at risk. A combination of habitat destruction, monocultures, pesticides, invasive parasites, diseases, and now toxic pollen from genetically modified plants are all collectively exterminating the forces of reproduction globally. According to Jeff Pettis of the USDA Bee Research Laboratory, "The take-home message is that we are very close to the edge. It's a roll of the dice now." The problem is particularly amplified by the fact that we now rely on a single bee species to pollinate about 1,100 species of plants. The following crops are now dependent on honeybees' pollination: almonds, 100 percent; apples, 90 percent; avocados, 90 percent; broccoli, 90 percent; onions, 90 percent, blueberries, 90 percent; asparagus, 90 percent; cherries, 80 percent;

and cucumbers, 80 percent. In other words, according to scientists like Claire Kremen of the University of California-Berkley, plants that require animal pollination make up 98 percent of the total vitamin C supplied by major global crops, 70 percent of the vitamin A, 55 percent of folic acid, and 74 percent of the fats. Studies by Kremen and colleagues found that it takes 1,000 grains of pollen to create a single watermelon.

But at the same time, we know that native pollinators are capable of doing the job. For example, in California over sixty species of native bees were found pollinating tomatoes, watermelons, and sunflowers. In Maine and Massachusetts, over eighty species of pollinators were found among the berry crops. In Wisconsin, over one hundred species were counted in cranberry bogs. In Michigan, 112 species were pollinating high bush blueberries. In New York and Pennsylvania, one hundred species were found in apple orchards. We do have alternatives, at least right now, to the endangered honey bee. The other encouraging news is that researchers at the University of California, Davis, found that honeybees become more effective at pollinating crops when they are flying amongst their native brethren. If honeybees are more efficient at pollinating crops because of competition from natives, then fewer are needed to pollinate a specific plot of farmland.

The honeybee, which has twenty-eight subspecies and is a nonnative import from Europe, is clearly our largest commercially important pollinator. Because we have become dependent upon this aggressive pollinator for so many fruit and nut trees, we now also rely on the honeybee for vegetables too numerous to count; legumes, especially alfalfa; berries; vines; herbs; and ornamental landscaping plants critical for food for our wildlife. But the honeybees are imploding, and rather quickly, from tracheal mites, varroa mites, and now a mysterious syndrome called colony collapse disorder, allegedly due to pesticides that have disoriented the bees and impaired their communication skills so that they apparently cannot find their way back from foraging to the hive body.

A strong smoking gun connection to nicotinoid insecticides, suspected of damaging critical parts of the bee's brain and nervous system, has consequently caused the European Union to ban the insecticides for at least two years. Meanwhile Bayer Crop Sciences, the agricultural chemical manufacturer, is still selling the poison in the United States, and as of this writing the Pesticide Action Network has initiated a lawsuit against the U.S. EPA for not banning it here in America. Ironically, Bayer Crop Sciences, who claims no scientific evidence supports the link between the declining bee population and neonicotinoids, is building a 5,500-square-foot "bee health

Honeybees and Caterpillars

In 2008 researchers in Bavaria, Germany, published in the journal *Current Biology* that just the noise of honeybees flying around blossoms is enough to deter caterpillars from feeding. According to Dr. Jürgen Tautz of the Biocenter of the University of Würzburg, caterpillars carry very fine hairs on the fronts of their bodies that alert them to subtle differences in the movement of air, including the sounds of approaching flying insects. Predatory wasps are primary enemies of caterpillars, and their flight creates a disturbance that warns caterpillars of an imminent danger.

However, the caterpillar hairs are not fine-tuned enough to distinguish the difference between a wasp and a nonthreatening honeybee. Both air disturbances cause the caterpillars to become stressed and they stop moving or drop away from the plant, which means they are less likely to eat vegetation. How much less? Dr. Tautz and his researchers found that sweet peppers growing in a tent with honeybees suffered 60–70 percent less damage from caterpillars than those not in the midst of honeybees.

So honeybees are not only pollinators, they also create an atmosphere of psychological warfare against the plants' enemies as a side effect of their gathering nectar and pollen, thereby becoming inadvertent bodyguards for plants. Yet another reason to be focused on saving honeybees not only for honey and pollination, but also the critical importance of having forage for all our pollinators and beneficial predators in order to have a resilient ecosystem.

center" in North Carolina and, with fellow chemical giant and neonicotinoid manufacturer Syngenta, has developed a comprehensive action plan for bee health. Neonicotinoids are now used on 140 crops and in home gardens. They and other pesticides no doubt negatively impact bees' overall health, creating more susceptibility to pests like varroa mites.

The huge monocultures of soybeans and corn have reduced dining options for the pollinators while seeds doused in neonicotinoids contaminate the pollen and nectar of the grown plant. These highly toxic pesticides may be the most widely used insecticides globally.

A study published last year by Purdue University was prompted by a massive bee die-off around corn fields that contained high levels of neonicotinoids. According to the study's lead author, Christian Krupke, "It [neonicotinoids] blows out behind the planter and gets in the air, it lands on dandelions, it lands on the bees even. . . . Anything that's a stressor is a concern now. We know they're weaker because of it."* Additionally, research reported in *Science News* has found that one of the critical compounds found in pollen and hive honey is a plant secondary metabolite (PSM) called p-Coumaric acid, which is responsible for activating genes involved in detoxifying chemicals and augmenting the immune system.† Detoxification of chemicals in the bees is now more of a challenge than ever because a 2010 survey in twenty-three states and one Canadian province has found 121 pesticides and their breakdown products in bees. This "medicine" in pollen is now compromised by pesticides. An organism can only be so efficient in detoxification.

The latest alarming news about pollinator decline published in *PLOS ONE* in May 2013 comes from research conducted by the USDA and the University of Maryland.‡ Pollen was collected from apples, watermelons, pumpkins, cucumbers, blueberries, and cranberries and examined for fungicides, insecticides, miticides, and herbicides that bees would have been exposed to while pollinating these crops. There were several interesting and disturbing findings. First, there was an average of nine pesticides found in the collected pollen. Second, fungicides were the most frequently found pesticide. The most common find in this study was chlorothalonil. It was discovered that bees fed pollen that contained this fungicide (commonly applied to apples), as well as another fungicide called pyraclostrobin, were almost three times more susceptible to acquiring a gut parasite called Nosema. This is breaking news because up until now the concern about pesticides affecting bees had been on insecticides, and fungicides had been considered "safe" to spray during blooming. The third discovery was that in many cases the pollen brought back to the hive came from wild plants, which bees have a preference for. Wild plants are being increasingly eliminated by monocultures and habitat destruction. The wild plant pollen was also contaminated with pesticides.

---

* Keith Robinson, "Researchers: Honeybee Deaths Linked to Seed Insecticide Exposure," Purdue University News Service, January 11, 2012, http://www.purdue.edu/newsroom/research/2012/120111KrupkeBees.html.
† Susan Milius, "Bees Need Honey's Natural Pharmaceuticals," *Science News*, April 29, 2013, http://www.sciencenews.org/view/generic/id/350023/description/Bees_need_honeys_natural_pharmaceuticals.
‡ Jeffrey S. Pettis, Elinor M. Lichtenberg, Michael Andree, Jennie Stitzinger, Robyn Rose, and Dennis van Engelsdorp, "Crop Pollination Exposes Honey Bees to Pesticides Which Alters their Susceptibility to Gut Pathogen *Nosema ceranae*," *PLOS ONE* (May 2013), http://www.plosone.org/article/info%3Adoi%2F10.1371%2Fjournal.pone.0070182.

Evidently, it's this toxic cocktail of biocides that is affecting all life forms by interfering with critical metabolic pathways, affecting unhealthy gene expression, and shutting down enzyme activity, all of which manifest as immune weaknesses and malfunctions, inviting all sorts of diseases and parasites to become opportunistically deadly. But once again, those profiteering on "better living through chemistry" proclaim that we need "more research" and that our scientific findings are (perennially) "inconclusive." Factor in the practices of commercial beekeepers, who typically feed bees primarily sugary substitutes like high fructose corn syrup as a winter feed, devoid of medicinal compounds and other nutrients found in the honey and pollen, and the unintended consequences are clear: Sixty years ago there were 6 million honeybee colonies in the United States. Currently, there are 2.5 million hives remaining—and according to the USDA, a study conducted in 2013 declared that the current bee colony population "is too low for us . . . to meet the pollination demands of U.S. agricultural crops."*

Last, but hardly least, is the loss of beekeepers, down 75 percent in the last fifteen years. How do you replace a beekeeper gone bust after forty years of experience? Some folks are musing that the new honeybee industry may need to become "feedlot" in style; that is, confine the bees and bring them nectar and pollen substitutes.

As a previous beekeeper myself, I investigated how to deal with mite challenges and was encouraged to find recipes to deal with these ectoparasites as well as microbes (e.g., foulbrood) and fungal antagonists. The answer: plant secondary metabolites. One recipe is as follows: add 25 drops (1 cc) of oil of wintergreen essential oil (or rosemary, spearmint, lemongrass, melaleuca, or peppermint) to one pint of honey; add 1 cc of lecithin as an emulsifier. Add this to a one-quart jar, fill with warm water, and allow the bees to take as much as they desire. You may want to alternate the essential oils to enhance the amount of terpenoid coverage the bees can ingest. The terpenes ingested act as natural insect repellents to the parasitic mites; they are also antibacterial and antifungal.

Another useful recipe is for grease patties, which are a simple blend of 2 cups of lard and 4 cups of cane sugar. Add 25 drops of the same essential oils (1 cc) to the mix, blend well, and make into four equal size (4 oz) patties. Place two patties on top of the brood box. This will invite the bees to lather with the fortified grease, which will kill and repel any ectoparasites, be they insect or microbe.

---

* "Report on the National Stakeholders Conference on Honey Bee Health," USDA, October 15–17, 2012, http://www.usda.gov/documents/ReportHoneyBeeHealth.pdf.

Honeybees produce an amazing substance called "bee glue," or propolis. This amazing substance is a collection of resins gathered from the buds of trees prior to their leafing out or flowering. The resins contain diterpenes, which are highly antiseptic in nature.

A report titled "Biological Activity of Bee Propolis in Health and Disease" discusses the more than three hundred compounds found in propolis, depending on the geography and the time of the year that it is produced. Propolis has been found to be antibacterial, antiviral, anti-fungal, antiparasitic, anti-inflammatory, antitumor, antiulcer, liver protective, brain protective, heart protective, and an immunostimulant.[*] Once, when opening my hive body in late spring, I noticed an amorphous substance on the bottom floor of the brood chamber. It was several inches in length and about two inches in width. It looked like dog dung. Using my hive tool to remove it, I then fractured the encrusted object only to find a mouse! Apparently, a mouse attempted to enter and steal some honey and brood, was discovered by the hive, executed, and then embalmed with propolis to prevent the cadaver from contaminating the colony. Perhaps our mortuaries would be better off, as would our environment, if our expired carcasses were preserved with propolis rather than a carcinogen called formaldehyde.

Honeybees can actually distinguish between cultivars of a plant species. Typically, a "scent" contains up to one hundred volatiles, usually somewhere between twenty to sixty, and honeybees utilize all volatiles to discriminate the subtle differences among the cultivars.

The irony of course is that when honeybees were first introduced into America in the seventeenth century, they rapidly spread throughout the continent, actually able to outcompete native pollinators because of their superior ability to detect, forage, communicate, and harvest the nectar and pollen. Because of their ability to distinguish preferable forages over others, they can quickly decide whether or not they will expend resources searching for a specific flowering plant.

The implosion of our industrious imported honeybees creates an urgent need to establish habitat for North America's native pollinators, whose numbers have dropped off precipitously—ironically because of their being initially overwhelmed by the more aggressive honeybees—so that we now

* Mahmoud Lofty Khalil, "Biological Activity of Bee Propolis in Health and Disease," *Asian Pacific Journal of Cancer Prevention* 7 vol. 1 (January–March 2006): 22–31.

have low numbers of both native and introduced pollinators. In fact in Australia, the imported honeybee became recognized as an invasive species not merely because it outcompeted native bees for pollen and nectar but because it also adversely affected vertebrate pollinators such as nectar-feeding birds, like wattle birds and honey eaters, and honey possums. Introduced honeybees have successfully outcompeted beetles, butterflies, moths, ants, flies, and wasps.

As Stephen Buchmann and Gary Paul Nabhan state in their seminal 1996 work *The Forgotten Pollinators*, "Honeybees are, after all, Lilliputian livestock—fuzzy herbivores with wings, that are just as capable of taming a landscape as any cow, sheep or goat infestation . . . they pack a big ecological wallop when it comes to altering, perhaps forever, the potential mix of forages out in the range, in the bush, in the outback or boonies!" Thus it comes as no surprise to both growers and to ecologists that there is a need to fill the vacuum of pollinators that we have created. Three factors contributed to this vacuum:

1. Overwhelming our native pollinators with imported "invasive" honeybees;
2. Severely compromising honeybee health with the stress of moving them for pollination services, feeding them sugar instead of honey, and exposing them to many doses of multiple insecticides; and
3. Destroying the habitat of our native pollinators by replacing crop diversity with monocultures and eliminating windbreaks, conservation buffers, and hedgerows, which are habitats for pollinators and other beneficial insects.

So, our challenge is twofold: Because we are now so dependent on honeybees to pollinate so many foods, we must eliminate practices that are reducing their numbers. In the United States alone, the value of pollination services provided by honeybees is estimated to be approaching $20 billion, and one out of three bites of food depends on pollinators in general—but especially honeybees—where large tracts of food are produced, be they orchards of nuts and fruits, fields of vegetables, or land devoted to specialty crops. Pesticides are clearly a major factor here, and it is insane to elongate the never-ending conversation about pesticides being *safe when used as directed*. If they are persistent, systemic, migratory, and produce equally toxic degradable by-products, pesticides are going to continue to have the cumulative effect of decimating not only honeybees but all pollinators. Secondly, not only must we cease and desist from destroying pollinating habitat, we now need to restore the habitat that is lost. The American suburbs have become a toxic wasteland of monocultures of rye grass, herbicides, insecticides, and fungicides, with alien species of ornamental trees and shrubs, rarely a vegetable plot to be found, and the only "livestock" being dogs and cats and perhaps a parrot indoors. And farmers take note: a study conducted in Alberta, Canada, discovered that by converting 30 percent of cultivated land back to natural habitat, farmers increased their total yields even though they decreased their cultivated acreage. These gains were apparently due to the return of native bee populations. In California, cherry tomato production tripled when native pollinators were enticed to the landscape by improved habitats.[*]

Consider the following: there are about 20,000 bee species worldwide, an estimated 4,000 in North America, and about 450 species in the eastern United States. About 90 percent of these species are made up of solitary bees, which means that a female constructs a nest consisting of a tunnel and a series of chambers or cells. They provide these cells with a provision of nectar and pollen, lay a single egg in each cell, and seal the chamber. The larva hatches from the egg, feeds on the "larder," and develops into a pupa, all without parental care. After months in this chamber, the pupa metamorphosizes into a winged adult and digs its way out of the chamber to begin the cycle once again.

An important series of considerations are required for pollinator restoration. In addition to pollen and nectar, pollinators also need standing water, as well as nesting materials (such as gums, resins, and sap) to construct their homes. Protecting complete habitats includes cliffs, marshes, bogs, deciduous woodlands, river banks/riparian buffers, fens, sand dunes, and levees, etc. Especially missing in urban and suburban landscapes are "holes" required for nesting, such as hollow trees, snags, miniature caves beneath rocks, rodent burrows, cactus boots, abandoned beetle burrows, etc. Consequently, building bee habitats for solitary bees could consist of stuffing paper straws into an empty waxed milk carton and attaching it to a tree branch.

Bumblebees, which are ground nesters, can be attracted by leaving clay pots upside down on the ground. Hanging wooden blocks measuring four by four or four by six inches drilled with miscellaneous diameter holes will attract pollinating wasps and bees. Bamboo, corrugated cardboard, or grooved sheets of laminate wood can provide readily appreciated pollinator real estate.

---

* www.pollinator.org

A Little Help from Our Friends:
Beneficial Predatory Insects

Beneficial insects are some of the most underappreciated, barely known, underutilized, and environmentally impacted creatures of the agricultural landscape.

Beginning with parasitic wasps, decades-long research of inventory of the family Braconidae has about 15,000 described species in the world, and it's been estimated to have 50,000 to 60,000 species, the same number of species as all vertebrates—all fish, birds, mammals, amphibians, and reptiles.

The reason for such diversity is that many wasps are species-specific as to their caterpillar hosts. For example, within a subfamily known as the Microgastrinae, more than 90 percent of the wasp species were found to target only one or a very few species of caterpillar (out of the more than 3,500 caterpillar species sampled). Researchers from University of Rochester, New York, and Baylor College of Medicine in Texas described the tiny wasps of the Nasonia genus, which number over 600,000 species, many of them smaller than the head of a pin. Also found to be species-specific relative to their preferred hosts, Nasonia wasps lay eggs in agricultural pests, acting as smart bombs.

The Trichogramma wasps are those that target the eggs of perhaps more than two hundred pest moth species, such as corn earworm, tobacco budworms, cotton bollworm, cabbage looper, diamondback moth, leaf rollers, codling moth and navel orangeworm, among others.

The Aphidus and Aphelinus genera of wasps contain multiple species that attack over forty species of aphids. The Dacionusa and Diglyphus wasps attack leafminers.

Lacewings (*Chrysoperla rufilabris*) are called "aphid lions, but it is the larvae, not the adult, that is the predator. This generalist feeds on all soft-bodied insects including aphids, mites, scale, mealybugs, thrips, whitefly, psyllids (and their lerps), leafhopper, and small caterpillars. It's important to know that the adults require both nectar and pollen in order to lay eggs, so be sure you have your pollinator refuges in place. The larvae are aggressive, hiking as much as seven miles within a hundred-foot radius. Its mere lifespan of two to three weeks can mean the consumption of 11,000 spider mites, 400 aphids, 250 leafhopper nymphs, and 6,500 scale eggs—per lacewing!

Ladybugs (Hippodamia) love aphids and white flies, and the primary food for both adult and larval stages of ladybugs is aphids. They too need some forage for pollen and nectar and are hibernators in protected areas over the winter.

Midges like Aphidoletes are predatory flies. Insects in the larval (maggot) stage consume over sixty species of aphids and psyllids. They can colonize a property over time once they've been introduced from an insectary.

Soldier bugs (*Podisus maculiventris*) prey upon caterpillars, web worms, bettlegrubs, loopers, hornworm, armyworm, Colorado potato beetle and Mexican bean beetles.

Parasitic nematodes (*Heterorhabditis* spp and *Steinernema* spp) prey upon pests that either dwell in the soil or migrate to the soil to pupate, including fungus gnats, thrips, white grubs, fleas, weevils, parasitic nematodes, the larvae of cucumber beetles, Colorado potato beetles, corn root worms, black vine weevils, root mealybugs, sod web worms, codling moths, and more. Identifying the primary pest target is necessary in order to choose the specific nematode species that would be most effective.

Predatory mites can be a variety of species belonging to genera such as Amblyseius, Galendromus, Phytoseiulus, and Neoseiulus, with multiple subspecies suited for a variety of pests and climates, such as two-spotted spider mites, thrips, red mites, etc.

Predatory Beetles
- *Lindorus lophanthae* is called the scale destroyer.
- *Orius insidiosus*, or the minute private bug, is a general predator that preys on mites, aphids, thrips, and small caterpillars.
- *Stethorus punctillum*, also called the spider mite destroyer, is especially useful for crops that do not have hairy leaves, like peppers.

- *Cybocephalus nipponicus* is a beetle that preys upon several scales.
- *Delphastus catalinae* is primarily a white fly predator.

Spiders are those colonizing predators that use ballooning strategies to migrate. They release strands of their web out into an air current, creating a sail of sorts, which then can airlift them from their terrestrial site and transport them to places completely dependent upon the direction of the wind, just as a hot air balloon's direction of movement is totally at the mercy of the prevailing breeze.

The number of spiders researchers estimate occupy forest or pasture land is enormous—a range of 200,000 to 600,000 per acre! One can readily see evidence of their presence when walking a pasture covered in morning dew and spotting their webs glistening like crystals reflecting the sunlight refracted in the dew drops.

Clearly, this is only a sampling of some of the innumerable numbers of predatory, beneficial insects that are either already in your environment, if it's really healthy, or can be used as a tool to control miscellaneous pests both in the greenhouse and in the field. To make full use of these insects, there must be: 1) an appropriate schedule release of predators, contingent upon pest populations and climatic conditions (that means you may need to learn how to monitor pest thresholds); 2) ample forage in the form of pollen and nectar; and 3) minimal use of pesticides (including synthetic chemicals or natural botanicals). The advantage of the natural botanicals is that they leave no toxic residue, so the beneficials can return.

Some comments on nectaries: some research suggests that plants with an "open" architecture are more attractive than plants with hidden blossoms. Examples are dill and clovers (the color white seems to be an added attraction to the bloom's architecture, as with yarrow, buckwheat, and alyssum). If planting nectaries within vegetable rows, every seventh or tenth row is a good plan. If using beds, then every tenth to twentieth bed should be a forage refuge and nectary. Ecologically sound landscapes should dedicate 1 percent of their arable surface area to a nectary, while conventionally farmed landscapes should do this with 5 percent of their cultivated land.

As far as the bees are concerned, there are three primary categories:

1. Cavity nesters refer to, for example, bumblebees (*Bombus* spp.) and honeybees (*Apis mellifera*). Both of these bees are generalists (meaning they have broad food preferences), and they are social insects with a community of a queen, workers, and drones. Because these bees are active all summer long, they require continuous floral resources in the vicinity of the hive. These bees can forage beyond a mile of their nesting site. Studies have sadly pointed out that four species of bumblebees have lost up to 87 percent of their habitat, reducing their numbers by 96 percent.

2. Tunnel nesters either excavate their tunnels in wood (e.g., carpenter bees) or utilize abandoned cavities such as cracks in masonry (e.g., mason bees) or beetle burrows. Types of mason bees include the blue orchard bee (*Osmia lignaria*) or the hornfaced bee (*Osmia cornifrons*). The large carpenter bees (*Xylocopa virginica*) can forage beyond a mile of their nesting cavity. The small carpenter bee (*Ceratina* spp.), which likes to nest in pithy stems such as brambles, and the mason bee (*Osmia* spp.) typically have a foraging range of less than five hundred yards from their nesting site.

3. Ground nesters, perhaps the most important wild pollinating bee, have a nesting strategy of excavating underground nests, a practice shared by 70 percent of bees worldwide. They obviously need well-drained soil with access to some bare ground but don't do well with excess tillage, mulching, soil compaction, or toxic herbicides such as paraquat (a.k.a. Gramoxone). This category includes the large mining bees (*Andrena* spp.), solitary bees that can be either forage generalists or specialists and which typically have a forage radius between five hundred yards and a mile; small mining bees (*Andrena* spp.), solitary forage generalists that have a forage range of less than five hundred yards; and cellophane bees (*Colletes inaequalis*), named for the iridescent coating that lines their nest walls. Cellophane bees are considered solitary, generalist foragers, but they usually aggregate their solitary abodes in "communities" in grass-covered sandy soil. Their forage range can exceed one mile. Dark sweat bees (*Lasioglossum* spp. and *Halictus* spp.) are generalist social bees that have a foraging range of five hundred yards to a mile. Blue-green sweat bees (*Augochlora pura, Augochlorella aurata, and Agapostemon* spp.) consist of generalist foragers, both social

and solitary in their habits, and their foraging range is less than five hundred yards from their nesting cavity.

Building habitats and refuges for our pollinators includes not only favorite haunts for the bees but also for the bats, moths, butterflies, birds, wasps, hornets, and predatory insects like ground beetles and ladybugs, predatory mites, spiders and such. These habitats can and should include a mosaic of hedgerows, windbreaks, alley cropping, conservation buffers, savannahs, riparian edges, and such.

In Pennsylvania, we have an urgent need to rapidly create habitats for the little brown bat, which has been devastated to the tune of a 98 percent loss in its population in Pennsylvania in the last five years. This decline apparently has been caused by white nose syndrome, a fungal infection on the face that interrupts the bat's hibernation, causing them to consume stored energy prematurely. Affected bats die of starvation or immune failure.

The second-largest bat cave in Pennsylvania is the Durham Mines in Bucks County. Normally, it hosts ten thousand healthy bats. The last count taken on February 21, 2013, showed that there were only twenty-three bats remaining, and half of them had white nose syndrome.* Keep in mind that one bat will consume 900,000 insects per year, including mosquitoes, rootworm adults, codling moths, biting flies, and a legion of agricultural pests that injure crops and spread diseases to plants, livestock, pets, and humans. In other words, that one bat colony can eliminate 9 billion insects from the environment every single year.

Absent these natural predators, how many more pesticides will be called in to spray for mosquitoes carrying West Nile virus, as well as insects that feed on our orchards, corn, vegetables, and forages? Toxic sprays will further disturb even more beneficial predators and poison the gene pool with substances that may contribute to chronic illnesses like cancer, neurological malaise, and autoimmune disorders. The United States already has 1,200 registered pesticides, three times as many as the European Union.

Windbreaks reduce wind chill effects, providing heat energy savings between 10 percent and 40 percent, and can also reduce air conditioning demands in areas of hot, dry winds in open, arid areas. They can also supply wood products as harvestable timber/firewood. For those with livestock the benefits are additionally significant, as animals can be protected from

---

* Amanda Cregan, "All but 23 of 10,000 Bats in Durham Bat Mine Have Died," PhillyBurbs.com, April 1, 2013, http://www.phillyburbs.com/my_town/palisades/all-but-of-bats-in-durham-bat-mine-have-died/article_19e44845-452b-5ffe-ba71-110122304402.html.

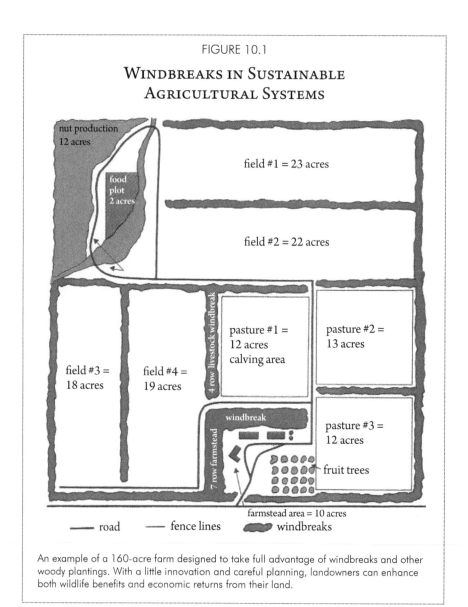

FIGURE 10.1

WINDBREAKS IN SUSTAINABLE AGRICULTURAL SYSTEMS

nut production
12 acres

food plot
2 acres

field #1 = 23 acres

field #2 = 22 acres

4 row livestock windbreak

pasture #1 =
12 acres
calving area

pasture #2 =
13 acres

field #3 =
18 acres

field #4 =
19 acres

windbreak

pasture #3 =
12 acres

7 row farmstead

fruit trees

farmstead area = 10 acres

—— road   —— fence lines   windbreaks

An example of a 160-acre farm designed to take full advantage of windbreaks and other woody plantings. With a little innovation and careful planning, landowners can enhance both wildlife benefits and economic returns from their land.

Minnesota Department of Natural Resources; "Conservation Buffers and Beneficial Insects, Mites, and Spiders," NRCS Conservation Information Sheet, 1998.

the dangers of wind chill. This translates into less cold-temperature stress and improved reproductive success. Windbreaks can be especially valuable during the calving/lambing/kidding season, when protection from late winter and early spring storms is most critical. In dry northern rangelands, the trapping of snow may be a valuable source of water for livestock.

Agroforestry is a term defined as a blend of practices designed to yield a desired mix of crops that can include timber, fruit and nuts from trees, and annual grains, crops, and forages. Proper management of a hedgerow or windbreak can translate into timber or fuel wood such as a managed existing woodlot. Black locust, Osage orange, cedar, and juniper all qualify for effective fence posts. Larger poplar and ash can provide needed lumber for crates, pallets, and baseball bats. I've been on livestock farms where "edible landscaping" has been incorporated into the mix, including fruit trees, berry bushes such as elderberry, brambles such as raspberries and blackberries, and vines such as table grapes and kiwi fruit.

A variation of the fencerow/hedgerow/windbreak is a layout called alley cropping, which is the planting of trees and/or shrubs in two or more sets of single or multiple rows with horticultural, agronomic, or forage crops cultivated in the alleys between the rows of woody plants.

The spacing between the woody plants is determined by the primary purpose of the alley cropping. Woody plants are mostly selected for their value for wood, nuts, or fruit crops. Obviously, canopy density and sunlight requirements for the horticultural/agronomic/forage crops will determine the width of the alley and the succession of crop changes associated with light requirements of the specific crops. Narrow alleys (less than or equal to forty feet wide) will require more adjustments as the crop varieties will need to change over time from, say, row crop to small grain to forage to all trees, because of the thickening canopy that reduces sun exposure.

Conservation buffers can collectively refer to filter strips, which should include bunch grasses like orchard grass and switch grass as a preferred habitat for beneficials over sod-forming grasses, as well as legumes for pollen and nectar. Large buffers should be linked together with smaller buffers to provide a network of habitats. In essence, you want a quilt of eco-niches that includes hedgerows/fencerows, woodlots, contour grass strips, shallow water swales, grassed waterways and filter strips, riparian buffers, and others.

Habitats along streams (riparian buffers) should include a diversity of woody plants such as trees, shrubs, vines, forbs, and ground cover. Willows are especially beneficial to honeybees and bumblebees as they provide pollen early in the spring. Standing dead trees, called snags, attract solitary nesting bees as well as cavity-creating birds, like flickers. Hedgerows and windbreaks are climate modifiers and a cafeteria of nutrients for pollinators, predatory beneficials, and livestock as well as being a natural pharmacy for all animals. Temporary pollinator pastures—such as fields planted in buckwheat, canola, and brassicas (kale, turnips, broccoli) gone to seed—will supply pollen and

FIGURE 10.2

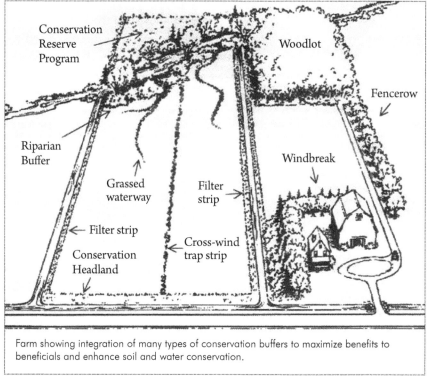

Farm showing integration of many types of conservation buffers to maximize benefits to beneficials and enhance soil and water conservation.

Minnesota Department of Natural Resources; "Conservation Buffers and Beneficial Insects, Mites, and Spiders," NRCS Conservation Information Sheet, 1998.

nectar. Fallow fields and undeveloped natural areas are also able to harbor beneficials, as can edges along fields and roadsides, and a diverse garden is very edibly useful to beneficials as well as its human beneficiaries.

A comprehensive study conducted at Michigan State University showed a dramatic increase in ground beetle species dwelling in legume-grass filter strips (+150 percent) and switchgrass filter strips (+300 percent) compared to an adjacent soybean field. Considering that ground beetles commonly found in Midwestern soils can remove up to four thousand cutworms per acre per day, and as many as forty weed seeds per square foot per day, it would be very wise to create refuges where ground beetles can thrive.

A European study found that a crosswind trap strip installed through a small grain field harbored over one thousand predatory beetles per square meter, and the cereal grains adjoining the strips suffered less aphid damage than those without the strips.

FIGURE 10.3

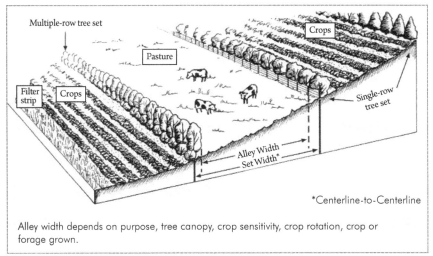

Alley width depends on purpose, tree canopy, crop sensitivity, crop rotation, crop or forage grown.

"Conservation Buffers and Beneficial Insects, Mites, and Spiders," NRCS Conservation Information Sheet, 1998.

SOME FORAGE PLANTS FOR WILD POLLINATORS
Trees
basswood (*Tilia americana*)
pussy willow (*Salix discolor*)
black willow (*Salix nigra*)
Saskatoon serviceberry (*Amelanchier* spp.)
silver maple (*Acer saccharinum*)

Shrubs
meadowsweet (*Spiraea alba*)
American plum (*Prunus americana*)
chokecherry (*Prunus virginiana*)
fireberry hawthorn (*Crataegus chrysocarpa*)
nannyberry viburnum (*Viburnum lentago*)
highbush cranberry (*Viburnum trilobum*)

Flowering Forbs
lupine (*Lupinus perennis*)
lance-leaf coreopsis (*Coreopsis lanceolata*)
smooth penstemon (*Penstemon digitalis*)
milkweed (*Asclepias* spp.)

purple coneflower (*Echinacea* spp.)
wild bergamot (*Monarda fistulosa*)
Joe-Pye weed (*Eupatorium purpureum*)
blue giant hyssop (*Agastache foeniculum*)
giant sunflower (*Helianthus giganteus*)
New England aster (*Symphyotrichum novae-angliae*)
butterfly milkweed (*Asclepias tuberosa*)
purple prairie clover (*Dalea purpurea*)
tall blazing star (*Liatris aspera*)
showy penstemon (*Penstemon grandiflorus*)
silky aster (*Aster sericeus*)
smooth aster (*Aster laevis*)
swamp milkweed (*Asclepias incarnata*)
yarrow (*Achillea millefolium*)

"Pollinator pastures" essentially need to supply an abundant bloom throughout the nesting period. For temporary pastures, both native and nonnative species that provide forage are appropriate examples — the latter including both annuals and perennials such as buckwheat, yellow sweet clover, berseem clover, crimson clover, red clover, alfalfa, canola, purple vetch, phacelia, and birdsfoot trefoil. The dual purpose of these crops is that they also are utilized as cover crops for building organic matter, suppressing weeds or fixing nitrogen.

Building habitats can be a productive and fun pastime. Create a "snag" by drilling holes in a dead tree or stump, or, take a log and drill holes in it and erect it like a fence post. The hole diameter should be between 3/32" and 3/8" (2.5–10 millimeters). Hole diameters less than a quarter of an inch (6.5 millimeters) should be three to five inches deep (8–13 centimeters). Holes larger than a quarter of an inch should be five to six inches (13–15 centimeters) deep. The distance between the holes should approximate three quarters of an inch (19 millimeters) center to center and the same distance from the edge (if using a wooden block).

Should you choose a wooden block to creating nesting habitat, a four by four inch by eight to twelve inches in length preservative-free block should be used when drilling nesting holes less than a quarter of an inch (6.5 millimeters). For nesting holes larger than a quarter-inch diameter, use

Via Wikimedia Commons

a four-by-six-inch (10 by 15 centimeter) block by eight to twelve inches (20–30 centimeters) in length. Drill holes three to five inches deep (8–13 centimeters), but be sure that the holes are not tunnels (open at both ends) as bees will not use them. Use a sharp bit to create a smooth surface.

Stem bundles can also easily be made. Using reeds, teasel stalks, or bamboo, cut sections after a natural node to create a back wall, and strap these together into a tight bundle with wire, string, or nylon-reinforced tape, keeping the open and closed ends of the bundle uniform on the same side. Or, one can pack these stems, or drinking straws into paper milk cartons, square plastic buckets, tin cans, etc. Turn both the nesting boxes, snags, and stem bundles to the east, facing the morning sun.

These are mere samplings of what can be introduced into your landscape, and it would be very advisable to consult with your local *Natural Resources Conservation Service* (NRCS) office or extension agent to find out which species are appropriate based on your climatic conditions and your pollinator/ beneficial species nearby. Additionally, what may be native in one locale may be invasive in another, so some plants that you are interested in may be prohibited in your bioregion. What you should consider is the window of time that each plant species is in bloom, so you can put in plantings of multiple species that will provide nectar and pollen through the entire frost-free growing season.

Pesticides to be Aware Of

It astounds me how ignorant we are of poisons we regularly and unknowingly ingest through our skin, respiratory tract, and digestive system and the degree of toxicity that they pose to all of us who collectively inhabit and constitute the environment. We leave it up to regulators and bureaucrats, who are constantly under pressure by moneyed lobbyists to marginalize the significant impact of these persistent poisons.

It's amazing that farmers and commercial applicators need a license to apply these toxins, which requires that they sit in on a class presentation given by an extension agent on the so-called safe use of these poisons. But John Q. Anybody can walk into a box store and pick up the same substances and spread them all over his lawn, trees, shrubs, and garden with nary a label warning beyond the small-print generic caveat that isn't much different than warnings found on a container of Pine-Sol.

The following list is a list of chemicals and products that are considered toxic to honeybees, classified as either high or moderate toxicity. A disclaimer: the data only incorporates studies looking at acute, short-term, adult toxicity. The longer-term effects on egg, larvae, and pupae development are not really known, nor are the effects on other pollinators. Other concerns are that so-called inert ingredients in the pesticide formulations can also be toxic. For example, organisilicone surfactants and adjuvants were most toxic, while other non-ironic surfactants showed some toxicity, and drop oils were least toxic.

One of our most important advocates in holding the pesticide industry's feet to the fire, along with government agencies that are at best lax in enforcing the regulations for pesticide use and at worst complicit in keeping very toxic compounds in the environment, is Pesticide Action Network (PAN). These folks have done yeoman's work in bringing to light not only the dangers of these substances, but also the absence of oversight by those in the regulatory arena who have allowed the misuse, even abuse, of these damaging compounds in our habitats, whether it's our homes, hives, nests, soil, water, and air. And lest we forget about our migrant workers: the EPA estimates there are 10,000-20,000 annual pesticide poisonings among our 2 million laborers who plant and harvest our produce.

It is propitious that the European Union has now issued draft regulations amounting to 266 pages designed to protect bees. Essentially, these regulations stipulate that farming practices must not affect more than 7 percent of the bee colony's size. Many pesticides will have to undergo studies involving 196 colonies as well as other tests measuring bees' chemical exposure to poisons in everything from water to dust.

TABLE 10.1
High Toxicity

Chemical Class/Group	Common Name	Trade Name
Carbamates	carbaryl, methomyl	Sevin, Lannate
Nicotinoids	clothianiden, imidacloprid	Clutch, Promado,
	triamethoxam	Actara
	acetamiprid, thiacloprid	Assail, Calypso
Organo Phospates	azinophos-methyl,	Guthion, Lorsban
	cloropyrifos, diazinon,	Diazinon, Dimethoate/
	dimethoate malathion,	Dimate, Melathion
	phosmet	Supracide Imidian
Pyrethroids	bifenthrin, cyfluthrin	Brigade, Baythroid
	deltamethrin, esfenvalerate	Decis, Asana
	fenpropathrin, lambda-	Danitol, Warrior
	permethrin	Ambush/Pounce
Insect Growth Regulator	novaluron	Rimon
Miticides	pyridaben	Nexter/Pyramite
Other Insecticides	formetanate HCl	Carzo

Moderate Toxicity

Chemical Class/Group	Common Name	Trade Name
Carbamates	oxamyl	Vydate
Chlorinated Hydrocarbon	endosulfan	Thiodan/Thionex
Pyrethroids	pyrethrum	Pyganic
Miticides	bifenazate	Acramite
Other Insecticides	azadirachtin,	Aza-Direct/Nermix,
	mineral oils	Stylet oil
	indoxacarb, spirotetramat	Avaunt, Movento

Helen Thompson of the United Kingdom's Food and Environment Research Agency stated that most of the pesticides would probably fail the new requirements. And remember, the EU already has only one-third the registered pesticides of the United States, about 400 to our 1200.

The July 2013 issue of *National Geographic* showcases the meadows of Romania, which are kept as virtual ecological treasures of grasses and flowering forbs by the practice of haymaking, all by hand labor. One can find fifty species of grasses and flowers in a single square yard.[*]

---

[*] Adam Nicolson, "Hay. Beautiful.," *National Geographic*, July 2013.

Viktor Schauberger, the "water wizard" of Austria, discovered there was a factual basis for local Austrian farmers' claims that fields grazed by animals and the hay cut by hand scythes were more enriched in the flowering herbs. Schauberger went so far as to say that if the scythes were sharpened by hammering their blades against a wood block, it would be better than grinding them. He suggested that hand scything, like grazing, tore the plants in a way that closed the cut surface of the remaining stalk, whereas a machine cut kept the plant wound open for a long time, allowing the "growth energy" to escape into the atmosphere. Butterfly orchids, meadow salvia, sanfoin, globeflowers, hawkweeds, companulas, yellow rattle, sorrel, snapdragon, gentian thyme and marjoram are a few species referred to in the *National Geographic* article. Local folks over the age of twenty can on average recognize and name more than 120 species of plants. Young children know 45–50 percent of the species. Local folks know 70–84 percent of their botanical neighbors. In the words of one of the farmers, Attila Sarig, "I know that I make this landscape by what I do." Humankind can enrich and contribute to our web of life as much as we are currently destroying it. The fabric can be of many colors, patterns, and textures if only we could recognize that we, too, are part of the quilt.

Bob Pyle of the Xerces Society, the primary organization overseeing the restoration and preservation of our pollinators, stated that "virtually every endangered butterfly remaining in England has declined because of the abandonment or destruction of traditionally modified landscapes— hedgerows, hay fields, excavation sites, and coppiced woodlands." The Xerces Society has also partnered with USDA's NRCS to build a pollinator enhancement program. Based upon the data generated by Claire Kremen's team, since 2009 this collaborative has trained more than 20,000 people from all backgrounds including farmers, cooperative extension agents and NRCS agents on the importance of native bees, including instituting guidelines for farmers, such as how to create the aforementioned "Romanian meadow" or a continuous flowering hedgerow and how to minimize pesticide use.

USDA has also funded a program called Integrated Crop Pollination, or ICP, to provide options like expanding pollinator habitat and bringing in other managed pollinators such as the blue orchard bee, a native species. ICP was the brainchild of Rufus Issacs, the resident blueberry entomologist at Michigan State University, who discovered that in small fields native bees provided 82 percent of the pollination. As the fields got larger, native pollinators were less effective because their habitats were eliminated. According to Issacs, farmers who restore native bee habitat could recover the cost of such habitat reestablishment in three or four years because of extra yields from the blueberries. Fortunately, farmers can potentially recover 50–90 percent of their costs even sooner from NRCS reimbursements.

Similar observations made at the University of California have shown that when 30 percent of the landscape in an agricultural area within three quarters of a mile of crops is planted to bee forage, rich in pollen and nectar, native bees could provide 100 percent of the pollination of watermelons, a critical discovery in light of the fact that domesticated honeybees are imploding. California's almond crop, substantially larger economically than the infamous California vineyards, is now totally dependent on honeybees. According to Kremen and her team, including Neal Williams of U. C. Davis, they were able to record 130 native species in California, but historical records indicate California once had 1,600 native bee species.

On the East Coast, comparable discoveries were made by researchers at Rutgers University in New Jersey (the Garden State), where in field sizes of ten to twenty acres, surrounded by natural areas, 90 percent of those farms receive 100 percent of their pollination from native pollinators.

The take-home message for farmers here is to contact the NRCS and Xerces Society and begin to create the biomes that your landscape is hungering for—habitat for pollen gatherers.

We will not preserve what we don't love, and we cannot love that which we do not know in some fashion. The encouraging news is that 40–50 million Americans have flower gardens, 30 million grow some vegetables, and 26 million are actively landscaping their yards. Approximately half of American households include at least one person involved in these three activities. Even though we are a highly surburbanized nation, infatuated with toxic lawns, the interest in healthy food and biodiversity is growing. Our educational institutions need to prioritize the critical significance of these activities for the health and safety of our citizens, for the restoration and conservation of our ecosystems, and for the sustainability and resilience of our communities. It can be accomplished because it once was. During World War II, the Victory Garden initiative inspired Americans to grow 40 percent of their produce in their back yards consisting of twenty million gardens producing 10 million tons of produce. That 40 percent is the amount of produce that is thrown out today because of spoilage in our super markets and home refrigerators. Pollinators, be they bees, beetles, moths, butterflies, or bats, don't only pollinate crops. They are a keystone species, vital to an energy-rich food web.

If we can also bring back this kind of restorative consciousness to those who are and will be custodians of the hundreds of millions of acres of private and public lands currently dedicated to fossil fuel–based, industrialized monocultures of a few select annuals, we could achieve an ecological renaissance in which humankind is a cocreator of wealth, health, beauty, and restoration. Curiously, it is precisely the quiltwork of human hands and stewardship alongside the majesty of our wilderness that has cultivated the ecotones, microclimates, and varied habitats that encourage a proliferation of pollinators and beneficials.

In summation, the best resistance against pests is a confusing quilt work of ecotones—that is, a very biodiverse farm ecosystem. There are many possible methods for building biodiversity on your land, including:

1. Leave undisturbed areas for predators and parasites that attack pests, such as hedgerows, riparian buffers, grassy waterways, weedy borders on edges, and even between rows within fields. No-till systems with these kinds of refuges attract ground beetles, crickets, ants, and field mice that consumed twice the weed seeds in soy fields than in conventionally tilled fields. In Georgia, cotton fields that were cover cropped had carabid beetle and spider populations that were fourteen times higher than in convention fields.

2. Include perennials in the equation, again with hedgerows, streamside banks, etc., as well as hay crops that can provide support for more biodiverse species of soil organisms, pollinators, and predators, Perennials can build more soil carbon infiltration and reduce soil compaction better than annuals.

3. Increase plant diversity across your landscape throughout the season by using different crops in the same landscape at different stages of growth. Use at least three rotations of three or more crops from year to year.

Creating this quilt work not only insulates the farm from weather extremes but also confuses pests, for which monocultures are magnets.

USDA research in 1997–1998 in Beltsville on tomatoes found that a mere hairy vetch cover crop reduced annual grass/weed pressure by 83 percent, reduced early blight severity by 52 percent, reduced Colorado potato beetle numbers by 82 percent, and increased beneficial lady beetle numbers by 250 percent compared to tomatoes grown with black plastic mulch. Other researchers found weed plant density in rotations was less than in monocultures in nineteen out of twenty-five cases, weed seed density in crop rotations was lower in nine out of twelve cases, and yields of crops in rotations were higher than in monocultures in nine out of twelve cases.

We cannot restore precious topsoil loss with "silver bullets" like GMOs and imported fossil fuel–based fertility. We cannot substitute biodiversity with monocultures that require higher and higher doses of pollinator-killing pesticides. Biology and ecology cannot be replaced with patented, fossil fuel–based technology. It's as simple and yet complex as that. If we do not adequately mimic natural systems, we will have squandered the most precious resources we have been blessed with: topsoil, water, and biodiversity.

Cover Crops

Farming in Nature's Image

We live off what comes out of the soil, not what's in the bank. If we squander the ecological capital of the soil, the capital on paper won't much matter.

—Wes Jackson, cofounder of the The Land Institute

THE ecological and environmental benefits of cover cropping are immense. The extreme storms the Earth has been experiencing, many of them quite localized, are most destructive when hillsides have been left barren and millions of tons of precious topsoil are swept into the watershed. Suffocating sediment smothers the food chain there: the macroinvertebrates and the critical grasses growing in the estuaries necessary for mollusks and crustaceans to reproduce.

Along with the topsoil comes an entire suite of manmade chemicals (such as nitrogen and phosphorus), which incites algae blooms and cause a condition known as eutrophication. The algae, once it dies and begins to decompose, consumes critical dissolved oxygen levels in the water, asphyxiating the aerobic organisms in that body of water and creating large dead zones, or hypoxia. The Chesapeake Bay is the largest estuary in the United States. Its ecological scorecard rates a "D." The oyster industry, now collapsed, was once a major economic flywheel on the eastern shores of Delaware, Maryland, and Virginia (Delmarva). The crabs that have been harvested by "watermen," such as those living on Smith and Tangier Islands, are now endangered, as are the livelihoods of those folks who have made a living on them since the mid-seventeenth century. The dead zone that occurs annually in the Gulf of

Mexico can range in size from an area the size of New Jersey to Maryland, up to 10,500 square miles.

Because of the massive amounts of soil erosion, estimated by USDA to be at four tons per capita in the United States alone, both our landscape and watersheds are in peril. There is a burgeoning movement, however, that evolved out of the no-till and minimum-till practices instituted back in the 1960s and 1970s and standardized with practices like ridge tilling.*

Between 1990 and 2000, no-till farming increased from 16 million acres to 52 million acres. Today about 35 percent of U.S. cropland is no-till, and that number is rising at a rate of 1.5 percent annually. Nevertheless, the average U.S. topsoil loss is still an unacceptable three tons per acre a year. Pennsylvania's rate was as high as over five tons per acre, and, depending upon the slope, fields in Iowa and elsewhere could be twice that amount.

The one thing back then that was missing in no-till or minimum-till practices was a cover crop; it was assumed that the residue remaining on top of the soil after harvest was an adequate protective cover to blanket the fields from the eroding precipitation of winter and spring. It certainly was an improvement over the bare ground remaining after a soybean or corn crop was removed, which inevitably invited severe erosion on even the slightest grade. But no-till without cover crops left a lot to be desired, particularly the healthy decomposition of the organic residues and a living root systems to invigorate soil life with living (liquid) carbon, the plant root exudates, while taking up leachable nitrogen into their plant tissues.

Curiously, most erosion is associated with rare, intense rain events—only about 0.10 percent of the rain events cause 75 percent of the soil erosion. Only a small amount of soil must be exposed for it to receive a lot of damage from powerful storms, which are more common in the spring and summer when most crops are young and a lot of soil is exposed.

Research at USDA's North Appalachian Experimental Watershed in Coshocton, Ohio, showed that during a four-year period, the annual rate of soil erosion from no-till fields was only six pounds per acre. From conventionally tilled fields it was 4,750 pounds per acre—seven hundred times greater! Sadly, the USDA has benchmarked what is referred to as "tolerable soil loss"—which ranges from three to four tons per acre per year—apparently under the assumption that growing crops have the opportunity to rebuild such losses with their residues. This is hardly accurate and downright reckless. We are barely building topsoil in the United States, and the sheet erosion, aggravated by gully erosion, is not only taking a horrible toll on some

---

* For more information, see *No-Till Farmer* magazine at www.no-tillfarmer.com.

of the best farmland in the world, it is destroying the most food-productive ecosystems on the globe: our estuaries, home to crustaceans like shrimp and crabs, mollusks like oysters and clams, fish, aquatic plants, marine mammals, amphibians, and reptiles that were sustainably harvested for thousands of years by indigenous people.

The advantages of cover crops for the grower go far beyond making the farmer a better neighbor. Building soil fertility and soil tilth, managing pests (including the reduction of pressure from insects, weeds, and diseases), and enhancing the resilience against drought and excessively wet conditions are all perks that cover cropping will provide.

Where no-till is used without a cover crop, even though little sediment leaves the landscape it's quite typical for nitrates (NO_3^-) to drain through the soil and field tiles into surface waters and aquifers because nitrates having a negative charge ($-$) readily leach away from the negatively charge soil particles. This is appropriately referred to as a "leaky soil."

The first drain tile was laid by John Johnston in 1835 near Geneva, New York. Drainage problems have continually worsened since that time because of the conversion from draft horses to heavy machinery, an unforgivable loss of soil organic matter, and continuous soil disturbance by tillage that destroys aggregates and creates plow pans/hardpans that disallow water infiltration.

One example of nature's ability to hold onto water is "cove soil," described by Edward Faulkner in his classic text *Plowman's Folly*. These are soils created at the base of mountain ranges covered in deciduous forests, which have an annual leaf drop. No water leaves these sites because the entire mountainside becomes a carbon-rich "blotter paper" that holds onto the water slowly draining into a cove, feeding it with moisture to generate an explosion of biology even with 90 percent slopes.

There are a few questions the grower needs to ask relative to each field that is a candidate for a cover crop. Is the cover crop for:

1. Fixing nitrogen?
2. Increasing organic matter?
3. Providing weed control?
4. Breaking up hard pan/improving tilth?
5. Providing habitat, nectar, and pollen for beneficial insects?
6. Eradicating soil pests (e.g., nematodes or root diseases)?
7. Releasing tied-up nutrients?

Answering these questions will determine what kind of cover crop will be best for the soil.

CARBON TO NITROGEN RATIOS ("GO" FOODS VS. "GROW" FOODS)

Using a legume as a cover crop can reduce or even eliminate nitrogen fertilizers. Of course, they do so by "fixing" nitrogen, an inert gas in the atmosphere, into ammonium and nitrate. When a legume-based cover crop is plowed down, all of that nitrogen that it synthesized via rhizobia and other bacteria is digested by numerous soil organisms that dine on the proteins and carbohydrates, which in turn increases the microbial population, which is soil protein, which is nitrogen.

High-protein legume plowdowns can supply as much as 140 pounds of nitrogen per acre in as little as a week because their carbon to nitrogen (C:N) ratios are so narrow, like 10:1 to 15:1. Even for non-legume grasses, such as winter rye, annual ryegrass, and wheat, the C:N ratio is narrow, about 15:1 when young. The following reference in biomass production and nitrogen accumulation is from Penn State University's *Agronomy Guide* with input from the Rodale Institute. The data reflect values based on cover crops established in late August or early September and killed in late April or early May.

The following table is a peek at the kinds of C:N ratios of some cover crops.[*]

Cover Crop	C:N Ratio
Young Rye Plants	14:1
Rye at Mid Boot Stage	40:1
Hairy Vetch	10:1–15:1
Crimson Clover	15:1
Corn Stalks	60:1
Sawdust	250:1

Higher carbon cover crops that are more lignified and are not legumes, such as winter rye, require a longer period of time to break down, and so a subsequent crop should ideally be planted two or three weeks after a plow down so as to not deprive that crop of nitrogen. Otherwise, additional nitrogen may need to be applied to the soil.

Non-legume cover crops are also high enough in protein and can produce a hefty enough amount of biomass that the residue of nitrogen can be significant, especially considering that those crops are also nitrogen scavenger crops (that is, they remove soluble nitrogen remaining in the soil at the end of the growing season by taking it up in its leaf tissue, thereby preventing it from leaching).

Some rules of thumb:

• Annual legumes are approximately 3.5–4.0 percent nitrogen prior to

---

* Source: ATTRA 2001. "Overview of Cover Crops and Green Manures."

flowering, and 3.0–3.5 percent nitrogen at flowering.
- Perennial legumes, which are more fibrous, have pre-bloom nitrogen levels of 2.5–3.0 percent and post bloom nitrogen levels of 2.0–2.5 percent.
- Most grasses approximate 2.0–3.0 percent pre-bloom and 1.5–2.5 percent post-bloom, when the seed is beginning to set.

Thus, to estimate how much nitrogen you are growing, multiply the dry matter per acre by the percentage of nitrogen to give you the pounds per acre of N. That's assuming a 100 percent established stand. If you would only have an 80 percent stand, then you would multiply the subtotal by 0.80 to give you a total estimated amount of lbs of N/acre. Dry matter (DM)/acre x (%) N x% of the stand. To determine dry matter/acre a general rule is: at 100 percent ground cover, at a 6-inch height = 2,000 lbs/acre of DM. For each additional inch, add 150 lbs/acre of DM.

So the nitrogen grown by a legume 18 inches tall at 100 percent ground cover would be:

18" - 6" = 12"

12" x 150 lbs/inch = 1,800 lbs/acre DM

1,800 + 2,000 lbs/acre DM (for the first 6 inches) = a total DM of 3,800 lbs/acre. Now, calculate the (%) stand and multiply by the (%) of nitrogen in the selected cover crop.

DM/acre x(%) stand x(%) nitrogen of legume = total nitrogen in a green manure crop.

It's also noteworthy that tilling in a green manure will provide more nitrogen than a no-till system because some of the nitrogen in the leaf will vaporize into the atmosphere in a no-till system. So, one needs to now divide the total nitrogen by 2 if it is conventionally tilled in, and divide by 4 if it's surface residue on a no-till system. Research with hairy vetch and rye/vetch mixes has shown that much of the nitrogen requirement of the subsequent corn crop can be provided by the vetch with a plow down or incorporation. If the vetch is mixed with the winter rye, the nitrogen will be released more slowly. This is good news for the minimum-till crowd who want to limit soil disturbance.

Conversely, low organic matter soils may leach more than a little nitrogen, as nitrate (NO_3), because it's the bacteria in the soil organic matter that gobble up the nitrate on the cover crop while using carbon from both the cover crop and the organic matter as an energy source. Low organic matter soils have fewer bacterial populations that act like sponges to capture the cover crop nitrogen.

Since new crops are planted as seeds or young transplants, there may be a lot more nitrogen in the system than can be taken up by the very young crop. Also, deep tillage may place nitrogen-rich residues far below the young, small root systems, inviting the nitrogen to leach away before roots become large enough to access it. Thus, it is preferable when using tillage tools to keep the cover crop in the top "A" soil horizon, where the microbes can make the best use of it to increase soil humus and nitrogen. As Don Schriefer used to ask, referring to the fence post principle discussed in chapter 3, "Where does the fence post rot?"

Some strategies that could help is to shallow incorporate the green manure to reduce gaseous migration of NH_3, NO_2, and NO, and to prevent NO_3 leaching into the subsoil from deep tillage. Tillage equipment like the Howard Rotavator, the Falc (made in Italy), and the Gen-Till are all designed to mix residues where they are most needed.

Mixing some lower-nitrogen, higher-carbon grasses into the mix can slow down the spike of nitrogen release from a legume-only stand. Table 11.1 list the top regional cover crop species throughout the United States as provided in the Sustainable Agriculture Network publication *Managing Cover Crops Profitably*, third edition.

WEED SUPPRESSION AND ALLELOPATHY

This section provides each crop's performance and roles ranking, their cultural traits, planting recommendations, potential advantages, and potential disadvantages. Weed suppression is a fringe benefit of cover cropping because there is an overwhelming amount of competition for soil nutrients by the cover crop at the expense of the weeds. Moreover, certain cover crops have been recognized to have what is known as the allelopathic effect, which is the cover crop roots' secretion of biochemicals that suppress the germination of weed seeds. Rye, wheat, oats, hairy vetch, and brassicas have been found by researchers to contain these allelopathic substances. Because we don't fully understand what plants are affected by these compounds, it is generally advised to either change the cover crops or diversify them with cocktails to avoid a possible buildup of the allelopathic substances that may inhibit the growth of a desired crop.

A couple of cover crops not mentioned in earlier editions of *Managing Cover Crops Profitably* that have merit are brassicas and mustard (cruciferous) species, for nematode and root disease control, and tillage radishes, also in the cruciferous family, which provide soil compaction/hardpan loosening benefits.

TABLE 11.1

TOP REGIONAL COVER CROP SPECIES

Bioregion	N Source	Soil Builder	Erosion Fighter	Subsoil Loosener	Weed Fighter	Pest Fighter
Northeast	red clover, hairy vetch, berseem clover, sweet clover	ryegrass, sweet clover, sorghum-sudangrass hybrid, rye	rye, ryegrass, subterranean clover, oats	sorghum-sudangrass hybrid, sweet clover, forage radish	sorghum-sudangrass hybrid, ryegrass, rye, buckwheat	rye, sorghum-sudangrass hybrid, rapeseed
Mid-Atlantic	hairy vetch, red clover, berseem clover, crimson clover	ryegrass, rye, sweet clover, sorgham-sudangrass hybrid	subterranean clover, cowpeas, rye, ryegrass	sorghum-sudangrass hybrid, sweet clover, forage radish	rye, ryegrass, oats, buckwheat	rye, sorghum-sudangrass hybrid, rapeseed
Mid-South	hairy vetch, subterranean clover, berseem clover, crimson clover	ryegrass, rye, subterranean clover, sorghum-sudangrass hybrid	subterranean clover, cowpeas, rye, ryegrass	sorghum-sudangrass hybrid, sweet clover	buckwheat, ryegrass, subterranean clover, rye	rye, sorghym-sudangrass hybrid
Southeast Uplands	hairy vetch, red clover, berseem clover, crimson clover	ryegrass, rye, sorghum-sudangrass hybrid, sweet clover	subterranean clover, cowpeas, rye, ryegrass	sorghum-sudangrass hybrid, sweet clover	buckwheat, ryegrass, subterranean clover, rye	rye, sorghum-sudangrass hybrid
Southeast Lowlands	winter peas, subterranean clovers, hairy vetch, berseem clover, crimson clover	ryegrass, rye, sorghum-sudangrass hybrid, subterranean clover	subterranean clover, cowpeas, rye, ryegrass, sorghum-sudangrass hybrid	sorghum-sudangrass hybrid	berseem clover, rye, wheat, cowpeas, oats, ryegrass	rye, sorghum-sudangrass hybrid
Great Lakes	hairy vetch, red clover, berseem clover, crimson clover	ryegrass, rye, sorghum-sudangrass hybrid, sweet clover	oats, rye, ryegrass	sorghum-sudangrass hybrid, sweet clover, forage radish	berseem clover, rye-grass, rye, buckwheat, oats	rye, sorghum-sudangrass hybrid, rapeseed
Midwest Corn Belt	hairy vetch, red clover, berseem clover, crimson clover	rye, barley, sorghum-sudangrass hybrid, sweet clover	white clover, rye, ryegrass, barley	sorghum-sudangrass hybrid, sweet clover, forage radish	rye, ryegrass, wheat, buckwheat, oats	rye, sorghum-sudangrass hybrid
Northern Plains	hairy vetch, sweet clover, medics	rye, barley, medic, sweet clover	rye, barley	sorghum-sudangrass hybrid, sweet clover	medic, rye, barley	rye, sorghum-sudangrass hybrid

Bioregion	N Source	Soil Builder	Erosion Fighter	Subsoil Loosener	Weed Fighter	Pest Fighter
Southern Plains	Austrian winter peas, medic, hairy vetch	rye, barley, medic	rye, barley	sorghum-sudangrass hybrid, sweet clover	rye, barley	rye, sorghum-sudangrass hybrid
Inland Northwest	winter peas, hairy vetch	medic, sweet clover, rye, barley	rye, barley	sorghum-sudangrass hybrid, sweet clover	rye, wheat, barley	rye, mustards, sorghum-sudangrass hybrid
Northwest Maritime	berseem clover, sub-terranean clover, lana woollypod vetch, crimson clover	ryegrass, rye, sorghum-sudangrass hybrid, lana woollypod vetch	white clover, rye, ryegrass, barley	sorghum-sudangrass hybrid, sweet clover	ryegrass, lana woollypod vetch, oats, white clover	rye, mustards
Coastal California	berseem clover, sub-terranean clover, lana woollypod vetch, medic	ryegrass, rye, sorghum-sudangrass hybrid, lana woollypod vetch	white clover, cowpeas, rye, ryegrass	sorghum-sudangrass hybrid, sweet clover	rye, ryegrass, berseem clover, white clover	sorghum-sudangrass hybrid, crimson clover, rye
California Central Valley	Austrian winter peas, lana wool-lypod vetch, subterra-nean clover, medic	subterranean clover, medic	white clover, barley, rye, ryegrass	sorghum-sudangrass hybrid, sweet clover	ryegrass, white clover, rye, lana woollypod vetch	sorghum-sudangrass hybrid, crimon clover, rye
Southwest	medic, sub-terranean clover	subterra-nean clover, medic, barley	barley, sorghum-sudangrass hybrid		medic, barley	

Managing Cover Crops Profitably, 3rd Edition (Beltsville, MD: Sustainable Agriculture Network, 2007), 66.

The forage and oilseed tillage radishes apparently make their yield differences due to their unique plow pan/hardpan dissolving tap root, which has been measured to grow to a depth of thirty inches. This occurs when the root hits a psi pressure of close to 300 psi, whereby it diverts its energy to grow a tap root,

The Nordells

Some of my favorite low-tech, low-input organic vegetable growers are Anne and Eric Nordell of Trout Run, Pennsylvania.

The Nordells rely on aggressive but timely cultivation and they utilize a comprehensive rotation of cover crops integrated with their seven-acre market garden in north central Pennsylvania, growing greens, onions, potatoes, vegetables, herbs, and flowers. Cool season veggies are their specialty, and they have the skills required to run such an operation without irrigation and with little human input. Their horsepower is, literally, horses. Weed elimination and building soil structure are their substitutes for irrigation.

The basis of the Nordells' system is fallowing half the market garden each year, allowing the land to rest from vegetable production while utilizing cover crops to discourage weeds, which according to the Nordells are present either to build soil structure or to scavenge surplus fertility. They refer to their system as a "Bio-Extensive System" because they are building soil while eliminating weeds with their combined fallowing of the land, utilizing both cover crops planted in the spring and the autumn with shallow tillage lasting six weeks (beginning in June), whereby fallow land is shallow cultivated every ten to fourteen days in order to kill weeds before they have a chance to become established, and before the full cover crop is sowed.

The Nordells have put together a detailed template that includes a seventy-two-minute DVD and a forty-two-page booklet, called "Weeding the Soil, not the Crop," that details their twenty-four years of bio-extensive farming experience of reduced tillage, managing weeds, and fertility with limited off-farm inputs. It also showcases their "Cover Crop Clock" that provides an at-a-glance look at the time each plot is dedicated to crop growing and soil building.

Anne and Eric Nordell's DVD and booklet can both be obtained from them at 3410 Route 184, Trout Run, PA 17771.

instead of a tuber. The radishes are also efficient nitrogen scavengers, taking up as much as 150 pounds of nitrogen in the autumn and storing until spring to release it again. Spring weed suppression is also a benefit, even though low freezing temperatures in the teens kill the radish, which needs to be planted three to six weeks prior to the killing frost and at about five to eight plants per square foot, or two to three pounds per seed/acre. Being a cruciferous plant, it contains sulfur compounds called glucosinilates that discourage root diseases in many crops, as well as parasitic nematodes.

Other glucosinolate-rich crucifers include mustards, arugula, rapeseed, turnips, kale, swedes, rutabagas, collards, cabbage, brussels sprouts, and broccoli, most of which are also grown for human consumption and of which the glucosinolates have been recognized as profound liver detoxifiers and cancer deterrents.

COCKTAIL COVER CROPPING

A practice that fortunately appears to be catching on quite infectiously amongst the cover crop community is "cocktail cover cropping," growing multiple species (five to twenty) instead of one or two as has been traditionally done.

Steve Groff, of Cedar Meadow Farm in Lancaster County, Pennsylvania, closely observes "conventional" farming (for example, he uses GMO seeds and glyphosate). He has nevertheless demonstrated that soil erosion, nitrate losses, and off-farm input costs are no longer a given on his acreage when he grows corn, soybeans, pumpkins, tomatoes, and forages. His organic matter has risen from 2.7 percent to about 4.5-5.0 percent in a dozen years, and he farms slopes from 3 percent to 17 percent without erosion.

Steve's practices can readily be adopted by any farmer to reduce costs, improve profitability and minimize environmental impacts while increasing soil organic matter. He relies on shorter season corn varieties (eighty-three to ninety-seven days) in order to have a longer window of time to get his cover crop, which is becoming increasingly more diverse. His cocktails may include a combination of tillage radishes, sun hemp, crimson clover, hairy vetch, annual ryegrass, triticale, sorghum sudan, phacelia, winter peas, and lupins. In table 11.2, Steve's research demonstrated the following on corn in USDA Hardiness Zone 6B, back in 2010–2011.

As can readily be seen, the profits from 191 bushels of corn yield without a drop of nitrogen applied wasn't far behind his 205 bushels/acre with only 60 units applied. According to the industry rule of thumb, one needs 1.25 units of nitrogen to produce 1 bushel of corn. Thus a 191-bushel yield would

TABLE 11.2

1. Yield	190.8 bu/acre	205 bu/acre	198.1 bu/acre	196.9 bu/acre
2. Cover Crop (Fertilizer, Seed, $17.60 drill cost)	$46.80	-0-	-0-	-0-
3. Nitrogen ($0.795/lb) (cost + $12.00 app. cost) (60/40 mix urea & ammonium sulfate)	0	$59.70 60 units	$83.55 90 units	$107.40 120 units
4. Gross profit/acre (@ $7.00/bu Corn)	$1,288.80/ac	$1,379.50	$1,303.15	$1,270.90
5. Net Profit/acre (Input Costs only included)	$1,242/acre	$1,319/ac	$1,219/ac	$1,163.50/ac

Chart reproduced from www.cedarmeadowfarm.com.

require 239 units of nitrogen per acre, and a 205-bushel yield would need 256 units of nitrogen. No doubt that Steve's many years of building humus on his soil generated huge reserves of organic nitrogen that could be mineralized as sustained-release nitrogen on all of his corn plots. If cover crops were to be abandoned and his organic matter expectedly drop, his dependence on off-farm purchased nitrogen (and phosphorous, potassium, and trace elements) would undoubtedly rise.

In 2012, Illinois was exceptionally dry, yet the results of the Cover Crop Solution trials that included soybeans were telling:

2012 Illinois Soybean Yields*

1. Bare field   23.5 bu/acre
2. Deep root annual ryegrass   42.9 bu/acre
3. Tillage radish and deep root annual ryegrass   42.7 bu/acre
4. Tillage radish and deep root annual ryegrass   54.3 bu/acre
   (plus crimson clover)

With these kinds of results and less than 10 percent of American farmers cover cropping (less than 2 percent in the Mississippi River Basin), all I can say is that there either "ought to be a law," or if the conventional operators want to continue to receive taxpayer-subsidized government checks for crop insurance, they should do so provided that they implement a systems

---

* Chart reproduced from www.cedarmeadowfarm.com.

approach that keeps that topsoil on their property. Because it would prevent crop failures much more often than not, it is a win-win proposal. The government crop insurance program suffers less loss, while the farmer enhances his profit margins due to reduced purchased inputs and better yields. Again, the bible on cover crops, what they do, where geographically they are best adapted, the optimal time to plant them (e.g., summer annual, winter annual, biannual, perennial), seeding rates, fertility requirements, and such is *Managing Cover Crops Profitably*, third edition, put out by the Sustainable Agriculture Network of USDA.

One innovator who is getting a lot of attention these days is Gabe Brown, a rancher and farmer practicing no-till farming and holistic management grazing near Bismark, North Dakota, who is working in concert with Jay Fuhrer, the NRCS district conservationist.

Although Gabe has been no-tilling since the early 1990s, he became inspired about cocktail cover cropping by the work of Brazilian agronomist Ademir Caligari, PhD, who began incorporating cocktail cover crop strategies on the lighter, sandier soils of Brazil with a growing season providing two annual cash crops. Building an organic matter reserve in a subtropical environment where oxidation rates of organic matter are more of a challenge resulted in a sound, cost-effective concept.

Clearly, North Dakota isn't Brazil, so it would be a trailblazing experiment to try something like this where wintertime temperatures can approach fifty below zero. And perhaps that's why Gabe was the recipient of the Natural Resource Defense Council's Growing Green Award in 2012. Reducing his fertilizer inputs by 90 percent and herbicide by 50 percent could only be achieved by planting a couple of dozen cover crops to nourish his soils so that he could cost effectively grow spring wheat, winter triticale, oats, corn, sunflowers, peas, alfalfa, and hairy vetch.

His cover crops, planted as a mix of up to a dozen species, consisted of pearl millet, sorghum sundan grass, proso millet, buckwheat, sunn hemp, oil seed radish, turnips, pasja, ryegrass, canola, phacelea, cowpeas, soybeans, sugar beets, red clover, sweet clover, kale, rape, lentils, mung beans, and subterranean clover, thus incorporating cool season grasses, cool season broad leaves, warm season grasses and warm season broad leaves.

His seventy-two- to seventy-nine-day corn, no-tilled into his legume rich cover crop, yielded an average of 127 bushels per acre, the countywide average being 100 bushels. This in a region that only receives fifteen inches of precipitation annually! His expenses ran him $1.10–$1.20 per bushel while his corn sold for $6.48 per bushel. Even though he rotates other crops into his corn rotation, he still nets $855 per acre on all of his acreage, including crops and cattle. The secret is the organic content of his soils, which started out at 1.70–1.90 percent in the early nineties when he switched to no-till. Today, most of his soil samples are running 4.7–5.3 percent. Gabe's model is the virgin rangeland nearby that's never seen a plow, with organic matter levels as high as 7.3 percent.

Since Gabe is also a cattle rancher, the use of grazing animals has made a significant difference on the recovery of his landscape by utilizing holistic management practices of high animal densities for short periods of time with adequate recovery rest periods. In 1991, his operation could run sixty-five cow/calf pairs and twenty yearlings. In 2012, the carrying capacity had increased to four hundred cow/calf pairs and eight hundred yearlings, with live weight densities as high as 680,000 lbs to 900,000 lbs per acre!

All of this translates into more than just more income per acre. The farm is now virtually drought-proof because the water infiltration rate has increased from half an inch per hour to eight inches per hour.

In Ohio, extension researcher Jim Hoorman is collaborating with growers like David Brandt, who has increased his organic matter from 0.5 to 4.0 percent and claims he now knows how to do this in a five-year span using eight- to nine-way mixes of cover crops. In the drought of 2013, Brandt's farm received only 8.5 inches of rain, and Brandt still got 236 bushels of corn per acre on his farm! One reason why drought proofing a farm with cover crops works, according to research at the Paul Scherrer Institute of Switzerland (www.psi.ch), is that: a) roots are 90 percent water, b) soil within a few millimeters of roots has 30 percent more water than surrounding soil, and c) roots exude a gel-like mucilage (mucigel) that can absorb ten thousand times its own dry weight of water.

Hoorman says that forty tons of crop residues will digest into ten tons, yielding a 1 percent increase of organic matter, which is equivalent to $900 in nutrients. Over twenty years, a no-till cover crop field will produce only seven inches of total runoff. Healthy, organic-rich soil can actually be nine inches higher than adjacent soil that has been reduced to clay, silt, and sand from destructive monoculture and tillage practices.

These cover crop innovators are yet another promising paradigm shift, as are the pasture-cropping practices of Colin Seis of Winona Farms and his colleagues seeking to answer how we can "feed the 9 billion" without GMOs, habitat destruction, loss of biodiversity, annihilation of our pollinators, the massive erosion of topsoil, and an epidemic of chronic human illnesses such as cancer, Parkinson's, and autoimmune disorders that are clearly associated with continual exposure to herbicides, fungicides, insecticides, and nematocides.

GROWING HUMUS WITH COVER CROPS—A BED AT A TIME

On a much smaller scale, I have found that using cover crops in my 6,000 square foot vegetable beds can really raise the bar on moisture conservation and weed suppression. My beds are typically about four feet wide. Beginning in August, I seed the beds—which may be growing tomatoes, peppers, brassicas, etc.—with a mixture of winter rye, crimson clover, red clover, hairy vetch, and tillage radish, which germinates but doesn't grow much due to the shade canopy. Once the killing frost has arrived in mid-October, I remove and compost the dead plants, and the cover crop really takes off, establishing a thick stand within two to four weeks.

In the spring, I allow the rye to become lignified, to get in the "boot" stage; that is, when the seed head is just forming and the stalk becomes higher in its straw-like constitution. I then mow it down with a trimmer and use the mulch as a barrier against heat/drought and weeds. Highly lignified rye can suck a lot of carbon out of the soil, so when putting in transplants use a cupful of good compost at the bottom of the transplanting hole if the clovers are not yet well established. For small seeds, like beets, carrots, kale, turnips, lettuce, radishes, etc., the soil is tilled to create a good seed bed. Depending what the ratio of lignified rye to red or crimson clover/vetch is, I may apply compost and/or organic nitrogen, like fish hydrolysate, to the seed furrow. Periodic drenches with an organic-based or commercial fertilizer may be needed through the first half of the growing season as the high-carbon rye breaks down into humus. Hairy vetch and rye/hairy vetch combinations maintain a consistent, more narrow C:N ratio, averaging slightly below or slightly above the 10:1 ratio respectively from fall through late spring. Winter rye alone, on the other hand,

climbs dramatically from an approximate 12:1 ratio in the fall to over a 40:1 ratio by late spring.

Another practice of mine is to set aside a few beds for continuous and successive cover crops. Thus, after mowing the "fallow" bed containing legumes and winter rye, I will overseed (without tilling) that same bed with buckwheat in May or June, allow it to flower, mow it down, overseed with sorghum-sudan in July, mow it, and overseed with oil seed radishes. Then in September, I will overseed with winter rye, clovers, and vetch, and that bed then can be used the following spring; this allows the soil to build both carbon and nitrogen reserves while providing an untold amount of plant root exudates—including amino acids, carbohydrates, lipids, and plant secondary metabolites—to be dumped into that ecosystem, strengthening the microbial communities that in turn can create "immune soils" that prevent diseases. This practice can also encourage more assimilation by the successive crop because it has an improved "digestive" system, namely a soil food web consisting of microbial and botanical diversity. And last but not least, my interim cover crops provide nectar and pollen for pollinators and predators.

12

The Tools
of the Trade

*We are exhausting the quality of our soils. As we do so the quality
of our plants goes down. And we are accepting this.*

—William A. Albrecht, PhD

O THER than the laboratory resources that provide soil analysis, forage tests/tissue tests, and water analysis, there are a number of practices that the grower can utilize on-site in real time. To ascertain one's limitations and level of progress—or lack thereof—one can easily amass a great deal of information necessary to improving crop performance long before lab analysis results are returned. Additionally, taking the "pulse of your land" can be done quite inexpensively at any time to determine its vitality and biological resilience.

Fortunately the USDA Natural Resources Conservation Service (NRCS) has assembled a soil quality guide, also called a soil health card, which can reflect what they refer to as the "dynamic quality" of soils, defined as the changing nature of soil properties resulting from human use and management.

Soil quality indicators can be assessed by qualitative and/or quantitative techniques. *Qualitative* assessments are reports on the nature of an indicator and would have an element of subjectivity. They are also done by the same person over time to minimize variability in the results. These determinations can be done simply and quickly with minimal tools, if tools are needed at all. Because of their subjective nature, results cannot be compared to any target levels for various soil properties, and results shouldn't be compared among different users of different farms. Although more time consuming, a *quantitative* assessment is the accurate measurement of an indicator having a precise numeric value; thus different people conducting the same measurement should be able to produce very similar results.

The *Soil Health Card* integrates physical, biological and chemical properties and has a scoring system ranging from "poor" to "good" or a numerical scale from 1 to 10 for each indicator. The cards can be obtained from local NRCS, the extension, or your Conservation District offices. They can also be accessed at the Soil Quality Institute website, www.soils.usda. gov/sqi. It typically takes less than thirty minutes to complete the tests in the Soil Test Kit.

The *Soil Quality Test Kit* was developed by USDA Agriculture Research Service (ARS) and is an on-farm soil quality assessment tool set. Included in the kit are tools to measure soil respiration, water infiltration, bulk density, pH, electrical conductivity, aggregate stability, slaking, and earthworms. Completing the entire set of measurements for twelve soil quality diagnostic tests may take as long as four to six hours. However, the results can be determined immediately following the tests.

The *NRCS Soil Health Card* template is a subjective assessment of the soil, but it is a very comprehensive outline of where to look and what to look for. Table 12.1 relates the best times to look for the indicators. The *NRCS Soil Health Card* template has one score, or rank, for each of the nearly twenty indicators as low, medium, or high. This template provides the farmer with an overview of the many facets that should be observed in order to get a read of the overall health of the landscape.

The *NRCS Indicator Table* is also a boots-on-the-ground, simple-to-use, albeit subjective, approach to both big picture and the details that make it up.

The *Assessment Sheet* allows you to keep track of the changes a particular field is making over time for each of the nearly dozen indicators.

USING THE SOIL TEST HEALTH CARD

Although similar to the NRCS Soil Health Card, this test entails more hands-on evaluation, though it takes very little time to conduct the tests.

Some considerations to adhere to, in order to get the best information:
1. Make the requisite equipment
    • First, construct a wire quadrant by bending a wire coat hanger, opening outward to make a square. Each side is approximately 9–10 inches (24–25 cm).
    • Fabricate your own penetrometer. Take a 20 inch (50 cm) length

TABLE 12.1

| Indicators | Best Time For Assessments Of Indicators | | |
	Stage of Crop Growth	Moisture Conditions	Tillage
Earthworms	Pre-plant, active growth	Good soil moisture	Before
Soil Organisms	Pre-plant, active growth	Good soil moisture	Before
Smell	Anytime	Adequate soil moisture	Anytime
Organic Material	Pre-plant, active growth	NA	After
Residue Decomposition	Anytime	Adequate soil moisture	NA
Compaction	Anytime	Adequate soil moisture	Anytime
Workability	Pre-plant, post harvest	Adequate soil moisture	During tillage
Soil Tilth/ Structure	Pre-plant, active growth	Adequate soil moisture	Anytime
Soil Aggregates	Pre-plant, active growth	Adequate soil moisture	Not too soon prior to or after tillage
Porosity	Pre-plant, active growth	Adequate soil moisture	Not too soon prior to or after tillage
Crusting	Pre-plant, active growth	Adequate soil moisture	Anytime
Water Infiltration	Anytime	After irrigation or rain	Not too soon prior to or after tillage
Drainage	Anytime	After irrigation or rain	Anytime
Water Holding Capacity	Pre-plant, active growth	After irrigation or rain	Anytime
Wind or Water Erosion	Anytime	Any	Anytime
Crop Vigor/ Appearance	Active growth	Adequate soil moisture	NA
Plant Roots	Active growth	Adequate soil moisture	NA
Root Mass	Active growth	Adequate soil moisture	NA
Salts	Any	Any	Any
Sodium	Any	Any	Any

NOTE: This calendar is approximate. Tailor it to local climates, cropping systems, and soil types.

United States Department of Agriculture, *Guidelines for Soil Quality Assessment in Conservation Planning*, Natural Resources Conservation Service Soil Quality Institute, January 2001, 38.

FIGURE 12.1

NRCS Soil Health Card Template

Operator Name_____Date of Visit_____ Field/Farm ID_____

Indicator	Ranking			Scoring
	Low	Medium	High	Circle one
Earthworms	Few worms per shovel, no casts or holes	More worms per shovel, some casts or holes	Many worms per shovel, many casts or holes.	L M H
Soil Organisms	Few insects, worms, fungi, or soil life	Some insects, worms, fungi, soil life	Many insects, worms, fungi, soil full of variety of organisms	L M H
Smell	Swampy smell	Little or no smell	Fresh earthy smell	L M H
Surface Organic Material	No visible roots or residue	Some residue	Lots of roots/residue in many stages of decomposition	L M H
Residue Decomposition	Very slow decomposition, or rapid decomposition	Some visible, nondecomposed residue	Residue at various stages of decomposition	L M H
Compaction	Hard layers, tight soil, restricted root penetration, obvious hardpan, roots turned awkwardly	Firm soil, slightly restricted root penetration, moderate shovel resistance and penetration of wire flag beyond tillage layer	Loose soil, unrestricted root penetration, no hardpan, mostly vertical root plant growth	L M H
Workability	Many passes and horsepower needed for good seedbed, soil difficult to work	Soil works reasonably well	Tills easily and requires little power to pull implements	L M H
Soil Tilth/ Structure	Soil clods difficult to break, crusting, tillage creates large clods, soil falls apart in hands, very powdery	Moderate porosity, some crusting, small clods, soil breaks apart with medium pressure	Soil crumbles well, friable, porous	L M H
Soil Aggregates	Soil surface is hard, clumps and does not break apart, very powdery	Soil crumbles in hand, few aggregates	Soil surface has many soft small aggregates which crumble easily	L M H

United States Department of Agriculture, *Guidelines for Soil Quality Assessment in Conservation Planning*, Natural Resources Conservation Service Soil Quality Institute, January 2001, 35.

NRCS Soil Health Card Template Cont'd

Indicator	Ranking			Scoring
	Low	Medium	High	Circle one
Porosity	Few worm and root channels	Weak plow pan, some new and old root and worm channels	Many worm and root channels, many pores between aggregates	L M H
Crusting	Soil surface seals easily, seed emergence inhibited	Some surface sealing	Soil surface has open or porous surface all season	L M H
Water Infiltration	Water on surface for long period of time after rain or irrigation	Water drains slowly after rain or irrigation, some ponding	No ponding after heavy rain or irrigation, water moves steadily through soil	L M H
Drainage	Excessive wet spots in field, ponding, root disease	Some wet spots in field and profile, some root disease	Water is evenly drained through field and soil profile, no evidence of root disease	L M H
Water Holding Capacity	Plant stress immediately following rain or irrigation, soil has limited capacity to hold water, soil requires frequent irrigation	Crops are not first to suffer in area from dry spell, soil requires average irrigation	Soil holds water well for long time, deep topsoil for water storage, crops do well in dry spells, soil requires less than average irrigation	L M H
Wind or Water Erosion	Obvious soil deposition, large gullies joined, obvious soil drifting	Some deposition, few gullies, some colored runoff, some evidence of soil drifting	No visible soil movement, no gullies, clear or no runoff, no obvious soil drifting	L M H
Crop Vigor/ Appearance	Stunted growth, uneven stand, discoloration, low yields	Some uneven or stunted growth, slight discoloration, signs of stress	Healthy, vigorous, and uniform stand	L M H

United States Department of Agriculture, *Guidelines for Soil Quality Assessment in Conservation Planning*, Natural Resources Conservation Service Soil Quality Institute, January 2001, 36.

NRCS Soil Health Card Template Cont'd

| Indicator | Ranking | | | Scoring |
	Low	Medium	High	Circle one
Plant Roots	Poor growth/ structure, brown or mushy roots	Some fine roots, mostly healthy	Vigorous, and healthy root system, good color	L M H
Root Mass	Very few roots, mostly horizontal	More roots, some vertical, some horizontal	Many vertical and horizontal roots, deep roots	L M H
Salts	Visible salt/alkali, dead plants	Stunted growth, signs of leaf burn from salts	No visible salt, alkali or plant damage espe- cially after rains	L M H
Sodium	Soil surface seals after rain or irrigation, fluffy when dry, uneven crop stand	Only some spots with sealed surface	No sealing or fluff at surface, no plant damage	L M H
Other				L M H
Other				L M H

NOTES:
1) Take all measurements under adequate moisture conditions (e.g., not excessively dry or wet).
2) Certain measurements, such as soil life, earthworms, structure, and tillage are affected greatly by field operations. They should be assessed before major tillage operations.
3) Select the best time for assessment and take measurements at the same time every year. See Maryland Card for an example of assessment time or calendar.
4) Include only regionally relevant indicators and descriptive terms.
5) This list is not all-inclusive. Add indicators as necessary, and leave blank spaces for field determined indicators.

United States Department of Agriculture, *Guidelines for Soil Quality Assessment in Conservation Planning*, Natural Resources Conservation Service Soil Quality Institute, January 2001, 37.

FIGURE 12.2

INDICATOR TABLE

Indicator	Poor	Medium	Good
Earthworms	0–1 worms in shovelful of top foot of soil. No casts or holes.	2–10 in shovelful. Few casts, holes, or worms.	10+ in top foot of soil. Lots of casts and holes in tilled clods. Birds behind tillage.
Organic matter color	Topsoil color similar to subsoil color.	Surface color closer to subsoil color.	Topsoil clearly defined, darker than subsoil.
Organic matter roots/residue	No visible residue or roots.	Some residue, few roots.	Noticeable roots and residue.
Subsurface compaction	Wire breaks or bends when inserting flag.	Have to push hard, need fist to push flag in.	Flag goes in easily with fingers to twice the depth of plow layer.
Soil tilth mellowness friability	Looks dead, like brick or concrete, cloddy. Either blows apart or hard to pull drill through.	Somewhat cloddy, balls up, rough pulling seedbed.	Soil crumbles well, can slice through, like cutting butter. Spongy when you can walk on it.
Erosion	Large gullies over 2 inches deep joined to others, thin or no topsoil, rapid runoff the color of soil.	Few rills or gullies, gullies up to two inches deep. Some swift runoff, colored water.	No gullies or rills, clear or no runoff.
Water holding capacity	Plant stress two days after a good rain.	Water runs out after a week or so.	Holds water for a long period of time without puddling.
Drainage, infiltration	Water lays for a long time, evaporates more than drains, always very wet ground.	Water lays for short period of time, eventually drains.	No ponding, no runoff, water moves through soil steadily. Soil not too wet, not too dry.
Crop condition (how well it grows)	Problem growing throughout season, poor growth, yellow or purple color.	Fair growth, spots in field different, medium green color.	Normal healthy dark green color, excellent growth all season across field.
pH	Hard to correct for desired crop.	Easily correctable.	Proper pH for crop.
Nutrient holding capacity	Soil tests, dropping with more fertilizer applied than crops used.	Little change or slowdown trend	Soil tests trending up in relation to fertilizer applied and crop harvested.

United States Department of Agriculture, *Guidelines for Soil Quality Assessment in Conservation Planning*, Natural Resources Conservation Service Soil Quality Institute, January 2001, 2.

FIGURE 12.3
ASSESSMENT SHEET

Date_____ Crop_____

Farm/Field ID_____

Soil Quality Indicators	Poor			Medium			Good		
	1	2	3	4	5	6	7	8	9
Earthworms									
Organic Matter Color									
Organic Matter Roots/Residue									
Subsurface Compaction									
Tilth/Friability Mellowness									
Erosion									
Water Holding Capacity									
Drainage Infiltration									
Crop Condition									
pH									
Nutrient Holding Capacity									
Other (write in)									
Other (write in)									

United States Department of Agriculture, *Guidelines for Soil Quality Assessment in Conservation Planning*, Natural Resources Conservation Service Soil Quality Institute, January 2001, 4.

of 10-gauge, high tensile wire. Curl the end of it into a loop handle using about 5 inches (or 12 cm) to do so. The remaining 15 inches (94 cm) is then scribed with a line every inch (or 2.5 cm), using a file to make the markings.
  • Construct an infiltrometer ring by taking a 6-inch-diameter (15 cm) PVC pipe at a length of 4.5 inches (11 cm) in length. Bevel the edges to make it easier to push into the soil.
2. When to test: Typically, more uniform results can be obtained in autumn, two to three days after a rainfall. Sample yearly at about the same time and under comparable conditions. Avoid flooded or drought-stressed soils or times of very high or low temperatures. Wait a few weeks following lime or fertilizer or manure applications.
3. Where to test: For the most meaningful results, test your best and worst locations. This gives you a benchmark of where to place other soils on the property.
4. Determining the number of soil cards: At each site, multiple cards may be warranted:
  • If there is more than one soil type in the field.
  • To compare conditions in the pasture to along the fence line or hedgerow.
  • To compare conditions in the row of a crop to those soils in between the rows.
  • To compare soils adjacent to, but not part of the orchard, vineyard, cropland, or pasture.
5. Each card has ten tests as well as space allotted for you to draw a sketch map of the site. Do at least five sets of tests to give you both a familiarity with the tests as well as the lay of your land.
6. Follow-up tests. Keep checking the low scoring areas at least once yearly to see how much progress any improvement protocols have made. Ideally, repeat every six to twelve months.

Testing Equipment Needed

1. Wire clothes hanger quadrant
2. Wire penetrometer
3. PVC infiltrometer tube
4. Spade
5. Small wide mouth jar with lid, marked at 125 ml level (4 oz)
6. 500 ml measuring cup (16 oz)

7. Container of water (allow 1250 ml [40 oz] water per sample site if soil is dry, 750 ml [24 oz] if soil is moist)
8. Soil pH kit (probe, meter for fifty-fifty soil, pH Hydrion paper)
9. Heavy duty plastic sheet three by three feet
10. Soil Health Card for each site to be tested
11. Clipboard and pencil
12. Watch with second hand display
13. Eight-by-eight-inch unbleached calico strips (one per test)
14. Felt pen
15. Twenty-inch (50 cm) length of a two-by-four (10 cm x 5 cm) board
16. Six eight-inch nails

Site Sampling Procedures
1. Begin from a designated point (e.g., flag attached to fence post or hedgerow tree).
2. Confine samples to similar soil types for each Soil Health Card.
3. Sketch a layout of the sample sites on the back of the assessment sheet. Mark any soil type boundaries as defined by the FSA/NRCS soil maps for your farm. Or define the soil types yourself (e.g., sandy loam, clay, clay loam, etc.).

The Soil Tests
1. **Ground Cover:** Throw the coat hanger quadrant randomly upon the surface and make an estimate of the amount of bare soil, subtracting this from 100 percent to determine ground cover. This test is applicable to pastures, meadows, orchards, vineyards, and cropland (if it is not tilled with a cover crop). Make a note of the amount of depth of surface litter, thatch, and mulch.
2. **Penetrometer:** Push the homemade wire penetrometer into the soil as deeply as you can without heavy exertion. If you hit a root or rock, move it to a new location. Record the depth on the assessment sheet. If using a purchased manufactured penetrometer (I believe every farmer needs one), apply slow, even pressure to push the penetrometer into the soil at a rate of four seconds per six inches or less. Record the highest pressure reading of psi (pounds per square inch). Ideally, a compaction test should be done at zero to six inches of depth and another at six to eighteen inches of depth by removing the top six inches with a spade. Roots cannot penetrate soils with penetrometer readings greater than three hundred psi unless you are using hardpan-

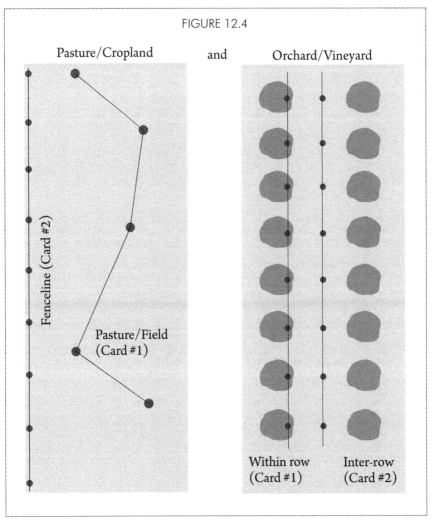

FIGURE 12.4

Pasture/Cropland   and   Orchard/Vineyard

Fenceline (Card #2)

Pasture/Field
(Card #1)

Within row   Inter-row
(Card #1)   (Card #2)

Northern Rivers Soil Health Card: Coffee, SoilCare Inc., June 2008, http://www.soilcare.
org/documents/Soil%20Health%20Card%20Coffee21-7-08.pdf.

fracturing plants like forage (tillage) radishes, chicory, burnet, warm-season perennials, etc. It is recommended that such a test be done at field capacity for moisture, several days following free drainage.

3. **Infiltrometer:**

    a. Remove all organic residues (mulch, thatch, etc.) and trim the living vegetation as close to the soil surface without disturbing the soil structure.

    b. Tap or push the infiltrometer PVC pipe ring into the soil about

FIGURE 12.5

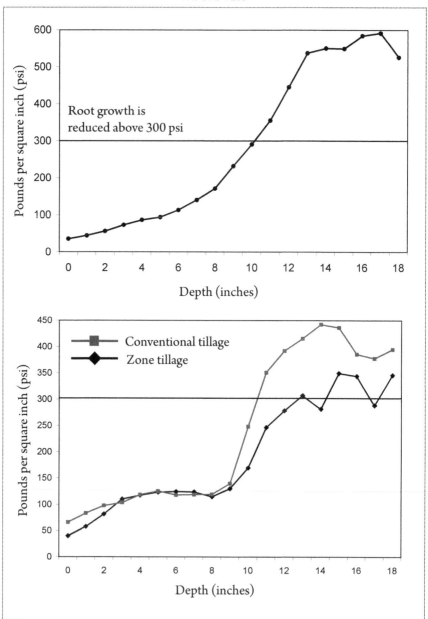

B. K. Gugino, O. J. Idowu, R. R. Schindelbeck, H. M. van Es, D. W. Wolfe, B. N. Moebius-Clune, J. E. Thies, and G.S. Abawi, *Cornell Soil Health Assessment Training Manual* (Geneva, NY: New York State Agricultural Experiment Station, 2009), 17, http://soilhealth.cals.cornell.edu.

three-fourths an inch (2 cm). Avoid stones, roots, and cracks or holes in the ground. Ensure the top of the ring is level.

   c. "Caulk" the inside edge of the ring by gently firming the soil against the edge, creating a seal to prevent water leakage around the ring.

   d. Carefully pour a pint (16 oz or 500 ml) of water into the ring, noting the time on the watch.

   e. Time how long it takes for the water to infiltrate the soil. Record the time when the soil surface is still glistening as the end point.

(Note: if the top three inches (7 cm) is dry, this test needs to be done twice, with the second test recorded as the most accurate. If the field is oversaturated, wait at least two days prior to conducting this test.)

4. **Diversity of Soil Life:** This is an evaluation of the diversity of species, not the numbers of organisms. Use the coat hanger quadrant to randomly pick an area not disturbed by previous tests. First, examine the surface of the litter and vegetation growing there. Then, methodically, carefully sift through any litter. Make a note of the varieties of soil life you encounter: spiders, millipedes, centipedes, earthworms, beetles, mites, springtails, and ants.

5. **Root Development:** Using a spade, cut a square block of soil eight-by-eight-by-eight-inches deep (or 20 cm square by 20 cm deep). This is 512 cubic inches (8,000 cubic centimeters) in volume, or 0.30 of a cubic foot, (which is 1,728 cubic inches, 12" x 12" x 12"). Lift the block of soil out, placing it on the plastic sheet. Without breaking the lump apart, examine the distribution of roots, noting where the fine roots are located and recording it on the card.

6. **Soil Structure:** Break a handful of soil away from the block near the surface and examine this sample for the size and arrangement of the soil aggregate or "crumb" structure. Using your fingers, apply pressure to break the clump up into crumbs of various sizes up to 0.40 inches (10 mm). Look for root hairs throughout the crumbs, which penetrate through the pore space. Overly solid soil (clods, plates, hard crumbs) would be poor structure, as would too loose a soil having little to no crumbs, such as a very sandy soil. Smell the soil. It should have an aromatic, earthy, fragrant odor. Soils that smell sour, mildewy, or putrid are probably associated with poor crumb structure.

7. **Aggregate Stability:** Put 4.5 oz (125 ml) of water into the wide mouth jar. Select three to four pea-size crumbs from an inch (10 cm) depth of soil block. Drop them into the water. Allow them to stand for one minute. Observe if the crumbs break apart or remain intact. If

intact after one minute of submersion, gently swill the jar several times and observe again. If they're still intact, swill the bottle vigorously and observe again. Obviously, healthy soils have more "glues"—called glomalin, mucilage, and polysaccharides—to hold them together. This is a sign of microbial activity in the soil doing its job of granulating the soil for adequate aeration and water infiltration. Repeat the same test again, except at an eight-inch (20 cm) depth, and record your results for both.

8. **Earthworms:** Now break up the entire block of soil into crumbs and spread out over the plastic sheet. Count any worms larger than one inch (2.5 cm/25 mm). Record on the sheet and return worms to the hole. Higher earthworm counts indicate higher fertility, optimal pH, and low pesticide residues.

9. **Soil pH:** Take two samples from the sides of the hole, one at two inches (5 cm) deep the other from eight inches (20 cm) deep. Following the instructions with the kit or pH device, note what each pH is and record. Acidity (<6.0 pH) can affect soil microbial activity, plant root health, and optimal uptake of nutrients.

10. **Leaf Color:** Chlorophyll production is generally reflected in the healthy color of the leaf. Examine fully formed leaves away from the growing tips, which can be pale due to their youth. Older leaves near the stem can show normal mottling. And leaves closest to the ground can often be going through senescence or aging.

11. **Calico Strip Test for Microbial Action:** Microbes recycle nutrients that are the residues of previous and existing crops, and their activity can be estimated by measuring the breakdown or decomposition of calico cloth, an unbleached cloth similar to some muslins. Cut unbleached and washed calico into eight-inch (20 cm) squares. Using a felt pen, draw a line across the cloth two inches (5 cm) in from one edge. Make a slice into the soil with the spade to a depth of six inches (15 cm) and insert the calico cloth into the slot using the spade to shoehorn the calico, making sure the felt line coincides with the soil surface. Allow the calico strip to remain in place for three weeks. Gently extract the strip and rinse the soil particles off the calico strip in a kitchen colander. Allow to dry, and then place the calico strip over a sheet of graph paper. Calculate the percentage of the calico that was completely decomposed. The more decomposition, the more microbial activity in the soil and the more healthy biology present in the soil.

FIGURE 12.6

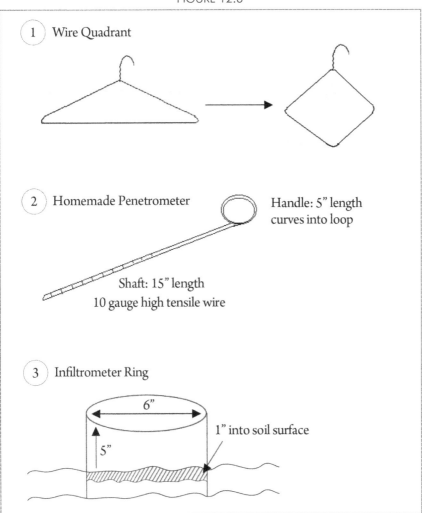

1. Wire Quadrant

2. Homemade Penetrometer

Handle: 5" length
curves into loop

Shaft: 15" length
10 gauge high tensile wire

3. Infiltrometer Ring

6"

1" into soil surface

5"

Northern Rivers Soil Health Card: Coffee, SoilCare Inc., June 2008, http://www.soilcare.org/
documents/Soil%20Health%20Card%20Coffee21-7-08.pdf.

12. Bioturbation: Bioturbation is the mixing of the surface organic matter
into the soil by organisms. Soil layers are categorized by "horizons."
The "O" horizon is the organic horizon, consisting of organic matter
in various stages of decomposition. Fresh litter is found on the surface.
As the "O" horizon depth increases, the vegetation has decomposed
into humus, with all signs of the original vegetal structure being
eliminated. In the "A" horizon, the organic material starts to mix with

The Tools of the Trade **273**

FIGURE 12.7
SOIL HEALTH CARD RESULTS SHEET

Date_____   Location/Management_____

Soil Type_____   Productivity_____

Days since 20mm rain_____   Soil moisture: dry / moist / wet

TEST ▼	RESULT ▶ 1 .... 2 3	4 .... 5 6	7 .... 8 9	Test Scores (1-9) 1	2	3	4	5
1. Ground Cover (Plants Or Mulch)	Less than 50% ground cover	50% to 75% ground cover	More than 75% ground cover					
2. Diversity Of Soil Life	Fewer than two types of soil animals	Two to five types of soil animals	More than five types of soil animals					
3. Penetrometer · Surface · 20 cm Depth (From Bottom Of Hole – After Test 5)	Wire probe will not penetrate	Penetrates with difficulty less than 20	Wire probe easily penetrates to 20 cm.					
4. Infiltration · Surface · 20 Cm Depth (After Test 5)	More than 7 minutes	3 to 7 minutes	Less than 3 minutes					
5. Root Development	Few fine roots only near the surface.	Some fine roots mostly near the surface.	Many fine roots throughout.					
6. Soil Structure	Mostly clods or with surface crust, few crumbs	Some clods but also many 10 mm crumbs	Friable, readily breaks into 10 mm crumbs					
7. Depth 'A-1' Horizon	0 to 1.9 cm	2 cm to 4.9 cm	5 or over					
8. Earthworms	0 – 3	4 – 6	more than 6					
9. Ph · 10 Cm Depth · 20 Cm Depth	pH 5 or lower	pH 5.0 to 5.5	pH 5.6 to pH 6.3					
10. Leaf Colour	Stunted plants, leaf discolouration	Some variation in growth and colour	Dark green glossy leaf colour & vigorous growth					

Northern Rivers Soil Health Card: Coffee, SoilCare Inc., June 2008, http://www.soilcare.
org/documents/Soil%20Health%20Card%20Coffee21-7-08.pdf.

FIGURE 12.8

Site Plan
(Showing a permanent reference point, 5 sample points, soil type changes, etc.)

	1.
	2.
	3.
	4.
	5.
	6.
	7.
	8.
	9.
	10.

Northern Rivers Soil Health Card: Coffee, SoilCare Inc., June 2008, http://www.soilcare.org/documents/Soil%20Health%20Card%20Coffee21-7-08.pdf.

FIGURE 12.9

Test Result	Situation Indicated	Possible Causes
1) Low ground cover	ground plants absent or growth is poor	unsuitable plant type(s), soil compaction, erosion, shading
2) Low variety of soil fauna	lack of habitat or food for fauna, poor soil structure, presence of harmful chemicals	sparse litter, low soil organic matter, lack of soil spaces and channels, mortality from recent use of insecticides or regular use of cumulative chemical(s) such as copper
3) Low probe penetrability	soil is generally hard, hard at the surface only, hard layer at greater depth	compacted by traffic or by over-working, low soil organic matter, compacted by traffic, especially if soil is wet at the time, compacted by heavy vehicles or 'hard pan' formed by soil inverting cultivators

Test Result	Situation Indicated	Possible Causes
4) Slow water infiltration	high proportion of clay particles, lack of spaces, channels or, burrows in soil	naturally high clay content of soil type, possible loss of topsoil, soil compaction, poor soil structure, lack of earthworms, surface crusting
5) Poor root development	hard soil lacking spaces, poor plant nutrition, root disease or attack	loss of topsoil, poor soil structure, soil compaction, soil pH not suitable for crop, lack of major or minor nutrients, presence of soil-borne pathogen, root-feeding nematodes or root-feeding insects
6) Poor soil structure	powdery soil, few crumbs, excessive clods	lack of soil-binding substances and processes, low soil organic matter (sparse ground cover), few worms, topsoil loss, soil compaction, low soil organic matter, excessive cultivation
7) Lack of depth of A1 (AO) horizon	low organic matter, low population soil organisms	loss of topsoil, sparse ground cover (see 1), copper toxicity, low variety of soil fauna (see 2), few earthworms (see 6)
8) Low earthworm count	pH unfavourable, poor food supply, lack of soil spaces, predators or parasites present, presence of harmful chemical	soil pH naturally low, pH reduced by use of acidifying fertilisers, sparse litter and/or ground cover (and roots), low organic content, low populations of fungi and bacteria, loss of topsoil, soil compaction, poor structure, predators (such as flatworms) and parasites (eg parasitic fly) may occur in 'plague' numbers, mortality from recent use of insecticides or regular use of cumulative chemical(s) such as copper
9) Low pH	high level of acidity	10 cm: excess of nitrogen from inorganic fertilisers and legumes, poor drainage, low organic matter 20 cm: shallow topsoil, unused N leached from above; if pH is less than 4 consider acid sulfate soil (grey clay/sometimes yellow veins)
10) Poor leaf colour	unthrifty plant	soil problem as indicated in tests 1–9, one or more essential nutrients deficient or unavailable (confirm via soil or leaf analysis), low soil organic matter, disease/cercospora, water-logging

Northern Rivers Soil Health Card: Coffee, SoilCare Inc., June 2008, http://www.soilcare.org/documents/Soil%20Health%20Card%20Coffee21-7-08.pdf.

the mineral soil. Measure how deep the "O" horizon is. The more an aerobic zone of microbial digestion there is to recycle nutrients and build soil carbon that holds moisture and prevents soil erosion, the thicker/deeper is the "O" horizon.

13. **Erosion:** Erosion can be visually monitored by taking a twenty-inch length of two-by-four-inch wooden stud (a board about 50 cm x 100 mm x 50 mm) and placing it wide side down on the surface of the soil, at the bottom of a slope, preferably below a long incline if possible. Secure the board in the ground by driving six eight-inch spikes through the board into the soil. After each major rainfall, check the wood board for a build-up of soil on the upper side. Erosion is a serious problem. Six pounds of topsoil are lost for every pound of food grown, an average of four to six tons of topsoil lost per person per year.

Cornell University now provides a comprehensive evaluation in its soil health assessment, which includes multiple parameters within the physical, chemical, and biological arenas. Cornell actually utilizes thirty-nine potential indicators in its soil health assessment.

Physical
1. Bulk density
2. Macro porosity
3. Meso porosity
4. Micro porosity
5. Available water capacity
6. Residual porosity
7. Penetration resistance at 10KPA
8. Saturated hydrolic conductivity
9. Dry aggregate size (<0.25 mm)
10. Dry aggregate size (0.25-2.0 mm)
11. Dry aggregate size (2.0-8.0 mm)
12. Wet aggregate size (0.25-2.0 mm)
13. Wet aggregate stability (2.0-8.0 mm)
14. Surface hardness with penetrometer
15. Subsurface hardness with penetrometer
16. Field infiltratability

Biological
17. Root health assessment
18. Beneficial nematode population

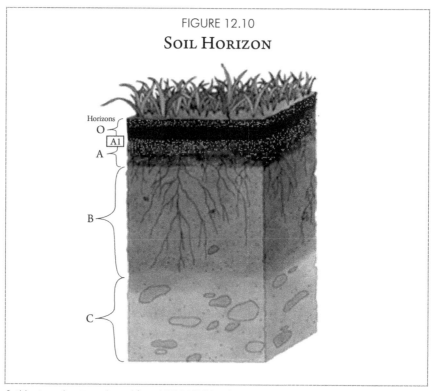

FIGURE 12.10

SOIL HORIZON

Soil horizon drawing adapted from USDA NRCS website.

19. Parasitic nematode population
20. Potential mineralizable nitrogen
21. Decomposition rate
22. Particulate organic matter
23. Active carbon
24. Weed seed bank
25. Microbial respiration rate
26. Glomalin
27. Organic matter content

Chemical

28. Phosphorus
29. Nitrate nitrogen
30. Potassium
31. pH
32. Magnesium

33. Calcium
34. Iron
35. Aluminum
36. Manganese
37. Zinc
38. Copper
39. Exchangeable acidity

The results of these thirty-nine measurements have been synthesized into a grower-friendly soil health report that can be used as an initial baseline assessment. The Total Soil Test Assessment distilled from those thirty-nine measurements include: aggregate stability, available water capacity, surface hardness or compaction, subsurface hardness or compaction, organic matter, active carbon fraction, potentially mineralizable nitrogen, root health rating, and soil chemical composition. Example results of the report and evaluation by the lab, are called the Cornell Soil Health Test Report (Comprehensive), are shown in figures 12.11 and 12.12. This example soil only received a grade of 43, a low score, even though the chemical parameter (fertility) scored high. Soil structure was poor and brought down the total grade.

In looking at the Cornell Indicator Table, the Assessment Sheet, and the Assessment Guide, one can recognize the striking similarities to those produced by NRCS and those published from the *Maryland Soil Quality Assessment Book* (1997) published by NRCS and available online at www.soils.usda.gov/SQI/assessment/state_sq_cards.html.

To evaluate your soil, specific scores are assigned between 0–100 to the values measured for the individual indicators. Scoring functions were developed separately for the major soil textural groups (sand, silt, clay) based upon data distributors. Thus, the scoring functions for many indicators consist of the cumulative normal distribution (CND) curves that are averaged based upon data collected over the northeastern United States. Specific scoring functions are then integrated, computing all the sums, and then expressed on a percentage scale. This translates into an overall quality score for the soil, thus:
>85%, very high
70–85%, high
55–70%, medium
40–55%, low
<40%, very low

FIGURE 12.11

① CORNELL SOIL HEALTH TEST REPORT (COMPREHENSIVE)				
Name of Farmer: GROWER A			**Sample ID:**	
Location:			Agent:	
Field/Treatment: VEGETABLES			Agent's Email:	
Tillage: PLOW TILL			Given Soil Texture: SILTY	
Crops Grown: PUMPKIN		④	Date Sampled: 5/18/07	

②	Indicators	③ Value	Rating	Constraint ⑤
Physical	Aggregate Stability (%)	18	18	aeration, infiltration, rooting
	Available Water Capacity (m/m)	0.18	64	
	Surface Hardness (psi)	348	2	rooting, water transmission
	Subsurface Hardness (psi)	472	3	subsurface pan/deep compaction
Biological	Organic Matter (%)	1.7	9	energy storage, C sequestration, water retention
	Active Carbon (ppm) [Permanganate Oxidizable]	312	5	Soil Biology Activity
	Potentially Mineralizable Nitrogen (µgN/gdwsoil/week)	2.0	0	N Supply Capacity
	Root Health Rating (1-9)	7.0	25	Soil-borne Pest Pressure
Chemical	*pH	7.3	89	
	*Extractable Phosphorus (ppm) [Value <3.5 or >21.5 are downscored]	17.0	100	
	*Extractable Potassium (ppm)	73	100	
	*Minor Elements		100	
⑥	Overall Quality Score (out of 100):		**43.0**	**Low**

Measured Soil Textural Class: → *silt loam*
           Sand (%): 37.0   Silt (%): 55.0   Clay (%): 8.0

Location (GPS): Latitude →   *Longitude* →

B. K. Gugino, O. J. Idowu, R. R. Schindelbeck, H. M. van Es, D. W. Wolfe, B. N. Moebius-Clune, J. E. Thies, and G.S. Abawi, *Cornell Soil Health Assessment Training Manual* (Geneva, NY: New York State Agricultural Experiment Station, 2009), 41, http://soilhealth.cals.cornell.edu.

FIGURE 12.12

CORNELL SOIL HEALTH TEST REPORT (COMPREHENSIVE)			
Name of Farmer: Chazy Plots			**Sample ID: E147**
Location:			Agent: Bob Schindelbeck Cornell University
Field/Treatment: CH14			Agent's Email: 0
Tillage: 7-9 INCHES			Given Soil Texture: SILTY
Crops Grown: COG/COG/COG			Date Sampled: 4/25/07

	Indicators	Value	Rating	Constraint
Physical	Aggregate Stability (%)	22	25	aeration, infiltration, rooting
	Available Water Capacity (m/m)	0.18	63	
	Surface Hardness (psi)	107	78	
	Subsurface Hardness (psi)	400	13	subsurface pan/deep compaction
Biological	Organic Matter (%)	2.1	14	energy storage, C sequestration, water retention
	Active Carbon (ppm) [Permanganate Oxidizable]	462	21	Soil Biology Activity
	Potentially Mineralizable Nitrogen (μgN/ gdwsoil/week)	2.0	0	N Supply Capacity
	Root Health Rating (1-9)	2.3	88	
Chemical	*pH	8.3	0	Toxicity, Nutrient Availability (for crop specific guide, see CNAL report)
	*Extractable Phosphorus (ppm) [Value <3.5 or >21.5 are downscored]	9.5	100	
	*Extractable Potassium (ppm)	20	11	Plant K Availability
	*Minor Elements		56	
	Overall Quality Score (out of 100):		**39.1**	**Very Low**

Measured Soil Textural Class: → *silt loam*
Sand (%): 17.0   Silt (%): 77.0   Clay (%): 6.0

Location (GPS): Latitude →   *Longitude* →

B. K. Gugino, O. J. Idowu, R. R. Schindelbeck, H. M. van Es, D. W. Wolfe, B. N. Moebius-Clune, J. E. Thies, and G.S. Abawi, *Cornell Soil Health Assessment Training Manual* (Geneva, NY: New York State Agricultural Experiment Station, 2009), 41, http://soilhealth.cals.cornell.edu.

A color-coded rating for continuous corn/grain on a silt-loam soil, managed using conventional plow tillage in a long-term soil management research trial in Chazy, New York, is quite telling. In this sample shown in figure 12.12, the biological parameters were quite compromised (except for root health), and the pH and potassium levels drove down the overall score as well.

The biological parameters available to the grower really intrigue me, because without a healthy vigorous microbial system in place, chemical or mineral values are not optimized.

TOTAL ORGANIC MATTER

Like most laboratories, the organic matter test is measuring both living and non-living fractions, including the well-decomposed humus. The percent of organic matter is derived based on the amount of carbon lost on ignition (LOI). Thus, a sample is first dried at 105°C (220°F) to remove all water. The sample is then ashed by heating it to 500° C (932°F) for two hours. The percentage lost on ignition is then converted to percent organic matter using the following equation: % OM = (% LOI x 0.7) – 0.23.

ACTIVE CARBON

Now, the next question is how much of the total organic matter consists of "active carbon"? Active carbon is a readily available energy source for the soil microbial community. This test is done by mixing soil with potassium permanganate, which has a deep purple color. Both are shaken so that the active carbon becomes oxidized by the permanganate, thus lightening the color. The sample is centrifuged, then the supernatant is diluted with distilled water and measured for light absorbance at 550 nanometers.

The significance of an active carbon test is that it is a good leading indicator of soil health responses to changes in crop and soil management usually responding to management much sooner (often years sooner!) than the total organic matter percent. Active carbon is positively correlated with percent organic matter, aggregate stability, and with measures of biological activity, such as soil respiration rates. This evaluation can be of help in enlightening farmers who are changing their practices (crop rotations, cover crops, tillage, compost, etc.) and can give key insight as to whether these changes are positively impacting the ecology, and therefore the productivity, of their soils.

POTENTIALLY MINERALIZABLE NITROGEN

Another Cornell test worth looking at is the potentially mineralizable nitrogen (PMN) test, which is an indicator of the soil microbial community's ability to convert the nitrogen complexed in the proteins of organic residues into the primary organic nitrogen of natural ecosystems, namely ammonium or NH_4.

Essentially soil samples are incubated for seven days, and the amount of ammonium produced in that period reflects the capacity for complexed nitrogen to become mineralized. Soils with high levels of nitrogen-rich organic matter, as for example where legumes are in the rotation, tend to have the highest populations of microbes that mineralize complexed nitrogen. Soils with a high PMN are also soils with high active carbon levels, high organic matter (OM) levels, and high aggregate stability levels.

ROOT HEALTH ASSESSMENT

The root health assessment test is a measure of the quality and function of the roots as indicated by size, color, and texture, as well as by the absence of disease symptoms and damage caused by root pathogens such as fungal adversaries like Fusarium, Pythium, Rhizoctonia, etc. and plant-parasitic nematodes such as root-knot nematodes. This test can be especially relevant to vegetable and forage producers because the test protocol utilizes bean seeds as the subject. Beans are susceptible to the major pathogens that impact vegetables, legumes and forages, so they are suitable indicator plants.

The protocol consists of planting a single seed in a cone tube filled with bulk soil from the site. The plants are maintained in a greenhouse under supplemental light and watered regularly for four weeks. The plants are then removed from the cone containers and the roots are washed under running water and rated on a scale of 1–9, with 1 being best and 9 worst:

1: white and coarse textured hypocotyls and roots.

3: light discoloration and lesions covering up to 10 percent of hypocotyls and root tissue.

5: approximately 25 percent of hypocotyls and roots have lesions, but tissues remain firm. There is a little decay, or damage to the root system.

7 to 9: 50–75 percent of hypocotyl and roots are severely symptomatic and at advanced stages of decay.

Good soil tilth and low populations of root pathogens as well as high populations of root symbionts (beneficials) are critical for the development of healthy roots essential for vigorous plant growth and higher yields via efficient extracting of nutrients and the feeding of those beneficial microorganisms in the rhizosphere. Together, a healthy root ball and a vigorous microbial community mean a reduced bulk density of the soil, more aggregates, more pore space, less soil compaction, and higher water infiltration.

Cornell's aggregate stability test is similar to the hands-on aggregate stability test in the Soil Health Card, except it's a bit more sophisticated because it uses a rain simulation. Sieves containing known weights of soil aggregates between 0.5 and 2.0 millimeters in size are placed at a distance of twenty inches (500 mm) below a rainfall simulator, which delivers individual drops of 4.0 millimeter in diameter. The "rain" is run for five minutes, delivering a 0.5 inch (12.5 mm) depth of water. Fifteen drops per second hitting the soil aggregates is equivalent to a heavy thunderstorm. Any stones or soil slaked out of the sieve are subtracted from the original weight to determine the percentage of stable aggregates.

It is encouraging to know that a grower has multiple resources available in acquiring critical information about his soil health and productivity potential, including the Soil Health Cards that can be used rapidly on-site, the NRCS Soil Health Template, the NRCS Soil Quality Test Kit, and laboratory analyses, which can include comprehensive chemical extraction such as Mellick 3 or ammonium acetate, as well as the Cornell Comprehensive Soil Health Test Report, which includes physical as well as biological parameters in addition to the chemistry tests (using a Morgan extraction of sodium acetate/acetic acid). Look into the resources available at Ward Laboratories—specifically their "Green Chemistry" tests, as discussed in chapter 4—when testing your soil. Available soil health tests include the Haney Test, which measures organic and inorganic amounts of carbon and nitrogen soil respiration and orthophosphate, and the phospholipid fatty acid (PLFA) analysis, which identifies functional group biomass and microbial diversity.

POCKET TOOLS: HIGH-TECH, FAST, AND EASY

However, there is even more. Bob and Cheryl Pike operate Pike Agri-Lab Supplies in Jay, Maine. I first met Bob back in the early 1980s when he began the company. Bob has, in my opinion, been the front-runner in explaining how to use an entire arsenal of hand tools to monitor crop and soil performance in "real time" on-site throughout the growing season. A few years ago, his daughter Cheryl has come on-board and has found value in correlating empirical evidence out in the field with scientific benchmarks discussed at academic institutions.

The following descriptions are written by Bob and Cheryl Pike for refractometers, penetrometers, electrical conductivity meters, pH meters, ion selective meters (nitrate, potassium, calcium and sodium), chlorophyll meters, ORP meters, infrared thermometer, Phil Callahan Soil Meter (PCSM), and the soil test kit using Morgan extract. They offer some excellent resources to further any inquiry or research. Contact information for Pike Agri-Lab Supplies can be found in the resources section of this book.

pH Meters

A pH meter tests hydrogen ion activity in soil, compost, plant sap, and foliar sprays. A pH meter should be calibrated using two standard solutions to ensure accuracy throughout the entire scale. There are two basic types of pH meters available. The most common is a meter with a probe-style electrode designed to be inserted into a container of liquid. The second type is a specialty meter with a flat sensor designed for testing very small samples, such as plant sap testing.

Soil pH is critical because it can control many chemical processes that take place in the soil, influencing the availability of nutrients to plants. Test soil pH by mixing equal parts (by volume) of distilled water and soil. Some nitrogen-fixing microbes cannot live in conditions where pH is lower than 5.8. Soil pH profiles can be a sign of compaction.

The pH of plant sap indicates the balance of nutrients taken up into the leaves and can be useful in identifying which elements might be missing. For many plant species a pH of 6.4 seems to be ideal. If the sap pH is higher than wanted, it may indicate that phosphorus and sulfates are lacking. If the sap pH is lower than ideal, the plant may be short of calcium, magnesium, potassium, or sodium. Insect and disease pressure increase as the sap pH moves away from ideal. The electrode surfaces of flat-sensor pH meters should be rinsed immediately after readings are taken.

Foliar spray pH can be adjusted to maximize nutrient uptake during either the vegetative growth phase or the fruiting phase. Add some apple cider vinegar to lower the pH and either baking soda, calcium hydroxide, or potassium hydroxide to raise the pH of the spray. A good practice is to make multiple versions of foliar spray solutions and apply them to test plots in the field. After an hour or so of sunshine, a refractometer can be used to see which version is most effective at improving the nutrient level in the leaf sap. An increase of 2 Brix or more is considered desirable. An excellent overview of foliar sprays can be found at: www.bountea.com/articles/foliarspray.html.

REFRACTOMETERS

A refractometer is an easy-to-use instrument for measuring total dissolved solids in the leaf sap of plants at all stages of growth or in the fruits and vegetables as they mature. Refractometers readings are expressed in Brix, which is defined as percent sucrose by weight. Often referred to as a "sugar" reading, Brix is much more than that. Any solids dissolved in the juice of the plant tissue are measured, including sugars, salts, proteins, amino acids, etc. These solids bend light rays in proportion to the temperature, quantity of atoms, atomic weight of the elements, and number of covalent bonds between the atoms. Refractometers that have automatic temperature compensation will correct for errors due to variations in temperature. Brix meters have been used for many years by grape growers but are increasingly being used by farmers and ranchers to evaluate a variety of crops and forages.

Fruits and vegetables with higher Brix will be sweeter tasting and also more nutritious due to their lower water content. Higher dissolved solid levels in plants also lead to a lower freezing point and a greater resistance to frost damage. Crops with higher refractometer readings show reduced susceptibility to disease and insects. As a general rule, plant leaf sap should be kept at twelve Brix or higher in order to achieve insect and disease resistance. For fruits and vegetables, your goal should be to maximize the Brix readings.

Growers wishing to use refractometers to evaluate their plants should follow a few simple guidelines when taking readings. Consistency is key—test Brix at the same time of day (ideally, after a minimum of two hours of sunshine), sample leaves of the same size, maturity and location, and use the same method for squeezing the sample. Also wash off any road dust or foliar spray residue and blot the leaves dry before squeezing samples. Results may be skewed when testing the leaves of dehydrated plants under severe drought conditions.

There are two basic versions of refractometers available at an affordable price. Simple optical instruments use ambient light and function via a prism with a cover plate and an eyepiece through which you view a number scale and determine your readings. There are also digital instruments that use an internal light source, have a sample well with a prism, and give the Brix value on a LED display. The digital versions are particularly useful when testing the darker-colored juices associated with high-Brix plants because the internal light of the digital meter does not have to pass through the cover plate and sample multiple times as it does with the optical instrument in order to get a reading. However, optical instruments allow the user to see whether the line of demarcation is fuzzy or sharp. A diffuse line is caused by the scattering of light by undissolved substances in the liquid. Carey Reams, an early proponent of Brix testing in agronomy, associated this phenomenon with low acidity (high pH) in citrus crops.

PENETROMETERS

A penetrometer measures the degree of soil compaction. This measurement relates to soil airiness, which indicates the amount of oxygen available for soil microbial life. Compacted soils can result in reduced water infiltration and root penetration, as well as increased soil runoff and erosion.

The penetrometer gauge displays the amount of pressure required as the probe end is steadily pushed through the soil. Although a steel rod or simple spade can give a general feel for compaction, the penetrometer gives the reading in pounds per square inch. This allows you to determine how severe the compaction is and at what depth. You can monitor improvements in compaction over time as you modify farming practices. Methods to alleviate compaction can include changing tillage operations, balancing soil chemistry, increasing soil microbiology, reducing field traffic, and avoiding field traffic entirely when soils are wet.

Readings should be taken when soils are neither too wet nor too dry, as these will under- or overestimate the actual compaction level, respectively. Most crops will not be able to push a root through soils that read psi or higher, though yield reductions can already be seen in soils at 200 psi or lower.

ELECTRICAL CONDUCTIVITY

Conductivity meters measure electrical conductivity (EC) of water, soil, compost, plant sap, and foliar sprays. EC meters read in microsiemens per centimeter or millisiemens per centimeter. A conductivity meter has two electrodes, and voltage is applied alternately to the electrodes. Small mobile ions can move readily between the electrodes, allowing them to be counted by the meter; larger ion clusters will not move quickly enough to be measured. You should calibrate EC meters with a standard solution that is about one-half to two-thirds the full range of the instrument. Many of the newer meters are programmed for calibration using a specific standard only.

Soil conductivity is measured by mixing equal parts (by volume) of distilled water and soil. Alternatively, there are meters that can measure EC by inserting a probe directly into the soil, provided there is adequate moisture. Carey Reams coined the term ERGS (energy released per gram of soil) when referring to soil conductivity expressed in microsiemens per centimeter. Those ions that are small and mobile enough to be measured by EC meters will be available to plants. If the soil contains a variety of active, healthy microbes, the large ion clusters can be broken down and made available to plants. ERGS should not be allowed to drop below fifty microsiemens for most plants. Generally, better growth will be achieved if ERGS is kept at a minimum of four hundred micosiemens. Soils that have excessively high EC levels can be susceptible to nematodes.

Plant sap EC is measured by squeezing a few drops from the plant leaves onto the flat sensor of a meter designed for that purpose. Plant sap EC should be kept between 2,000–12,000 microsiemens. If the sap EC readings are too low (and Brix readings are also low), not enough simple ions have been taken up into the plant leaves. Possible remedies would include foliar feeding, side-dress fertilizers, irrigation, fertigation, and microbial inoculants. A sap EC reading that is too high can often result from an excess of simple ions such as nitrate, potassium, or sodium.

ION-SELECTIVE METERS

These meters employ electrodes that are selective to a single ion. They give a direct readout in parts per million (ppm) for water, soil, and plant sap. These pocket-sized digital meters can also be used to evaluate fruits, vegetables, milk, and most any food or beverage. They can be used to measure foliar sprays and hydroponic fertilizers. Some fertilizers may need to be diluted in order to test ppm directly. Flat-sensor technology enables quick, simple, and accurate measurements with only a few drops of sample. To avoid contamination, the electrode surface of these meters should be rinsed immediately after the readings are taken.

Nitrate

Determine NO_3 levels in soil using water extraction and filtration. Only a few drops of filtrate are required for a reading. Successful nitrogen management can optimize crop yields and increase profitability while minimizing nitrogen losses to the environment. Nitrogen is a very mobile and reactive element that undergoes many complex transformations and movements into and out of the soil, causing levels to change rapidly. For this reason, more people are relying on plant sap nitrate readings to provide immediate on-site analysis.

The ion-selective meter can be used to measure nitrate uptake by squeezing sap directly from plant leaves. Nitrate is mobile in plants, therefore deficiencies show up in older leaves first. Some recommended ranges for nitrate and potassium levels in leaf sap for a variety of crops at various growth stages can be found at www.edis.ifas.ufl.edu/cv004. Another great study showing nitrogen sap levels for a few crops at various fertilizer application rates can be found at www.mdvegetables.umd.edu/images/Plant%20 Petiole%20Nitrate%20Sap%20Testing.update.pdf.

You can also test water quality directly in ppm NO_3 with this simple, quick, pocket-sized meter. According to the EPA, drinking water should be kept below 10 ppm.

Potassium

Measuring soil potassium levels can be done with a simple water extraction and filtration. Since K+ is relatively immobile in soils, any condition that restricts root growth can decrease root contact and absorption of potassium. Excess potassium will block uptake of calcium. Measuring potassium in leaf sap is very useful for determining uptake in plant tissue. Potassium is instrumental in the process of photosynthesis and in moisture regulation of the plant. It is also essential in activating certain enzyme processes.

Some recommended ranges for nitrate and potassium levels in leaf sap for a variety of crops at various growth stages can be found at www.edis.ifas.ufl. edu/cv004.

Calcium

The Ca+ meter is designed to measure free-calcium ion levels in plant sap and soil. Calcium mobility in plants is very low and takes place mainly in the xylem, together with water. Therefore calcium uptake is directly related to the plant transpiration rate. Calcium deficiency will appear in younger leaves as dieback or burns and in fruits as blossom end rot or bitter pit because they have a very low transpiration rate. Therefore, it is necessary to have a constant supply of calcium for continued growth.

The free-calcium level represents what is available for the many roles that calcium plays in plants. Calcium is required in large amounts by the plant. It is a major component of the cell wall, binding pectin molecules together. Since calcium is rarely redeposited within the leaf, it is important to have a consistent supply of free ions available for the plant to form new cells. Calcium uptake can be reduced when transpiration is limited or when excessive levels of competing ions such as sodium, potassium or magnesium are present. Monitor calcium throughout the growing season and take immediate action when levels drop.

Sodium

This simple tester determines sodium ion activity in plant sap, soil, and water. Sodium readings can be very useful, especially when irrigation is used. Sodium levels in soil can be determined by performing a simple water extraction and filtration. Long-term irrigation of farmland can build up an overabundance of sodium, which reduces crop yields. With high sodium levels in soil, extra precautions must be taken to avoid over-compaction.

The Na+ reading can also be used to determine what portion of a high conductivity reading is attributable to sodium. Excess sodium will block uptake of calcium.

Sodium levels in water can be easily tested directly by placing a few drops of water on the flat sensor. The World Health Organization (WHO) guideline limit for sodium in drinking waters is 200mg/L.

CHLOROPHYLL

A chlorophyll meter is a handheld, easy-to-use device for noninvasively measuring the relative chlorophyll content of green leaf plants. Chlorophyll content can be an indicator of the plant's condition. Tests have shown a strong correlation between leaf chlorophyll content and nitrogen content in a variety of crops. Since chlorophyll testing is faster and simpler than performing sap nitrate analysis, many people are taking advantage of a lower cost chlorophyll meter which was recently introduced.

Plant-relative chlorophyll concentration is measured by inserting a leaf into the device aperture. The leaf is not damaged during the test. The chlorophyll content reading is displayed on the digital readout. An individual reading is taken with a single press of the button, or readings are averaged by holding down the button as the meter moves over the leaf.

You can upload customized lists to the meter using the included USB cable and Windows software. This allows you assign categories to your readings as you take them. Classify them according to crop name, field location, or maturity level. Results can be downloaded to your computer, allowing them to be stored, graphed, and evaluated.

Many references are available showing tests performed with another (more expensive) chlorophyll meter. Many researchers have outlined the use of chlorophyll meters in assessing various crops, for example www.extension.psu.edu/plants/crops/grains/corn/nutrition/early-season-chlorophyll-meter-test-for-corn and www.ianrpubs.unl.edu/epublic/pages/publicationD.jsp?publicationId=648.

Oxidation Reduction Potential (ORP)

An ORP meter indicates the oxidation reduction potential of soil or compost. An ORP reading can be used to indicate the suitability of soil for biological life. ORP reactions in the soil are of major significance from a chemical as well as biological standpoint. The ORP tester is the simplest instrument for measuring the state of soil oxidation. It can also help you to determine when additional cultivation is unnecessary. The ORP meter is used to determine the stability and stage of completion of compost. It may also be used to measure H_2O_2/ H_2O mixtures. People have also found an ORP meter useful in evaluating their home water treatment equipment.

A simple formula using the readings from an ORP meter and a pH meter provides a redox (rH) value from 0 to 42. Optimum soil rH value is 27–29. The ORP and pH reactions involve ions and are both measured in a water solution.

Life obtains its energy from the transfer of electrons caused by the oxidation of reduced materials. Respiring life captures energy from a series of reactions involved in the movement of electrons to oxygen. In soil, organic matter is the major electron donor, and oxygen is the major electron acceptor. Oxygen is the only electron acceptor plant roots can utilize. In those cases where oxygen is not available, nitrate, ferric (Fe +3, the fully oxidized form of iron), Mn +2, and sulfate can act as electron acceptors, if the live organisms have the correct enzyme systems.

In soil, electrons are continually being transferred by the biological oxidation of organic matter. Electron flow reduces as organic matter is converted to humus and increases with the addition of fresh organic matter.

The ORP value will drop due to spreading of manure or organic matter. For this reason, by delaying planting, you can allow the potential to return approximately to its former value.

For neutral or alkaline pH soils maintaining the rH value at a level that is not too high might improve the availability of phosphorus, iron, and manganese. (In these situations, it might be better to have an rH of 26 than an rH of 30.)

INFRARED (IR) THERMOMETER

A non-contact infrared heat sensor measures plant stress by comparing temperature variance between ambient air and plant foliage, as researched by the USDA.

A major determinant of leaf temperature is the rate of evaporation or transpiration from the leaf. The cooling effect of transpiration happens because a substantial amount of energy is required to convert water to water vapor, and this energy is then taken away from the leaf in the evaporating water, thereby cooling it.

There are a few conditions required for reliable test results. Plant leaf surfaces must be dry. Use only when wind is blowing at less than 10 mph. Keep the sunlight at your back. Take IR readings from foliage only during the peak sunlight hours of the day, when stress is most likely to occur. Therefore, take readings from 11 a.m. to 4 p.m. during the summer and from 1 p.m. to 3 p.m. during the winter.

In general, a differential temperature of no greater than three degrees Fahrenheit is very good. If the foliage is 10°F warmer than ambient air, the plant is seriously stressed, and the cause of problem needs to be determined. Overall, the cooler a particular crop stays, the higher the yield and the better the quality of the crop.

PCSM (PHIL CALLAHAN SOIL METER)

A PCSM will test soil and rock dust to determine their paramagnetic value on a digital readout. The atoms or molecules of a paramagnetic substance have a net magnetic spin such that the spins are capable of being temporarily aligned to the direction of an applied electromagnetic field when they are placed in that field. This produces an internal magnetic field (magnetic moment), which differs from magnetic substances (such as iron, nickel, and cobalt) where such spins remain aligned even when they are out of the applied field, that is, permanent. Magnetic susceptibility is measured, according to the physics handbook, in millionths of a CGS unit (centimeters grams second), $1 \times 10\text{-}6$ CGS, or μCGS.

What does this mean for agriculture? According to Dr. Callahan's observations, soils with higher paramagnetism had better plant growth than similar soils without the paramagnetic force. Dr. Callahan's research showed that a soil magnetic susceptibility reading of 0–100 μCGS would be poor; 100–300 μCGS is good; 300–700 μCGS is very good; and 700–1,200 μCGS or higher is considered excellent. This force can be added to soil, where it has eroded away, by spreading ground-up paramagnetic rock (basalt, granite, etc.) into the soil. Dr. Callahan estimates that 60 to 70 percent of this volcanic paramagnetic force has been eroded away worldwide. The PCSM can be used to evaluate rock dust sources to add paramagnetism back to your soils. A locally available rock dust with a moderate reading could be a better choice than a higher paramagnetic source from another region due to higher transportation costs.

Other researchers have shown the positive effects that paramagnetic rock dust can have on plant growth, as described in www.harmonygardens. blogspot.com/2008/01/paramagnetic-rock.html.

SAMPLING TOOLS
Plant Sap Sampling
Vise-grip pliers are available, which have been modified with stainless-steel jaws to squeeze juice from plant leaves, fruits, or vegetables. This tool is portable and much easier to clean than other options, such as a garlic press. It works great for most row crops and other materials with average moisture levels. To help keep a bunch of leaves (or slippery fruits) from escaping the vise grips, use a small square of nylon mesh to form a pouch. You might want to discard the first couple of drops squeezed from the leaves, as these tend to be more watery liquid with lower Brix.

A stainless-steel hydraulic plant sap press will allow you to squeeze sap from difficult-to-juice materials. Even for those substances that are not difficult to squeeze, people have found that the hydraulic press provides a good, consistent juice sample. If the leaf is so dehydrated that it cracks when folding to take the sap sample, don't bother testing as it is too dry. Instead you should irrigate or wait until after rainfall to perform your plant sap testing.

Soil Sampling
A stainless-steel soil sampling probe with welded foot pedal can be used to pull a one-inch diameter, twelve-inch deep sample from your soil. The totally enclosed sample area provides a noncontaminated soil sample. The hinge

opens wide, allowing you to see the profile before removing soil. Different levels of soil can be removed without mixing, if desired, for testing.

SOIL TESTS WITH MORGAN EXTRACT

The Morgan universal solution is a chemical extract that was patterned after the exudates given off by roots. It was developed in the 1920–1930s by M. F. Morgan in Connecticut. Morgan named his extract a "universal" extract, meaning all major nutrients (including phosphorus) and many micronutrients can be measured in the one extract. Colorimetric test methods are used for most test factors, other than the calcium, potassium, sulfate, and chlorides, which are based on turbidity comparators.

The Morgan extract measures which nutrients are available to the plant. For example, there may be plenty of calcium in the soil, but a plant may show a deficiency because the calcium is tied up in an insoluble compound. The Morgan extract only measures what is available to the plant at that time. It was the soil extract of choice for the late Dr. Carey Reams. He used this soil extract when determining his range of ideal nutrient levels in the soil because he was interested in what nutrients were biologically active.

The good news to growers is that there are multiple resources available to determine the health and productivity of both crops and soils, in addition to the laboratories that can assess the chemical (mineral), physical, and biological attributes of soils. Growers can now utilize easy-to-implement diagnostics that can provide them with solid information in "real time" and that is also reasonably accurate. This valuable information can provide farmers and gardeners with options to either prevent or minimize crop damage and/or enhance crop quality and productivity. It's a systems approach that fosters the connecting of the dots: geology/minerals/chemistry, biology, physical soil structure, ecological diversity.

Back to the Future

A Permanent Agriculture

*Soil is not usually lost in slabs or heaps of magnificent tonnage.
It is lost a little at a time over millions of acres by the careless acts
of millions of people. It cannot be saved by heroic feats of gigantic
technology, but only by millions of small acts of restraints.*

—Wendell Berry

WE are continually being bombarded by so-called experts in academia, corporations, and our government with the notion that we must become more *biotechnologically* involved with agriculture because otherwise we will not be able to feed the anticipated 9–10 billion souls that will be hungry by 2050. I have no argument with predictions of such a possible mass of humanity on the scene in less than three decades, but I find it frightening that those who have been setting food policy in the most arable of lands could be either so ignorant of the facts or so corrupt and arrogant as to ignore those facts.

The undeniable fact is modern, annual monocrops are dangerously close to destroying the network of ecosystems that allow a resilient, productive food system to even be possible. Moreover, how sane is growing two or three annual cereal crops continuously on our best soils while we export four to six tons of topsoil per person per year down our rivers and into our estuaries? Is there even a scintilla of evidence that this will feed the hungry for the foreseeable future?

Why are we focused on corn and beans, whether grown conventionally, organically, or "biologically"? Is the goal of growing 300–400 bushels of corn a manifesto to truly feed the hungry, heal the planet, and nourish humanity with something other than calories? Or is it like a testosterone-induced athletic challenge, much like whose tractor has the most horsepower at a tractor-pulling contest at the state fair? Can we continue to ignore that every pound of food raised conventionally has a cost of six pounds of topsoil lost, and every pound of food—even raised organically—still has a cost of five pounds of soil lost?

Can we justify the incredibly toxic soup we breathe, drink and eat? What about the children, who are so much more vulnerable? Can we sit by while the greatest extinction of species is occurring since the dinosaurs? Pollinators are being wiped out exponentially, and bats are disappearing wholesale in literally a couple of years. Our macroinvertebrates, the basis of the food chain, are being eviscerated by sediment and farm and industrial chemicals, and as a result our fisheries are either imploding or becoming too toxic to eat.

Despite newfound interested in cover crops, only 8 percent of midwestern grain farmers utilize them (and only 2 percent in the Mississippi River Basin). Academic researchers have proven, along with their farming colleagues, that smart crop rotations and cover crops can reduce the need for fertilizers and herbicides by 90 percent while maintaining high yields and profits.

In the Midwest alone, eliminating marginal cropland and land that includes hedgerows, fields, woodlots, and stream border banks—which provide habitat for pollinators and beneficial predatory insects—has increased the use of insecticides by an amount that would cover over 5,400 square miles of crops, or over half the size of the state of Maryland.

Genetically modified organisms (GMOs), more chemicals, and even organic or biological alternatives are not a substitution for what is currently happening, although biological and organic farming certainly contribute immensely to a reduction in the pesticide insanity. Can the world be fed without such a centralized, industrialized system?

Not only can it be fed, the examples are already in place. Russia, a large country with a population of 145 million, has 35 million families living on either small farms or plots of land less than an acre. Collectively, these folks feed their fellow citizens, or at least 71 percent of them. They provide 92 percent of the potatoes, 87 percent of the fruit, and 77 percent of the vegetables consumed by the Russian people. In Romania, a peasant Euro nation, the average farm size is only eight acres, and 60 percent of the Romanians' milk is produced by farms with only two to three cows.

In the United States in 1950, the year I was born, we had 3.6 million dairy farms. Today, in 2013, we have less than fifty thousand, or a loss of 98.7 percent, with just 3 percent of the remaining dairies producing 40 percent of the milk. During World War II the patriotic fervor of U.S. citizens led them to raise Victory Gardens. More than 40 percent of the produce consumed then came from those backyard plots. Today, that much or more is discarded by the producers and the grocery stores due to spoilage. Because of consolidation, centralization, and industrialization of our food production, Americans now have to depend on a farm-to-plate infrastructure and an average food-miles distance that amounts to fifteen hundred miles—hardly food security.

Many more examples exist around the planet: the Mexican chinampas, the lagoonal bars in Tunisia, the mulberry dykes of China, the *hortillage* practices in rural France and Asia, and the Andean *camellones*.

An extraordinary example of how the nine billion could be fed, especially in developing cultures, is the *waru-waru*, a farming technology developed by ancient Peruvian Incas. The *waru-waru* were raised platforms of soil surrounded by moats of water that apparently produced bumper crops at altitudes of up to 12,000 feet (4,000 meters). Evidence of these "farms" can be found near Lake Titicaca, amounting to nearly 200,000 acres (80,000 hectares).

The *waru-waru* design is ingenious. Moisture from the ditches provides water to crops via the capillary action of the roots. Excess rain is diverted into the canals to prevent flooding. Water is a solar collector that stores daytime solar energy to be given off at nighttime, which can be cold at such high altitudes. Water also creates a mist or fog that insulates the air from killing frosts. Sediment collects in the ditches, which become nutrient rich with leachable plant food, algae, and plant residue, all of which can then be returned to the crop beds. Yields of potatoes in *waru-waru* have out flanked contemporary yields by a factor of 200–800 percent. No modern mechanized equipment or imported fertilizer was required. Manual (local) labor was the primary resource requisite, averaging 80–400 worker days per acre (200–1,000 worker days per hectare).

Ben Falk of Vermont has provided readers with a beautiful tour of his Vermont permaculture property in his book *The Resilient Farm and Homestead: An Innovative Permaculture and Whole Systems Design Approach.* His design incorporates almost unlimited possibilities to create innumerable close-looped systems of self-sufficiency, waste resources as a source of fertility and energy (e.g., hot water from the heat of a compost pile), and a landscape of immeasurable beauty. Ben even grows rice in Vermont!

In the spirit of the 1940s Victory Gardens there is a growing resurgence of urban farming in every metropolitan community. One I am familiar with is Kahanu Aina Greens in Wailuku, Hawaii, owned and operated by Vincent and Irene Mina and their son, Kekai. Approximately four hundred pounds of sprouted greens are harvested weekly, consisting of sunflower sprouts, green pea sprouts, Kawari radish sprouts, and wheatgrass grown in trays that range from eleven by seventeen inches to seventeen by seventeen inches. All the greens are grown in a plant-based compost that has been tested and is amended at rates of approximately eighty grams of minerals blended into four cubic feet of compost; the compost is made from the biomass of the harvested trays, vermicastings from their red wiggler workforce, and biochar.

The farm is a whopping two thousand square feet in size, or 1/22nd of an acre. The production area is twelve hundred square feet, or 1/36th of an acre. The composting area and processing areas are each about four hundred square feet. The trays are on tables beneath a misting system. This is equivalent to 14,400 pounds per greens per acre per week, or 748,000 pounds per acre per year—all without GMOs, pesticides, fossil fuel–based fertilizers, or environmental degradation, and without a need for large tracts of real estate!

Vince is one of those guys that brings a lot of sunflower sprouts to share when he travels, even when eating in a restaurant. I've been a beneficiary of these micro-greens when he has come to Pennsylvania visiting family, and I can attest to their nutrition based on not only their flavor but their shelf life—as long as three weeks in my refrigerator. Try saving hydroponic sprouts; they usually become mush in less than half that time.

Lancaster County, Pennsylvania, is approximately a hundred miles southwest of my home and is the second-largest Amish settlement in the United States, and one of the largest dairy-producing counties in the United States with about 1,200 family dairy farms, most of them run by Amish or Mennonite Plain Sect people.

A group of about four dozen family farmers in Lancaster and nearby communities formed an unincorporated, private buying association about a decade ago to provide a variety of healthy foods unburdened by the increasingly heavy yoke of food safety regulations. These rules are more and more implemented because of our broken, centralized, industrialized food system, a system that is contributing to the CDC statistics of tens of thousands of annual hospitalizations, hundreds of thousands of reported annual illnesses, and several thousand annual mortalities. The association called CARE, or the Community Alliance for Responsible Eco-Agriculture, provides nutrient-dense foods raised without toxins, while staying committed to healthy soils, plants, and livestock, to approximately seven thousand members, many if not most who subscribe to the dietary tenets of Weston A. Price, DDS.

Price was a Cleveland dentist who spent the 1930s searching for the healthiest populations worldwide and authored a groundbreaking summation of fourteen isolated cultures scattered from the Arctic Circle to Polynesia, from Swiss Alp villages to African tribes in Kenya, from the Outer Hebrides of Scotland to the Maori of New Zealand. His seminal achievement, complete with exhaustive photographs, is entitled *Nutrition and Physical Degeneration*. This book eventually spawned the Price-Pottenger Nutrition Foundation (www.ppnf.org) and in the late 1990s the Weston A. Price Foundation (www.westonaprice.org), both of which promote this timeless wisdom.

The Weston A. Price Foundation now boasts thirteen thousand members worldwide, with six hundred chapters, and hosts an annual conference attracting over 1,500 devotees of nutrition and holistic health to learn from scientists, farmers, nutritionists, physicians, chefs, biological dentists, and ecologists.

The foundation's quarterly journal, *Wise Traditions*, not only showcases the science of nature and the "nature of nature," it features a section where ecologically engaged farmers offer healing and regenerative foods, (such as the CARE farmers), who provide pastured raw milk, cheeses, cream, yogurt, butter, kefir, pastured eggs, poultry, pork, beef, fermented vegetables, nonalcoholic fermented beverages, organic produce, fermented (sourdough) breads and cereals, etc. These farms not only benefit the land, they are ensuring a future of good stewards, producing "food as medicine," and enriching their communities with health, wealth, and beauty.

Traveling west from Lancaster County into Perry County, one may be fortunate enough to visit Spiral Path Farm (www.spiralpathfarm.com) near Loysville, Pennsylvania, a 260-acre certified organic farm producing about forty annual vegetables and fruits. Owned and operated by Mike and Terra Brownback, granddaughter Ivory, sons Lucas and Will, his wife Dierdre, and their children Khayla and Jonas, their farm provides produce to subscription members (called a community supported agriculture model, or CSA), which now number over 2,200 families, and to customers at farmers markets in Bethesda and Silver Spring, Maryland. Additionally, Spiral Path wholesales its produce to a regional grocery chain of eighty stores called Wegmans, which puts a face on their produce in a kiosk that replicates a farmers market stall.

Spiral Path's farming practices include mineralizing the soil, cover cropping, crop rotation, composting, vermicomposting, natural/biological pest controls and mechanical weed control. This single family farm is feeding thousands of health- and eco-conscious patrons, stewarding the landscape, and providing know-how to up and coming farmers as well as conventional farmers wanting to transition away from toxic-rescue chemistry.

The rock star of alternative agriculture, Joel Salatin, and his wife, Teresa; son, Daniel; Daniel's wife and children; and Joel's mother, run Polyface Farms (www.polyfacefarms.com) in Swoope, Virginia, in the heart of the Shenandoah Valley, once the granary, or breadbasket, of the Confederacy. Polyface consists of owning/leasing hundreds of acres, raising grassfed beef, poultry, pastured eggs, rabbits, and pastured and wood-lot pork. Polyface harvests and mills timber sustainably from their 450-acre woodlot and direct markets its pastured animal protein foods both directly and to local restaurants. Salatin's "lunatic farming" practices have been featured in *Smithsonian, National Geographic,* and *Gourmet* magazines. His farm was featured in the *New York Times* bestseller *The Omnivore's Dilemma* by Michael Pollan and the award-winning, Oscar-nominated documentary *Food, Inc.* Their hundred acres of pasture consist of high-density mob grazing of cattle, "eggmobiles" moved into those same pastures three to four days following the cattle for fly and parasite control, "chicken tractors"—pens moved daily over top the grasses, legumes and forbs that supplement the meat birds. Tours and field days educate others and provide agri-tourism income. Polyface feeds five thousand families and supplies ten retail stores and fifty restaurants, all without a "skull-and-crossbones" method of feeding all those grateful clients while keeping his five hundred–plus acres of meadows, pastures, and forests intact, resplendent with both domesticated and wild inhabitants.

Joel is the author of several books, his latest bestseller, *Folks, This Ain't Normal,* explodes the myth that modern society is the culmination of humankind's genius. He shows that abandoning the natural system's blueprints to sustainability and resilience in exchange for bigger, faster, and more mechanized methods to grow food has been a recipe for far too many ills. These problems cannot be corrected by regulatory agencies trying to bandage a flawed and defective design with an avalanche of rules that completely ignore the fundamentals that are the scaffolding of a farm and food system that generates the least amount of risk to both ourselves and our environment.

Joel's evangelical speaking style can really incite both farmers and eaters to think profoundly about how the choices they make can affect so many outcomes—medically, environmentally, economically, and socially. Many interns and apprentices have gone off on their own, starting their own "personal Polyfaces," thanks to apprenticing with a hands-on mentor that no expensive academic boutique education could likely provide.

These are but a few examples of what an ecologically sound, beautiful agriculture can provide, and I would emphatically encourage growers and eaters to get involved with their local/regional food movements, be it the local chapter of Buy Fresh, Buy Local; Weston A. Price Foundation; sustainable organizations such as my own Pennsylvania Association for Sustainable Agriculture (PASA); the NOFA's (Northeast Organic Farming Association) respective state organizations of New York, Vermont, New Hampshire, Massachusetts, New Jersey, and Connecticut; MOFGA (Maine Organic Farmers and Gardeners Association); OEFFA (Ohio Ecological Food and Farm Association); Tilth (Oregon, Washington); MOSES (Midwest Organic and Sustainable Education Services); and CCOF (California Certified Organic Farmers) to name a handful. I would also encourage people to support publications like *Acres U.S.A.*, *Graze*, *Stockman Grass Farmer*, *The Natural Farmer*, *Organic Broadcaster*, and so many more. Eaters and healers need to find their farmers. Farmers need to find their patrons, as well as teachers, and mentors, whether they be other farmers, consultants, or the visionaries who figured out so much fifty to a hundred years ago and wrote it all down for us to read and learn from. Regarding the latter, I'm referring to Louis Bromfield, J. I. Rodale, Lady Eve Balfour, Friends Sykes, Newman Turner, William Albrecht, J. Russell Smith, Carey Reams, Phil Callahan, Francis Pottenger, Weston A. Price, and Frank King, Luther Burbank, George Washington Carver, to name a few.

The future has never been brighter, or more precarious. Policymakers are too distracted, or too ignorant, or too influenced by lobbyists, or too corrupt, or too partisan to politically address the problems for which we have clear, affordable solutions. We can "do this" because we did it once and are doing it again.

Size is a secondary issue. The primary issue is how much land can an individual properly steward? Perhaps one place it's an acre; perhaps someplace else, with a different geology, technology, topography, climate, and economy, it's one thousand acres. But the key here is how do we keep the landscape not merely sustainable, but resilient? If it is fragile because of its location or because of human abuse, how can it be regenerated and restored?

I first heard Bill Mollison speak in the early 1990s and soon after purchased his seminal work *Permaculture: A Designer's Manual*. Wow! Nothing was ever the same. The manual was a beautiful introduction to looking at landscapes like a canvas. Not an empty canvas, but one that invited the student, the

Lawns to Feed America?

During World War II, patriotic Americans grew Victory Gardens to feed themselves (40 percent of all produce consumed nationwide came from Victory Gardens) and help with the war effort. Over 20 million Victory Gardens produced 10 million tons of food. There weren't shopping malls, commercial and industrial "parks," or six-thousand-square-foot, five-bedroom McMansions planted in huge subdivisions that once were farms.

According to the Lawn Institute, as of 2004 there were 46.5 million acres, or 72,656 square miles, of turfgrass in the United States; more than an area the size of Pennsylvania, West Virginia, Delaware, and Rhode Island combined. Of that tidy sum, 25 million acres (up from 16 million acres in 1978) are private lawns. The turf grass industry is a $35 billion annual industry, and private homeowners expend $6.4 billion annually to fertilize, mow, and apply pesticides for merely cosmetic purposes.*

What's the big deal? Well, loss of farmland to those suburban developments has amounted to 3,000 acres *per day* in the United States. We squandered, for a variety of reasons, 23 million acres of farmland between 1982 and 2007. Meanwhile, the USDA reported that in 2009 in the United States imported 51 billion pounds of fruits and vegetables. (Are those "national security" ideologues and aficionados in D.C. having a conversation about food sometime, instead of drones, tanks, and Wikileaks?) Check out the American Farmland Trust (www.farmland.org) for how our landscape has been radically changing in a brief spit of time. We converted cornfields into bentgrass lawns; why not convert some of them back to squash, kale, tomato, and strawberry fields? Ironically, more nutritious food could be produced from small gardens on a fraction of those converted acres than when they produced mostly corn and soybeans for feedlots or ethanol plants.

---

* Speaking of pesticides, nationwide we dump 8 billion pounds of pesticides per year on U.S. cropland, turf grass, forests, etc. This amounts to about thirty pounds per person per year, twice what was used in 1964, two years after the release of Rachel Carson's *Silent Spring*. There are a hundred pesticides now found in drinking water in forty states, affecting 100 million people. The number of pesticides registered for use in the European Union is four hundred. In the United States it's twelve hundred, three times as much! For more information, visit the Pesticide Action Network, www.panna.org.

Lawns consume 20 percent of all fertilizers and utilize more water, fertilizer, fossil fuels, pesticides, and man-hours per acre than gardens or cropland. In fact, grass seed is the number two seed crop in the United States. Now let's imagine the amount and variety of local, fresh food that can be grown on a small fraction of those 46.5 million acres. Proper management of those landscapes could also create sanctuaries for pollinators, beneficial predatory insects, perennial/biannual flowering plants, fruit and nut trees, vines and berries, and a cornucopia of vegetables.

Small-scale livestock production—such as honeybees, poultry, rabbits, even flocks of mini ruminants like sheep—would readily fit into such a variegated expanse of land and contribute its own aesthetic resources to the suburban monoculture. Lest one think that such sounds like *Tobacco Road*, keep in mind that the front lawns of English manors were once mowed by sheep.

John Jeavons of the group Ecology Action in Willis, California, has provided for anyone who wants to be food self-sufficient a primer called *How to Grow More Vegetables: And Fruits, Nuts, Berries, Grains, and Other Crops Than You Ever Thought Possible on Less Land Than You Can Imagine*. His food-raising methods are now being used in over 140 countries. Jeavons is a national treasure teaching the "biointensive" farming and gardening method to non-governmental organizations, the Peace Corps, government agencies, and farmers and gardeners globally.

These days, children are entirely removed from the world of nature and where their food originates. These micro-farms could be educational modules for folks of all ages. For a little encouragement on how critically important such a concept is, I would suggest that the reader delve into the national bestseller *Last Child in the Woods: Saving Our Children from Nature-Deficit Disorder* by Richard Louv, who succinctly quotes from John Dewey's century-old *The School and Society*: "Experience [outside the school] has its geographical aspect, its artistic and its literary, its scientific and its historical sides. All studies arise from aspects of the one earth and the one life lived upon it." One of the driving forces instigating the installation of school gardens is the epidemic of childhood obesity and type 2 diabetes, which is clearly associated with the consumption of carbohydrates—especially refined carbs like sugar, high fructose corn syrup, and wheat flour. All of these empty calories drive surges of insulin while contributing virtually nothing in terms of minerals, vitamins, plant-based carotenes, essential fatty acids, fiber, and antioxidants. In the United States today, 8 percent of low-income children are obese, and 33 percent of *all* children born in 2000 are likely to become diabetic. Perhaps turning our lawnscapes into landscapes can help address the global medical catastrophe of diabetes, up from 153 million in 1980 to 347 million as of 2013. And just maybe it could reduce the incidence of cancer, now at 41 percent in the United States.

Children readily can make the correlation between their health and appearance and vegetables and fruits grown on healthy soil. While gardening they can learn so much more than what a textbook can teach about how natural ecosystems work and that we humans can rejoin the web of life.

observer, to see how he or she could become part of the painting, part of the landscape's story, to partner with a co-creator of this landscape and generate ecological capital, real wealth and health for the entire biological community, especially humans.

We can be designers of more fractal architecture in this remarkable quiltwork of meadow, pasture, orchard, field crops, garden, vineyard, streams, riparian edges, hedgerows, woodlot, range, savannah, marsh, wetland, estuary and the oceanside, tidal pools, lagoon, desert, steppes, pond, lake, and river. All of these are eco-niches, and all are inhabited by people who grow food nearby and are the organs of the corpus of Gaia. In Adam Nicolson's 2013 *National Geographic* article "Hay. Beautiful.," an article on the hay meadows of Romania, Nicolson commented on how throughout the world's cultures, each has on average twenty to forty words that describe or define an eco-niche. I stopped at about twenty a few sentences ago. Romanian peasants have 145 words for such places. In order for humanity to have a wholesome, healthy, and joyful existence, the extinction, destruction, and sterilizing homogenization of our landscapes must be terminated—and then restored.

Essentially, this whole-systems approach incorporates growing spaces both efficiently and cooperatively. Take the cooperation between orchard and nut trees with ground covers, grazing livestock, annual and perennial fruits and vegetables—not only do they *not* compete with one another, they increase the fertility year after year, thus increasing the land's productivity, enhancing biodiversity, and favoring the neighboring environments.

Orchards can be ground covered with legumes such as clover, spike root plants like comfrey, bulbs like daffodils, and insectary plants that attract pollinators—such as the Umbelliferae family of fennel, dill, tansy, carrot, Queen Anne's lace, and parsnip and the Compositae family of daisy and Echinacea. Placing small baby pools intermittently amongst the trees will attract frogs and toads to control leaf insects. Bringing in poultry early on at seventy to a hundred birds an acre will allow them to scavenge windfalls—including larvae or pupae pests—provide hen manure fertilizer while giving the flock about a third to half of their nutritional intake with insects, earthworms, legumes, seeds, forbs and cull fruit, all of which create flavorful and highly nutritious eggs and meats. As the trees mature from six to eight years of age they could withstand an introduction of swine to consume pest-ridden fruit on the ground. Research at Michigan State University demonstrated that pastured pigs controlled plum curculio at least as effectively as toxic insecticides. Following those eight years of growth, rotational grazing animals like sheep could be introduced, and from ten to twenty years on, tree orchards can withstand a rotation of grazing cattle.

This is obviously a quiltwork farm, and the vast majority of mechanized agrarians would find this kind of an example more suited to the homesteading aficionados who subscribe to the *Mother Earth News*. It is true enough that a perennial agriculture can be attractive and quite conducive to even an urban homestead where such a scale of farming feeds much of the developing world. However, the multilayered strategies of integrated farming are quite relevant everywhere in terms of adequate food production and landscape restoration. Instead of pretending that four or five cereal crops are an adequate food "larder" to feed humanity, why can't we see that a healthy nation, a healthy society, and a healthy people need a diverse access to hundreds if not thousands of foods?

Following the acquisition of Mollison's text and also *Permaculture: Principles and Pathways beyond Sustainability* by his brilliant colleague David Holmgren, I ended up with the out-of-print edition of J. Russell Smith's *Tree Crops: A Permanent Agriculture*, originally published in 1929 and republished in 1950. Smith's position was "that farming should fit the land," not force the landscape to fit our desires. Like Professor Walter C. Lowdermilk, Smith traveled the globe and observed the worldwide catastrophes of soil erosion creating—as he described it—a one-way avalanche of "Forest—field—plow—desert—that is the cycle of the hills under most plow agriculture, a cycle not limited to China, but so (also) Syria, Greece, Italy, Guatemala and the United States." According to Smith, to make matters worse in the United States, we have tilled row crops, especially corn, cotton, and tobacco, whereas Europe had small cereal grains that hold the ground better.

America is also beset by the thunderstorm, dumping two inches of rain per hour into hilly corn fields, equivalent to two hundred inches of gentle British or German rain. "Corn, the killer of continents, is one of the worst enemies of the human future," said J. Russell Smith. Wow, and ouch! This was from a USDA scientist.

Smith's primary concern for the United States was the serious destruction and loss of topsoil on our hill ground, which he said amounted to millions of acres from Maine to Alabama, up again through Tennessee, Kentucky, central Ohio, southern Indiana and Illinois, and into Missouri and Arkansas. Other similar topography appears on the foothills of the Rockies and the mountains of the Pacific Coast. The chief objective of his research and writing was to "urge new foods for animals," because livestock were already consuming the feeds grown on four-fifths of the farm acreage, much like the corn and soybean craze of today. This kind of permanent agriculture would be much more productive than even the existing alternatives to plowing the hillsides, which are either pasture or woodlots.

But Smith even proposed the radical idea of two-story agriculture for level land. The wonderful example he provided was the Spanish island of Majorca, where nine-tenths of the cultivated land was growing an annual crop beneath a tree crop. This apparently was a common practice in the Mediterranean Basin. A typical farm might have been planted with fig trees growing in rows forty feet apart. Beneath the fig trees was a regular rotation of wheat, clover, and chickpeas. The clover was allowed to grow for two years, and the second year it fed a flock of sheep, thus yielding five crops from the same land.

Other Majorca farms grew almonds or olives as a tree crop. The yields were about 75 percent of what a monoculture of figs, almonds, olives, or wheat were. But 75 percent of the tree crop plus 75 percent of a wheat crop equals 150 percent off the same land while dividing the risk of weather over at least two crops. Trees insulate the landscape from the extreme vagaries of weather, be they drought, heat, flood, or frost.

Smith foresaw farms integrating fodder trees like honey locust, chestnut, acorn oaks, persimmon, mulberry, and carob. Smith's visits to the

Mediterranean Basin countries demonstrated that in steep, rocky terrain, as in the foothills of the Atlas Mountains in Algeria, the hillsides—which were covered in olive and fig trees—supported human populations twenty-five times more dense than where the land was unplanted to trees.

Smith's vision was to see an institute that could find selected tree parentage, breed them for higher productivity or quality, and even hybridize them for local climatic conditions.

The lowly honey locust (*Gleditsia triacanthos*) was a favorite example of Smith's disdain for a lack of foresight and imagination amongst bureaucrats in charge of improving agricultural practices, crop production, and farm profitability. Smith incited John Hershey, who worked for the Tennessee Valley Authority, to seek out honey locust trees also rich in sugar in their pods. He found two such varieties: Milwood at 36 percent sugar and Calhoun at 39 percent sugar.

One experiment station in Auburn, Alabama, reported in 1942 that five-year-old Milwoods produced an average of 58.30 pounds of pods per tree (dry weight). At forty-eight trees per acre, this would equal 2,798 pounds of pods. The average from 1942 to 1945 (only four years) was 2,923 pounds of pods, equal to ninety-seven bushels of oats per acre. As in Majorca, Spain, there was also an understory crop of hay (*Lespedeza sericea*) averaging two and half tons per acre per year while completely protecting the soil from erosion. A few years later, some eight-year-old trees were producing over 250 pounds of pods per tree. At thirty-five trees per acre, this would be equivalent to 8,750 pounds of pods per acre—equal to 275 bushels of oats per acre, plus the hay or pasture!

President Franklin Delano Roosevelt began the Shelter Belt Plan in 1934 at the height of the Dust Bowl. About 19,000 miles of belts were planted on 33,000 farms. A 1944 survey of 1,079 belts showed that the highest percentage of tree survival was the honey locust at 79 percent, followed by black locust at 78.3 percent, and 59.4 percent for cottonwoods.

It is inconceivable that so many reports from experiment stations and farmers alike from New England, the Midwest, the South, the dry Western Range, the High Plains, the Southwest—including a USDA report consisting of 180 pages of valuable honey locust data—could be ultimately ignored and abandoned.

I won't in this text cover all the other food and fodder trees that Smith laboriously collected data about from Hawaii to Europe to China, but

TABLE 13.1

AVERAGE COMPOSITION OF NUTS AND OTHER FOODS

Kind of Food	Refuse %	Water %	Protein %	Fat %	Carbohydrates		Ash %	Fuel Value/ # Calories
					Sugars, Starch, etc.	Crude Fiber %		
Acorn, fresh	17.80	34.7	4.4	4.7	50.4	4.2	1.6	1265
Almond	47.00	4.9	21.4	54.4	13.8	3.0	2.5	2895
Beechnut	69.90	6.6	21.8	49.9	18.0		3.7	2740
Brazil nut	49.35	4.7	17.4	65.0	5.7	3.9	3.3	3120
Butternut	86.40	4.5	27.9	61.2	3.4		3.0	3370
Chestnut, fresh	15.70	43.4	6.4	6.0	41.3	1.5	1.4	1140
Chestnut, dry	23.40	6.1	10.7	7.8	70.1	2.9	2.4	1840
Chestnut flour	....	7.8	4.6	3.4	80.5		3.4	1780
Filbert	52.08	5.4	16.5	64.0	11.7		2.4	3100
Hazelnut meal	....	2.7	11.7	65.6	17.8		2.2	3185
Hickory nut	62.20	3.7	15.4	67.4	11.4		2.1	3345
Other Foods for Comparison								
Beans, dried	....	12.6	22.5	1.8	55.2	4.4	3.5	1650
Potatoes	20.00	78.3	2.2	0.1	18.0	0.4	1.0	385
Apples	25.00	84.6	0.4	0.5	13.0	1.2	0.3	290
Raisins	10.00	14.6	2.6	3.3	73.6	2.5	3.4	1605

J. Russell Smith, *Tree Crops: A Permanent Agriculture* (Greenwich, CT: Devin-Adair Publishing Company, 1950), 393.

ignoring the evidence of how woody perennials can feed humans and livestock in concert with annual cereals and forage crops while discussing how GMOs and pesticides are needed to feed the coming 9 billion is nothing short of the kind of behavior that the Church exhibited toward Galileo when he insisted that the sun was the center of our solar system.

Rather than repeat all the other examples that Smith illuminated to his readers about other tree crops farms and the long-lasting prosperity created for the landscape and his comments (such as chestnut orchards in Corsica over a thousand years old) the following table demonstrates the feeding value of some fruits and nuts as they compare to annual grain crops.

Apparently, what appears to be ideal as a food-producing landscape is neither the dense forest nor the cultivated grassland but the juvenile landscapes that resemble savannahs, where trees and grasses coexist to produce a rich, varied ecosystem, a park-like landscape that perhaps reminds us of our origins. The so-called second phase of human development—following our first phase of hunter-gatherers—was when and where grass became a nutritive multiplier in the Fertile Crescent of the Nile Valley and Mesopotamia and where domestication of both livestock and grasses created yet another quiltwork of biological reciprocity. Through the clearing of its dense beech forests, Europe became a Fertile Crescent spinoff where a tapestry of woodland, pastures, and meadows interspersed with trees—savannahs—bordered by hedgerows and plots producing fruits, nuts, wheat, and vegetables created an explosion of species expansion for those species that were originally marginalized by the thick forest canopy. Clearings inviting sunlight encouraged an abundance of meadowland species, both plant and animal. Numerous new species developed, either through cross fertilization or the colonization of these habitats by new arrivals (think of European dandelion in our American pastures, meadows, lawns, etc.). Along with the arrival of many new plants came animals, birds, and insects, including pollinators. In the eastern United States this activity of opening up the dense forest by Native Americans brought the grazers elk and bison into the Eastern Seaboard (hence the names Elk County, Pennsylvania, and Buffalo Gap, Pennsylvania and Virginia).

Charles Mann's seminal book *1491* explodes the assumption held by Eurocentric thinkers for many decades that Amazonia was always a wilderness inhabited by primitive hunter-gatherers. Tropical soils are positively not fertile, especially because heavy rainfall destroys soil structure and leaches nutrients when exposed without tree cover. Apparently, Amazonia's first inhabitants, those who created the remarkable terra preta soils from charcoal, clay pot shards, and animal/human waste, were tree crop farmers. Of the more than 138 domesticated species found in Amazonia, between 50–80 percent are trees such as sapodilla, calabash, tucuma, babacu, açaí, wild pineapple, cocopalm, American oil palm, Panama hat palm and peach palm.

The peach palm is a nutrient-dense food rich in oil, protein, and carotenes. It can also be dried into flour and fermented as a beverage. And in terms of yield per acre they are much more productive than rice, beans, or corn. Peach palm trees begin producing within five years and can produce for up to seventy years. Other resources on palm forests can be found in *The Subsidy from Nature: Palm Forests, Peasantry and Development on an Amazon Frontier,* by Anthony Anderson, Peter May and Michael Balick. The early Amazonians actually transformed much of the tropics into orchards, to the extent that one-eighth of the non-flooded forest was anthropogenic, that is, created by humans.

The terra preta food plots used to grow perennial food trees were typically five to fifteen acres in area, with black soil measuring one to two feet deep, sometimes as much as six feet deep, with the largest plot measuring three miles in length and a half mile wide, capable of supporting 200,000 to 400,000 people! Biochar, as terra preta is also called, is capable of retaining carbon in the soil for up to 50,000 years. Compare that to the current practices of slash-and-burn "modern" agriculture, exhausting the exposed fragile tropical soils to a dead-end window of beef cattle grazing, or planting GMO monocultures of soy and corn, requiring tremendous amounts of soil disturbance, fossil fuels for farm machinery, petroleum-based fertilizers, and ecologically toxic and destructive pesticides. Which of the two systems described has a likelier chance of feeding a growing population sustainably—the darlings of Bill Gates and Stewart Brand, namely the Monsantos, Syngentas, DuPonts, Cargills, et al., or those nameless artisans, farmers, and original conservationists who gave us a non-patented roadmap from which all can prosper from, and without exterminating untold numbers of our native brethren while exporting obscene amounts of topsoil and contaminating the gene pool?

The Iroquois made famous the Three Sisters planting of corn, beans, and squash or pumpkins. Jane Mt. Pleasant, a Cornell-educated PhD and an Iroquois descendent, pointed out that the Iroquois would first plant corn in hills about a yard apart, three stalks to a hill. Two weeks later pole beans were planted in those hills and squash planted in between the hills. The corn yields were estimated to be a fraction (twenty-five to forty bushels per acre) of the current average New York State corn yields (one hundred

Revisiting Chaboussou

The author of the text *Healthy Crops* gets an accolade of support from José A. Lutzenberger, who makes his own case for Francis Chaboussou's theory on trophobiosis in his article "How Agrochemicals Feed the Pests that Destroy the Crops."[*] Jose Lutzenberger began his agronomy career working for the agrichemical corporation BASF. He returned to his native Brazil in 1972 to become an avid opponent of reckless pesticide use on food crops, and he eventually became minister of environment in Brazil.

Lutzenberger met Chaboussou, a farmer, in France and consequently championed his work of reviewing fifty years of innumerable studies that demonstrated that the nutritional state of crops is what affects their susceptibility to disease and insects. Chaboussou died in 1985, heartbroken about the toxic direction agriculture had taken, and it was Lutzenberger who worked avidly to see that Chaboussou's work was eventually published in English.

It's now nearly thirty years after *Healthy Crops* was first published in French in 1984 and this theory seems to be really stacking up. Trophobiosis concludes that pests can only survive on plants that have an excessive level of soluble nutrients in their sap or tissues, such as amino acids, sugars, nucleotides, and even minerals. Excess can be a result of an inhibition of proteosynthesis (or complete protein production) or a predominance of proteolysis (a breaking down of proteins) over proteosynthesis, an excess production of free amino acids in the tissue, or enzyme interference by pesticides or by unbalanced nutrition. Sad to report that, in spite of all the evidence reported by many researchers,[†] those who have the primary influence over the agriculture practice of our growers (namely academics, extension agents, and industry reps) continually provide the erroneous, misleading advice that our crop pests are arbitrary enemies, that they appear out of nowhere and will inevitably destroy

---

[*] First published in *Ecologist* 14, no. 2 (1984): 77–81, and enlarged and revised in 1986.
[†] See *Mineral Nutrition of Crops*, edited by Zdenko Rengel; *Plant Disease: An Advanced Treatise*, edited by James G. Horsfall and Ellis B. Cowling; *Mineral Nutrition and Plant Disease*, edited by Lawrence E. Datnoff, Wade Elmer, and Don Huber; and *Mineral Nutrition of Higher Plants*, by Horst Marschner, to name a few.

our crops unless we intervene with toxic rescue remedies, both preventatively and defensively.

IPM (Integrative Pest Management) was set up by extension agents to lighten the load of our cancer-causing arsenal against insects, weeds, bacteria, fungi, nematodes, mites, rodents, and mollusks. Thus, with IPM, apple sprays still may be "only" a couple of dozen applications per season. Meanwhile, the pest damage accelerates as we continue to use more tonnage of the poisons, and resistance continues to increase.

One interesting observation given by Lutzenberger, which is a large exception to the ecological rule, is that even monocultures can be healthy. He provides some natural examples of monocultures in wild niches, such as Brazilian salt marsh stands of only one species of mangroves, reeds in salt marshes, and fields of one herb (Salicornia). Cultivated monocultures may be healthy or unhealthy, as Lutzenberger can attest to eucalyptus groves and acacia plantations. The acacia plantations may or may not attract the serrador beetle, which apparently prefers trees growing in waterlogged or extremely sandy soils.

Lutzenberger goes so far as to say that fungicides and other pesticides can invite more pest opportunism even if the predators have not been killed off by insecticides because the actual biochemistry of the plant has been altered to the benefit of the pest. He proclaims that pest opportunism is a result of: 1) inadequate or unbalanced nutrition, 2) weed competition, 3) interactions with companion plants, 4) allelopathy, (the interference of the growth of one plant because of the biochemicals excreted by another plant), and/or 5) climatic stress.

Healthy plants have low amounts of soluble nutrients because the turn over of them to be utilized in the cell is rapid. They are quickly utilized to build new structures, like proteins, RNA, DNA, cell walls, carbohydrates, fats and much, much more. Old leaves are experiencing proteolysis, where nutrients are recycled to newer parts of the plant. Soluble nutrients begin to accumulate in older leaves and that is why on the curcurbits, squash, melons, cucumbers, etc. one can witness heavy fungus attack in the old leaves while the rest of the plant is clear.

José Lutzenberger then moves on with some interesting examples of how he and other growers circumvented the bombardment of crops with pesticides (some growers spraying almost daily). One simple solution was to spray cheese whey—beginning at 100 percent, then at 10 percent, and finally at 2 percent dilutions—with great effect, reducing costs by over 90 percent on strawberries, while preventing insect and disease damage. Another example was a sixty-five hectare (160 acre) orchard of twenty-eight thousand guava trees, which were conventionally treated with once-yearly plowing, twice-monthly harrowing, and repeated applications of herbicides to maintain bare soil. Fungicides, insecticides, and occasionally acaricides were applied every two weeks, sometimes weekly. Lutzenberger's conversion was to quit soil disturbance, instead planting a cover crop of native forbs and legumes. They applied moderate amounts of rock phosphate every three or four years. Trees were sprayed every fifteen days with whey. The fruit fly was baited with molasses or sugar water, which eventually became unnecessary. One tanker load of whey costs less than a one-gallon canister of fungicide, and the other "crop" is a hundred cattle that are rotated under the tree canopy to graze the cover crop. Ten years after these practices were instituted, Lutzenberger states, the land became a beautiful, profitable, and toxic-free orchard, with input costs down to near zero.

Apple growers in southern Brazil have followed the example of a grower who once was an extension agent and came up with a treatment known as Super-Magro, named after Edelvino Magro, the grower. The mix consists of 50 percent water and 50 percent cattle manure mixed in an open drum or tank when temperatures are above 20°C or 68°F. He adds two and a half to five pounds of sugar or molasses and some milk, allows it to ferment for twenty days until all the gas has escaped, and then adds a suite of trace elements, even including molybdenum and vanadium. The brew is diluted to 1–2 percent before applying regularly (ten- to fifteen-day intervals). He also grazes sheep in the orchard. Super-Magro is now used successfully in citrus groves, vineyards, peach orchards, and vegetables.

Citrus trees attacked by aphids were brought back to health in only four days after only one application of either a humus concentrate fortified with trace elements, pure whey, or whey plus humus at only 1–2 percent. First the immature insects fell off, followed by the adult females, with the ants that "milk" them running about in despair. In the meantime, an intensive attack of predators increased, including wasps, ladybugs, and syrphid flies, which was not a phenomena in the intact colonies prior to the foliar spray. It appears that the host tree's physiology changed, similar to an "immune response," including an "immune response" that was also external; namely, predators were called in by both a healthier plant and an unhealthier parasite, the aphids.

In 2012, an open warm winter invited an onslaught of army worms into large sections of the northern United States. A few folks I visited, out of desperation, were using a mixture of whole raw milk (two to three gallons), liquid fish (two to three gallons) and molasses (two gallons) per acre. The army worms avoided the areas where this mixture was sprayed on pastures, even though army worm damage was significant in areas surrounding the treated area. Similar reports on grasshoppers were received, and some folks added five pounds of rock salt and three to five pounds of Epsom salts to the milk, fish, and molasses recipe and reported encouraging outcomes.

Do these sprays act as nutritional factors? Plant physiology stimulants? Encourage a disease outbreak on the pests? No doubt it's a combined, synergistic impact that should encourage the curiosity of plant pathologists, entomologists, and agronomists to collaborate on finding effective, economical, and safe alternatives to the onslaught of chemical warfare we have unleashed upon nature and ourselves for the last seventy years.

As Lutzenberger points out, a goal for agriculture should be getting several hundred thousand farmers to reduce their poison applications by 5–10 percent, which would have a larger net impact than having two or three dozen farmers going 100 percent organic. Additionally, those who take that first step of 5–10 percent poison reduction don't stop there because they realize without any dogma or ideology that it is to their advantage to continue farming more ecologically, no matter how close to certified organic they become.

bushels per acre). But when totaling up the calories of both types of farming, the Three Sisters method yielded over 4 million calories per acre versus 3.4 million for our current corn-alone agriculture. But that's only calories—what about protein, minerals, vitamins, carotenes, etc.? In addition to these vegetables, the nut orchards produced tons of "mast," namely hickory nuts, beechnuts, acorns, butternuts, hazelnuts, pecans, walnuts, and chestnuts. Prior to the Europeans cutting them down and a blight that finished them off in the early twentieth century, the American chestnut was estimated to make up to 25 percent of the eastern deciduous forests that ranged from southeastern Canada to Georgia, apparently because of Native Americans managing them via understory burning as well as planting them. Basically, park-like arrangements were instituted that included fruit and nut orchards, grazing pastures to invite game, and farmed patches of vegetables. Near my community is the township Plainfield, allegedly named so by European colonists in the eighteenth century because of the openness of the landscape, which was created by the native Lenni Lenape, who did not dwell in a deep, dark forest but a landscape of variegated ecotones of pasture, woodlots, orchards, and gardens.

The Three Sisters' beans supply nitrogen from the rhizobia bacteria in the roots and the protein in their leaves; the squash provide a living mulch to suppress weeds and conserve moisture. All three crops at harvest provide carbon-rich biomass for the next year's humus requirements. This carpet of three plants provides a refuge for predatory insects and pollinators for other vegetables and fruits grown on the property. Now imagine these crops grown in an alley where perennial nut or fruit trees create a border, or perhaps where grapevines or brambles like raspberries can thrive.

This is a laughable concept to an industrial monoculturalist who can quickly and precisely plant thousands of acres of corn or beans with GPS, GMOs, glyphosate, and an arsenal of biocides to cover the community of plants, animals, and humans in the name of food security. That is, until the devil's pantry of toxic rescue chemistry fails him and insects or blight become as resistant to this toxic soup as staph has become to penicillin. Meanwhile, the black soil of the prairie has become sterile and departs from the landscape raindrop by raindrop, while the calories required to produce this inedible "stuff" outweighs the harvest by as much as to 10:1 compared to the calories harvested.

We have far too many examples of how to sustain our ecological communities of plants, soil, water, beneficial insects, and animals (including humans), that contribute to wholesome, economically vibrant, and physically and emotionally healthy populations, while simultaneously having an in-depth, stark record of how to ruin civilizations by utilizing extractive (and now toxic) methods to grow food, fodder, and fiber.

Encouraging signs do exist. Mark Shepard, a Wisconsin farmer and biodiverse permaculturalist, is replicating J. Russell Smith's *Tree Crops* model utilizing pigs, poultry, ruminant grazers, nut trees, fruits, vines, berries, and annual plots as reported upon and detailed in his book *Restoration Agriculture*.

In the same vein, two other permaculture practitioners, David Jacke and Eric Toensmeier, have put together an exhaustive two-volume text they call "an ecological vision and theory for temperate climate permaculture," titled *Edible Forest Gardens*.

An extraordinary tale written by French author Jean Giono that should be on every bookshelf is a fable called *The Man Who Planted Trees*. It was appropriately titled *The Man Who Planted Hope and Grew Happiness* back in 1954 when it was published in English. The story is of a man named Elzéard Bouffier living near Provence, France. He is a peasant shepherd who collects and sorts acorns and beechnuts while managing his flock and plants healthy nuts to create a hardwood forest on a barren and denuded land. Fast forward forty years, and the region has not only become enlivened with many forms of animal and plant residents, but the springs have returned and the village people have grown more kindly and optimistic because of the beauty and bounty of their restored hills. Though a fiction, it reads as true as a compass. Visit such an area—whether in Europe, Pennsylvania, or Vermont—and then drive to an area ravaged by mining, clear-cuts, suburbia, or extractive monoculture agriculture and look around—the heart and soul has been cut out of the bioregion and of the community that includes people, plants, animals, soil, and water.

A living example of *The Man Who Planted Trees* is a woman named Wangari Maathai, who in 1977 founded the Green Belt Movement (www.greenbeltmovement.org), which organized women to plant trees for firewood, fruit, fodder, fencing, and ground cover/riparian buffers to restore water flow in streams and springs. Wangari Maathai's position is that "only through an equitable distribution of resources and their sustainable use will we be able to keep the peace." Her Green Belt Movement has since planted more than 30 million trees throughout Kenya and other African nations to "keep the peace" by creating equitable, renewable, natural resources necessary for sustainable livelihoods.

The diversity of life is the holy grail of Spaceship Earth and the yet-to-be-realized treasures available to us, such as the natural origins of medicines utilized by Western cultures, including the 119 substances used in their pure form. Interested readers will want to refer to *The Diversity of Life* by Edward O. Wilson.

The unprecedented rate of extinction, mostly the handiwork of resource-hungry and wasteful humans, has now perhaps crossed the threshold of the point of no return. Those who feel that extinction is a normal cycle eventually reconciled by Nature should pause to consider the following. Humanity has ushered in the Sixth Great Extinction. The other five great extinctions preceded humanity's presence upon Earth. The Ordovician Extinction occurred 440 million years ago; the Devonian, 365 million years ago; the Permian, 245 million years ago; the Triassic, 210 million years ago; and the Cretaceous Extinction, 65 million years ago. In geological time, these are a blink in God's eye. As we become seduced by mechanistic and militaristic ideas that technology will always solve our problems and that "might always makes right," the laws of unintended consequences are always with us.

After each downturn from extinction, the coevolutionary processes began again, the divine spark igniting the flow of the life from water, minerals, and sunlight to reinhabit the earth. But keep in mind that in geological or divine time, that recovery required tens of millions of years.

As E. O. Wilson, author of *The Diversity of Life*, Pulitzer Prize–winning author of two textbooks, and honorary curator of entomology at Harvard University, states "I will argue that every scrap of biological diversity is priceless, to be learned and cherished, and never to be surrendered without a struggle." Father Thomas Berry, a Passionist priest and author of *The Universe Story*, *The Dream of the Earth*, and *The Great Work*, sums it up succinctly. "The Universe is a communion of subjects, not a collection of objects."

Additional Resources

Listed here are just some of many additional books, websites, and journal articles that readers looking for further information might find helpful.

POLLINATORS
Pollinator Resources
Pollinator Partnership, www.pollinator.org

North American Pollinator Protection Campaign, http://pollinator.org/nappc/

USDA Forest Service, www.fs.fed.us/wildflowers/pollinators/

Wild Farm Alliance, www.wildfarmalliance.org

Xerces Society Pollinator Program, www.xerces.org

Illinois Natural History Survey, www.inhs.uiuc.edu

Native Plant Resources
Plant Conservation Alliance, www.nps.gov/plants/

Seeds of Success, www.nps.gov/plants/sos/

Lady Bird Johnson Wild Flower Center, www.wildflower.org/plants/

U.S. National Arboretum, www.usna.usda.gov

USDA, NRCS 2007-The Plant Database, www.plants.usda.gov

Native Bees
Alternative Pollinators: Native Bees, www.attra.org/attra-pub/nativebee.html

Agriculture Research Service Plants Attractive to Native Bees, http://www.ars.usda.gov/Services/docs.htm?docid=12052

Butterflies and Moths
Butterflies and Moths of North America, www.butterfliesandmoths.org

A Little Help from Our Friends
The following are some references to support the science behind the need for pollinating and predatory refuges and nectaries:

Deborah K. Letourneau et al., "Does Plant Diversity Benefit Agroecosystems? A Synthetic Review," *Ecological Applications* 21, no. 1 (January 2011): 9–21.

Timothy D. Meehan et al., "Agricultural Landscape Simplification and Insecticide Use in the Midwestern United States," *Proceedings of the National Academy of Sciences* 108, no. 28 (2011): 11500–5.

Teja Tscharntke et al. "Landscape Perspectives on Agricultural Intensification and Biodiversity—Ecosystem Service Management," *Ecology Letters* 8, no. 8 (2005): 857–74.

COVER CROPS
Abe Collins of Collins Grazing in Vermont is a real soil carbon activist. Abe has been collecting information and advising others on cover crop cocktails, key line subsoiling, and foliar sprays for forages based on the success stories found throughout the country and has posted the following resources for those who want to cover crop with cocktails profitably:

Jay Fuhrer's webinar on Cocktail Cover Cropping (www.youtube.com/watch?v-zjI2z4uMI)

USDA ARS Cover Crop Chart (http://www.ars.usda.gov/SP2UserFiles/Place/54452000/CCC/CCC_v13_5_2012.pdf)

Gabe Brown Ranch website (www.brownsranch.us)

Managing Cover Crops Profitably (www.sare.org/learning-center/books/managing-cover-crops-profitably-3rd-edition)

TOOLS OF THE TRADE
Bob and Cheryl Pike of Agri-Lab Supplies are most capable at explaining their craft and can readily be reached at: Pike Agri-Lab Supplies, Inc. 154 Claybrook Rd. P.O. Box 67 Jay, Maine 04239

Telephone: 207-897-9267 Toll Free: 866-PIKEAGRI (745-3247)
www.pikeagri.com

Penn State University Greenhouse IPM Manual. Emphasis on Bio controls page 108 free download. http://extension.psu.edu/ipm/program/greenhouse/greenhouse-manual

ATTRA: IPM for Greenhouse Crops http://attra.ncat.org/attra-pub/ghipm.html

http://www.appliedbio-nomics.com/crop_recommendations/

Lawns to Feed America

A relevant read on this topic is Barbara Berst Adams's *Micro Eco-Farming: Prospering from Backyard to Small Acreage in Partnership with the Earth.*

Some worthwhile websites on the Urban/Suburban Farming Movement can be found at www.microecofarming.com, www.suburbanhomesteading.com and www.theurbanfarmingguys.com.

Recommended Reading

Against the Grain: How Agriculture Has Hijacked Civilization, Richard Manning (2004).

An Agricultural Testament, Sir Albert Howard (1940).

Agriculture in Transition, Donald L. Schriefer (2000).

Agroecology: The Science of Sustainable Agriculture, Miguel Altieri (1995).

The Albrecht Papers, 8 vols., William Albrecht (1975).

The Art of Balancing Soil Nutrients: A Practical Guide to Interpreting Soil Tests, William McKibben (2012).

Attracting Native Pollinators: Protecting North America's Bees and Butterflies, Xerces Society (2011).

Biodiversity and Pest Management in Agroecosystems, Miguel Altieri and Clara Nicholls (1994).

The Biological Farmer: A Complete Guide to the Sustainable and Profitable Biological System of Farming, Gary F. Zimmer (2000).

Biology of Plants, Peter H. Raven, Ray F. Evert, and Susan E. Eichhorn (2005).

Common-Sense Pest Control, William Olkowski, Helga Olkowski, and Sheila Daar (1991).

Design in Nature: How the Constructal Law Governs Evolution in Biology, Physics, Technology, and Social Organization, Adrian Bejan and J. Peder Zane (2012).

Diseases and Pests of Vegetable Crops in Canada: An Illustrated Compendium, Ronald James Howard, John Allan Garland, and W. L. Seaman (1994).
The Diversity of Life, Edward O. Wilson (1992).
The Earth Moved: On the Remarkable Achievements of Earthworms, Amy Stewart (2004).
Eco-Farm: An Acres U.S.A. Primer, Charles Walters and C. J. Fenzau (1996).
Ecologically Based Pest Management: New Solutions for a New Century, National Research Council (1996).
Edible Forest Gardens, Dave Jacke and Eric Toensmeier (2005).
The Enlivened Rock Powders, Harvey Lisle (1994).
The Farmer's Earthworm Handbook: Managing your Underground Money-Makers, David Ernst (1995).
Farming in Nature's Image: An Ecological Approach to Agriculture, Judith Soule and Jon K. Piper (1992).
Flowforms: The Rhythmic Power of Water, John A. Wilkes (2003).
The Forgotten Pollinators, Stephen L. Buchmann, Gary Paul Nabhan, and Paul Mirocha (1996).
From My Personal Experience: The Pleasures and Miseries of Life on a Farm, Louis E. Bromfield (2011).
From The Soil Up, Donald L. Schriefer (2011).
The Fundamentals of Soil Science, 8th edition, Henry D. Foth (1990).
Hands-On Agronomy, Neal Kinsey and Charles Walters (2006).
Harnessing the Earthworm: A Practical Inquiry into Soil-Building, Soil-Conditioning and Plant Nutrition through the Action of Earthworms, with Instructions for Intensive Propagation and Use of Domesticated Earthworms in Biological Soil-Building, Thomas J. Barrett (1947).
The Healing Power of Energized Water: The New Science of Potentizing the World's Most Vital Resource, Ulrich Holst (2004).
Healthy Crops: A New Agricultural Revolution, Francis Chaboussou (2005).
The Holistic Orchard: Tree Fruits and Berries the Biological Way, Michael Phillips (2012).
How Soils Work: A Study into the God-Plane Mutualism of Soils and Crops, Paul W. Syltie (2002).
Introduction to Ecological Biochemistry, J. B. Harborne (1982).
Introduction to Soil Microbiology, Martin Alexander (1961).
Laws of Life in Agriculture, Nicolas Remer (1995).
Life in the Soil: A Guide for Naturalists and Gardeners, James Nardi (2007).
The Lives of a Cell: Notes of a Biology Watcher, Lewis Thomas (1974).

The Living Earth: The Organic Origin of Rocks and Minerals, Walther Cloos (1978).

The Lost Language of Plants: The Ecological Importance of Plant Medicines to Life on Earth, Stephen Harrod Buhner (2002).

Malabar Farm, Louis E. Bromfield (1948).

Managing Cover Crops Profitably, Sustainable Agricultural Network (2007).

Metabolic Aspects of Health: Nutritional Elements in Health and Disease, Karl H.Myes and John A. Schutte (1979).

Metals and Micronutrients: Uptake and Utilization by Plants, D. A. Robb (1983).

Mineral Nutrition and Plant Disease, Lawrence Datnoff, Wade H. Elmer, Don Huber (2007).

Mineral Nutrition of Crops: Fundamental Mechanisms and Implications, Zdenko Rengel (2000).

Mineral Nutrition of Higher Plants, Horst Marschner (1995).

Modern Soil Microbiology, Jan Dirk van Elsas, Janet K. Jansson, and Jack T. Trevors (2007).

The Nature and Property of Soils, Nyle C. Brady, Ray R. Weil (2008).

The New England Vegetable Management Guide, John Howell, ed. (annual).

Northeast Cover Crop Handbook, Marianne Sarrantonio (1994).

The One-Straw Revolution: An Introduction to Natural Farming, Masanobu Fukuoka (1990).

The Organic Gardener's Book of Natural Insect and Disease Control: A Complete Problem-Solving Guide to Keeping Your Garden and Yard Healthy Without Chemicals, Barbara W. Ellis and Fern Marshall Bradley (1992).

Humic, Fulvic, and Microbial Balance: Organic Soil Conditioning, William R. Jackson (1993).

Out of the Earth, Louis E. Bromfield (1950).

Paramagnetism: Rediscovering Nature's Secret Force of Growth, Philip S. Callahan (1995).

The Penn State Agronomy Guide, Penn State University (2013–2014).

Permaculture: A Designer's Manual, Bill Mollison (1988).

Plant Disease: An Advanced Treatise, 5 vols., James G. Horsfall and E. R. Cowling (1977–1980).

Plant Secondary Metabolites: Occurrence, Structure and Role in the Human Diet, Alan Crozier, Hiroshi Ashihara, and Mike N. Clifford, eds. (2008).

Plant-Microbe Interactions and Biological Control, Greg J. Boland, L. David Kuykendall, eds. (1998).

Pleasant Valley, Louis E. Bromfield (1998).

Plowman's Folly, Edward H. Faulkner (2012; reprint).

Plowman's Folly and a Second Look, Edward H. Faulkner (1988).

Seaweed: A User's Guide, Sonia Surey-Gent and Gordon Morris (1987).

Seaweed in Agriculture and Horticulture, William Anthony Stephenson (1968).

Secrets of the Soil: New Solutions for Restoring Our Planet, Peter Tompkins and Christopher Bird (1998).

Sensitive Chaos: The Creation of Flowing Forms in Water and Air, Theodor Schwenk (1965).

The Survival of Civilization Depends upon our Solving Three Problems—Carbon Dioxide, Investment Money, And Population: Selected Papers Of John D. Hamaker, John D. Hamaker, annotated by Donald A. Weaver (1982).

Teaming with Microbes: The Organic Gardener's Guide to the Soil Food Web, revised edition, Jeff Lowenfels and Wayne Lewis (2010).

Trace Elements and Other Essential Nutrients: Clinical Application of Tissue Mineral Analysis, David L. Watts (2006).

Tree Crops: A Permanent Agriculture, J. Russell Smith (1950).

Under Ground: How Creatures of Mud and Dirt Shape Our World, Yvonne Baskin (2005).

Water for Every Farm, P. A. Yeomans (1965).

Water, Pure and Simple: The Infinite Wisdom of an Extraordinary Molecule, Paolo Consigli (2008).

What's Wrong With My Plant? (And How Do I Fix It?): A Visual Guide to Easy Diagnosis and Organic Remedies, David Deardorff and Kathryn Wadsworth (2009).

The Work of Nature: How the Diversity of Life Sustains Us, Yvonne Baskin (1997).

The Worm Book: The Complete Guide to Gardening and Composting with Worms, Loren Nancarrow and Janet Hogan Taylor (1998).

Index

Mulder Mineral Wheel, 62-63
Murray, Doug, 155-156
Murray, Maynard, 165
Mustard, 126
Mycorrhizae, 113-114

Nardi, James, 84, 113
Natural Resources Conservation
    Service, 23
Nature and Properties of Soils, The,
    xiii, 25, 83, 85, 90, 95, 107, 121
Nature Farming, 142
Nematicides, 128
Nematodes, 120, 205
Nematodes, bacteriovore, 122
Nematodes, parasitic, 120,
    124-127, 226
Nematodes, pathogenic, 120
Neonicotinoids, 218-219
Nettle tea, 169
Nickel, 79-80
Night crawlers, 173
Nile River, 175
Nitrate, detoxification, 75
Nitrate, meter, 288-289
Nitrification, 97
Nitrobacter bacteria, 36
Nitrogen distribution, by
    earthworms, 179
Nitrogen fixation, 47
Nitrogen, 32-37, 56
Nitrogen, organic, 15, 33
Nitrogen, oxidizing, 98
Nitrogen, potentially mineralizable,
    282-283
Nitrogen, water-extractable, 122
Nitrogen-fixing bacteria, 31
Nitrosamine formation, 75
Nitrosomonas bacteria, 36, 97

Nordell, Anne and Eric, 251
Northeast Organic Farming
    Association, xiii
No-till, 244-245
NPK, 8, 53, 203
NRCS. See Natural Resources
    Conservation Service
NRCS Soil Health Card, 260-277
Nutrient functions, 41
Nutrient recycling, 120
Nutritional state of crops, 311
Nuts, nutritional composition, 308

Ohio Ecological Farm and Food
    Association, xiii
Omnivore's Dilemma, The, 300
Organic farming, 91
Organic matter, 15-16
Organic Soil Conditioning, 106
Organisms, thermophyllic, 143
ORP, meter, 291
Our Earth, Our Cure, 26
Out of the Earth, 130
Oxalic acid, 39
Oxidation reduction potential,
    meter, 291

Paramagnetism, 6, 9, 292-293
Parasitic wasps, 225
Pasture cropping, 16
Pathogen inhibition, 137
PCSM. See Phil Callahan Soil Meter
Peat, 102
Penetrometer, 10, 268, 287
Pennsylvania Association for
    Sustainable Agriculture, 300
Percolation, 89
Perennial legumes, 247

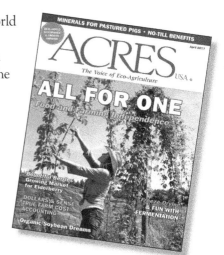